Applied FORTRAN for Engineering and Science

Applied FORTRAN for Engineering and Science

James Schwar   **Charles Best**
Lafayette College, Easton, Pennsylvania

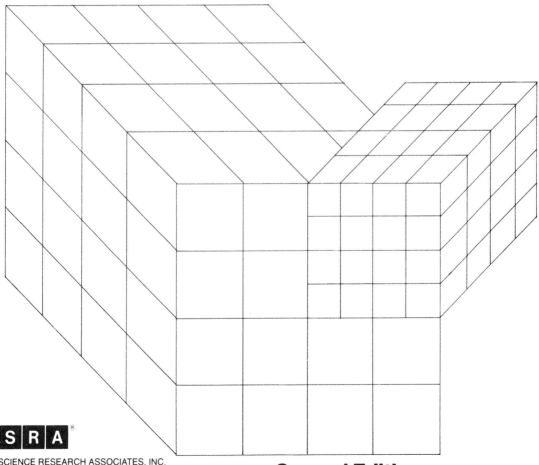

SRA ®

SCIENCE RESEARCH ASSOCIATES, INC.
Chicago, Henley-on-Thames, Sydney, Toronto

A Subsidiary of IBM

Second Edition

Acquisition Editor	John Levstik
Project Editor	Byron Riggan
Compositor	Graphic Typesetting Service
Illustrator	Diane Keller
Cover Designer	Arv Tessing
Text Designer	Judith Olson

Library of Congress Cataloging in Publication Data

Schwar, James P.
  Applied FORTRAN for engineering and science.

  Includes index.
  1. FORTRAN (Computer program language)   I. Best,
Charles L. II. Title.
QA76.73.F25S34   1985   001.64'24   85-10737
ISBN 0-574-21795-9

10   9   8   7   6   5   4   3

preface

This book is designed for a one-semester introduction to FORTRAN 77 programming for students in engineering and science. FORTRAN, the acronym for FORmula TRANslation, is the prevailing computer language in engineering and science. Since the introduction of FORTRAN in the mid-1950s, the language has undergone several generations of development. An unfortunate consequence of this development has been the introduction of various dialects peculiar to particular machines. FORTRAN 77 is an attempt to update and standardize the language of FORTRAN. It is the standard proposed by the American National Standards Institute (ANSI) and thus can be considered official FORTRAN. To quote ANSI, however, "An American National Standard is intended as a guide to aid the manufacturer, the consumer and the general public. The existence of an American National Standard does not in any respect preclude anyone, whether he has approved the standard or not, from manufacturing, marketing, purchasing, or using products, processes, or procedures not conforming to the standard." Hence, although FORTRAN 77 can be considered official, you may encounter some variations of the language for your computer.

Chapter 1 introduces the various parts of the computer and describes their functions. It also reviews the various types of languages that can be understood by the computer and how they are processed. Chapter 2 discusses data types and data structures, and the internal (binary) representation of data, all of which are helpful in understanding the limitations and rules associated with FORTRAN 77. This chapter can be omitted without interrupting the continuity of the text. So that you can start programming as soon as possible, Chapter 3 presents the elementary syntax of FORTRAN. Because formatting of input/output (I/O) is highly formalized in FORTRAN, its discussion is postponed until Chapter 7. Instead Chapter 3 includes what is called *list-directed* I/O. List-directed I/O is machine-controlled; hence, you can concentrate on the logical and syntactical flow of program writing without special regard for the details of form of the input and output. Chapter 4 discusses flowcharting and problem solving. This chapter includes details on such important concepts as flowchart symbols, and programming structures such as SEQUENCE, DOUNTIL, IFTHENELSE, and DOWHILE.

The most important capabilities of a computer are carrying out repetitive calculations and handling large arrays of numbers. The concepts of looping and arrays are closely related. Looping, however, is an important concept in itself. Hence, looping is presented as an idea separate from numerical arrays in Chapter 5, followed by a discussion of numerical arrays in Chapter 6. Chapter 5 also includes the very important decision-making (branching) capabilities of FORTRAN.

Chapters 1, 3, 4, 5, and 6 contain the essentials of FORTRAN programming. A thorough understanding of those five chapters will enable you if you are a beginning student to solve a host of computer problems.

Chapter 7 discusses formatted I/O, and Chapter 8 discusses the important specification statements: INTEGER, REAL, COMPLEX, DOUBLE PRECISION, LOGICAL, IMPLICIT, DATA, and PARAMETER. The CHARACTER specification statement for the manipulation of character strings is treated extensively in Chapter 8.

Intrinsic functions, user-defined functions, and subprogramming are discussed in Chapter 9.

A special feature of this book appears in Chapter 10, where some applications to numerical methods and matrices are introduced. The computer is of prime importance in solving problems of numerical integration, root search, simultaneous equation, and the like. Without it, hundreds of hours would be expended in hand-done calculations.

While not integral to the understanding of FORTRAN programming, Chapter 11 gives an overview of the processing of files. This chapter introduces the FORTRAN statements needed to access, process, and save files.

Finally, Chapter 12 deals with microcomputer implementations of FORTRAN. Several sample programs, along with a discussion of FORTRAN for microcomputers, are included in this chapter.

In the Appendixes a complete set of character codes and intrinsic functions are given as well as a glossary of FORTRAN programming statements.

In learning computer programming you must always remember that the actual writing and running of programs is essential. For this reason numerous exercises are provided at the end of each chapter. Computer programming is fun as well as a valuable experience in logical problem solving. You will find it a real thrill when your program runs smoothly and efficiently and, above all, provides the correct answers. Remember, a computer will do only what it is told to do!

ACKNOWLEDGMENTS

The authors would like to thank the following for their critical comments: Thomas Lynch, Northwestern University, Evanston, Illinois; Gilbert Van Brocklin, California State Polytechnical University; Hue Tran, Milwaukee School of Engineering; Don Sudweeks, Mesa College, San Diego, California; Stanley Niu, University of Missouri—Truman Campus; Henry B. Metcalf, University of Maine at Orona; Robert Clover, California State University. Special thanks are due to Mrs. Elizabeth A. Bullock who endured the authors' endless revisions.

J. P. S.
C. L. B.

contents

Applied FORTRAN for Engineering and Science

chapter 1

Introduction to Hardware and Software

The modern electronic digital computer is a high-speed device capable of serving many users performing varied tasks. *Time-sharing* is the ability of the computer to serve many users concurrently, and *multiprogramming* permits the computer to handle several tasks or programs.

A digital computer can serve many users concurrently through the interaction of the machine hardware (the physical components of the computer) and the software (the programs or instructions that cause the hardware to function in the desired way).

1.1 COMPUTER HARDWARE

Computer hardware consists of the *central processing unit* (CPU) and the *input/ output units* (I/O). The CPU can be further subdivided into a *memory unit*, an *arithmetic-logic unit*, and a *control unit*. The components of a CPU are diagrammed in Figure 1.1.

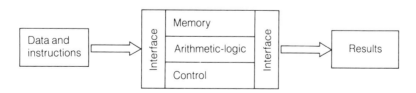

Figure 1.1 Central processing unit

1

Instructions and/or data are prepared by the user and entered into computer memory through an input device. The control unit decodes these instructions and directs the arithmetic-logic unit to the action to be taken in processing the data. The central processing unit will send the results, output data stored in memory, to an output unit. These instructions, when arranged in some logical sequence, are called a *computer program*.

Information, which may be data in, results (data out), or instructions, enters or leaves computer memory via an interface called a *controller*. The function of a controller is to interface the central processing unit to a specific physical input/output device.

Computer memory is the holding area for instructions and/or data. The arithmetic-logic unit performs actual data manipulations. The control unit decodes instructions; it directs and synchronizes those actions of the arithmetic-logic unit that are required to implement the instruction.

Input/output units are of many types. A widely used input/output device is the *computer terminal*. A terminal has a typewriterlike keyboard for input and either a printing mechanism to produce hard copy or a cathode-ray tube (CRT) for visually displaying output. A typical terminal and its keyboard layout are shown in Figure 1.2.

A computer terminal is commonly used to access a digital computer in an interactive (conversational), time-shared environment. Other input/output devices include magnetic tapes and magnetic disks. These magnetic storage units are capable of holding large amounts of information.

Certain units function only as input (card reader) or output (line printer) devices. Card input and printer output are not interactive. The amount of and speed with which information can be transferred to or from the computer is usually limited by the input/output device itself. Table 1.1 summarizes several types of input/output devices and some of their important operating characteristics.

TABLE 1.1   Input/Output Device Characteristics

Device	Characters per line	Transfer speed
printing terminal	80 to 132	10 to 120 characters/second
CRT terminal	80	10 to 960 characters/second
card reader	80	300 to 1000 cards/minute
line printer	80 to 132	300 to 2000 lines/minute
magnetic tape	user defined	36,000 to 562,500 characters/second
magnetic disk	user and/or system defined	100,000 to 3,000,000 characters/second

Figure 1.2 The ADM-22 Interactive Display Terminal (*Photo courtesy of Lear Siegler, Inc., Anaheim, California*)

1.2 COMPUTER SOFTWARE

Computer software is made up of user and system software. It consists of those instructions or programs that tell the computer what is to be done. They reside, along with data, in computer memory. *User software* consists of programs written by the user in a programming language that can be "understood" by the computer. *System software* consists of programs that are "built into" the computer system; these programs:

1. Monitor all system activities, such as computer logon, requests for other programs, execution of programs, and computer logoff.

2. Offer utility operations for listing programs and data, transferring information from one device to another, preparing programs and data in machine-readable form, and the like.

3. Implement computer programming languages such as FORTRAN.

1.3 INSTRUCTION WORDS AND DATA WORDS

The memory of a digital computer is divided into elementary units of storage called *words*. A word of computer memory is the fundamental unit of information accessed and operated on by the arithmetic-logic unit. A word of memory is itself made up of many *binary digits* or bits. A binary digit is a 0 or a 1. Most computers use either a 16-bit or a 32-bit *computer memory word*. The location of a computer memory word is called its *address*. Computer memory is made up of many contiguous locations; each location is directly addressable and each location is a memory word capable of storing 16 or 32 bits. Addressing starts at zero and proceeds serially upward. The maximum number of memory words available in a computing system is usually a power of 2. For example, 2^{20} or 1,048,576 memory words would be addressable beginning at location zero and ending at location 1048575. Figure 1.3 shows the serial nature of memory storage.

The binary nature of the computer is evident, since all information is stored in computer memory in one or more memory words. A single memory word is made up of a 16- or 32-bit (binary digit) number. This stored information may be either an *instruction word* or a *data word*. A single instruction may require part of a memory word, one memory word, or more than one memory word.

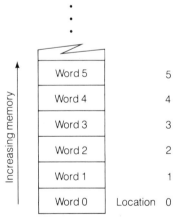

Figure 1.3 Representation of computer memory

Figure 1.4 shows a partial program and its associated data that have been loaded into computer memory. Locations 1000 through 1002 contain instruction words, one instruction per memory word. These instructions tell the central processing unit to load the data word found at location 3000 into a special hardware register called the *accumulator*. "Add 3001" instructs the processor to add to the contents of the accumulator the data word at location 3001. "Store 3002" stores the contents of the accumulator at location 3002. After these three instructions have been executed, the data word at location 3002 will be decimal 30.

The instruction and data words shown in Figure 1.4 have been represented in an external format that is easy to read. Actually, these words are stored internally as binary numbers. The logical grouping of instruction words, in binary form, is called a *machine-language program*. Only a machine-language program can be executed by the computer and only binary data can be acted on by the central processing unit. It is necessary to ensure that instruction and data words are properly located in memory so that they are not intermixed or mistakenly used in the wrong context.

1.4   THE CENTRAL PROCESSING UNIT

Figure 1.5 shows the details of a typical central processing unit and its associated registers. A *register*, usually equal in size to a word of memory, holds information such as an instruction word or a data word.

The *data bus* is a pathway for data and instruction words as they move to and from memory. The *accumulator* (A) is a register that stores the data word loaded

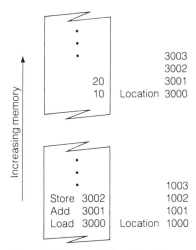

Figure 1.4   Representation of machine-language program and data stored in computer memory

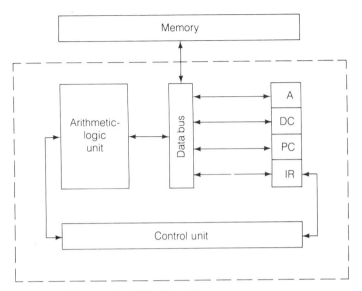

Figure 1.5 Representative CPU with registers

from memory and to be operated on by the arithmetic-logic unit. The *data counter* (DC) register stores the address or location of the data word that is to be loaded into the accumulator. The *program counter* (PC) register stores the address (location) of the instruction memory word that is to be loaded into the *instruction register* (IR). The IR stores the instruction word that is to be decoded by the control unit and used to direct the operation of the arithmetic-logic unit. Data words can be loaded from memory into the accumulator or from the accumulator into memory. The time needed to access a memory word and load it into the accumulator is in the range of nanoseconds (10^{-9} seconds). The time needed to execute an instruction is in the range of microseconds (10^{-6} seconds). Memory, whose access time is in the nanosecond range and whose words are each directly addressable, is termed *main* or *primary* memory. The program being executed and the data being processed by the CPU must reside in main memory.

Most computing systems offer several hundred different instructions that may occupy part of a memory word, one memory word, or more than one memory word. The control unit must be able to decode the information found in the IR and determine not only the nature of the instruction but also whether more than one instruction is present. Instructions, at the machine level, include capabilities for arithmetic, testing, branching, input, output, and similar operations.

In summary, the computer program, stored in memory, consists of binary information. This machine-language program directs the action to be taken by the CPU for data input, processing, and output. When programming at the machine level, it is necessary to keep track of the memory locations of data and instructions.

1.5   ASSEMBLY LANGUAGE

Assembly language permits instruction words, data words, and addresses to be represented by symbols. An assembly-language program is the first in a sequence of steps that ends in a machine-language program. An assembler, a system program (part of the system software), translates a program written in assembly language into binary code. This translation is usually on a one-to-one basis, one machine instruction for each assembly-language instruction. The next step is to load the binary code into computer memory to produce a machine-language program. This is accomplished by a system program, the loader. Once loaded into memory, the program is executed and assembly code such as

$$
\begin{array}{ll}
\text{LOAD} & \text{A} \\
\text{ADD} & \text{B} \\
\text{STOR} & \text{C}
\end{array}
$$

generates the machine-language code and data stored in memory, as was shown in Figure 1.4. Thus datum A will be assigned location 3000, datum B will be assigned location 3001, and datum C will be assigned location 3002. The instruction words will be located in memory beginning at location 1000. The system software handles the translation of the assembly-language program, the loading of the translated (binary) program into memory, and its execution, as shown in Figure 1.6, where the rightmost block represents a program in the process of execution.

Figure 1.6   Assembly-language program through execution

1.6   HIGH-LEVEL LANGUAGES

High-level languages allow the programmer to write instructions, called *statements*, in an algebraic format. The logically arranged sequence of statements is called a *source program*. A translator (or compiler) accepts as input the source program and translates it into binary code. The loader maps the binary code (instruction words) and data (data words) onto computer memory. The final step is program execution. These steps are shown in Figure 1.7.

Figure 1.7 FORTRAN source program through execution

In the previous example of assembly-language code, three instructions were needed to add B to A and store the results in C. A high-level language requires only the single statement

$$C = A + B$$

This one statement generates several instruction words, the three words shown in Figure 1.4. Each statement in a high-level language generally produces several instructions in binary code.

Important high-level languages are:

1. FORTRAN, an acronym for FORmula TRANslation, a language designed primarily for scientific and engineering programming
2. COBOL, an acronym for COmmon Business Oriented Language, designed specifically for business data processing
3. Pascal, a language developed for systems and application programming

Each of these languages would be implemented on a specific computer as a compiler. A *compiler* is a system program, part of the system software, that accepts as input source programs written in a particular language, such as FORTRAN. The compiler translates the source program into binary code. This binary code is then loaded into computer memory and executed. Translated (or binary) code can be saved. The saved code can be loaded and executed, without compiling, whenever the program is needed. Binary code can be executed only on a computer of the type on which it was compiled. Ideally, source code can be compiled and executed on *any* computer that supports a compiler for that language.

System software is generally included in the purchase of a computing system and thus is supplied by the computer manufacturer.

User software, as differentiated from system software, consists of those programs written by the user. These programs are commonly coded in a high-level language such as FORTRAN. Programs usually begin execution with the first statement and execution proceeds sequentially unless interrupted by some control or decision statement.

1.7   TIME-SHARED COMPUTING

Time-sharing is the capability of a modern digital computer to serve many users concurrently through joint use of the CPU. Multiprogramming is the capability of executing many different programs. A time-shared, multiprogramming computer has many users doing many different things.

In a time-shared environment, each user is allotted a slice of time, usually milliseconds, during which the CPU is dedicated to that user. When one user's time quantum or time slice expires, the next user will be served by the CPU. The users, as represented by individual programs, are held in a circular queue that advances from user to user upon expiration of a time quantum. Priorities are usually established among several circular queues so that critical system programs are executed before user programs, as shown in Figure 1.8. A modern digital computer will usually have one or more input/output processors (IOPs), which permit I/O to be processed in parallel with CPU operations. This frees the CPU to process data since it does not have to process data input/output. The computer memory will be accessible to both the CPU and the IOP. The IOP is a highly specialized processor that

Figure 1.8   Circular queues

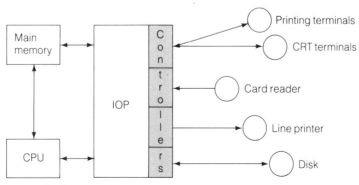

Figure 1.9   Time-shared computer system

Figure 1.10 A Tandy 2000 Microcomputer (*Photo courtesy of the Tandy Corporation, Fort Worth, Texas*)

interfaces input/output devices with the CPU. The IOP is connected physically to each type of I/O through a hardware device called a *controller*. For example, user terminals connect to the IOP through a single controller. Figure 1.9 on page 9 shows a complete time-shared computing system.

At times, main memory is not large enough to handle all the programs and data active in a multiprogramming environment. The system software, under control of the computer operating system, can automatically use disk storage to handle the overflow. Only the data and code currently being executed must be present in main memory. Programs and data not in use can be stored in (swapped out to) secondary or disk storage. Programs and data needed for execution, if not present in main memory, are swapped into main memory from disk storage. In a multiprogramming environment, swapping goes on continuously as each user's time quantum expires. Each user is guaranteed program code and a unique, private data area in memory. *Virtual memory* is the name given to this combination of main and secondary memory.

1.8 MICROCOMPUTERS

Microcomputers are small computing systems that support a wide range of software. They are frequently single-user systems consisting of a keyboard, CRT display, printer, microprocessing unit, main memory, and disk storage. Microcomputers are characterized by their small (desktop) size and low price. They are capable of running most of the applications supported on larger, time-shared computer systems. A typical, single-user microcomputer is shown in Figure 1.10. Such a system could compile and execute programs written in FORTRAN.

1.9 SUMMARY

The digital computer is an electronic device that can be programmed to perform a wide range of tasks. The programming of a computer involves stating the program in a language native to the machine, or a symbolic language that must be assembled to binary code, or a high-level language such as FORTRAN that must be compiled (translated) into binary code. The binary code, when loaded into computer memory, directs the actions to be taken by the central processing unit and the attached input/output units so that data can be entered and processed and the desired results displayed. The central processing unit consists of memory, the arithmetic-logic unit, and the control unit.

EXERCISES

Answer the following questions as they relate to the computing system you are using.

1. How many bits are in a computer word?

2. Describe the type, whether CRT or printing, and the speed of terminals attached to the computer. How many terminals does the computer support?

3. What is the capacity of the computer's main memory, in number of words?

4. Does the computer support magnetic tape? If so, what are the characteristics of the tape units?

5. How many disk units does the computer support? What is their combined storage capacity in number of words?

6. Is the computer a virtual-memory machine? If so, what is the ratio of words of virtual memory to words of main memory?

7. List the high-level programming languages available on the computer. In what application area(s) are these languages used?

8. How many machine-language instructions does the computer support? Do any of these instructions require more than one memory word?

9. Is an assembler available on the computer? Sketch diagrammatically how you would proceed from assembly-language program to output.

10. How does a compiler differ from an assembler?

11. What is an input/output processor? Of what value is an IOP?

12. Briefly describe the purpose and/or need for queues. How is a queue related to a time quantum?

13. Why are priorities useful in a time-shared environment?

The purpose of the following three exercises is to acquaint the user with computer access through punched-card or terminal input/output and to illustrate the compile, load, and execute sequence shown in Figure 1.7. The source programs are written in FORTRAN and they should be copied exactly as shown. It is not necessary at this point to understand this FORTRAN code.

14. Compile and execute the FORTRAN source program that calculates and outputs the square root of a number.

```
C234567
      WRITE(6,*)'ENTER A NUMBER '
      READ(5,*)VALUE
      ANS=SQRT(VALUE)
      WRITE(6,*)'SQ ROOT IS',ANS
      STOP
      END
```

15. Compile and execute the FORTRAN source program.

```
C234567
      WRITE (6,*) 'TABLE OF SQUARES AND CUBES '
      WRITE(6,*)
      DO 10 X=0.0,10.0
   10 WRITE(6,*)X,X*X,X**3
      STOP
      END
```

16. Compile and execute the FORTRAN source program.

```
C234567
      WRITE(6,*)'ENTER THE SIDES OF A RT TRIANGLE '
      READ(5,*)A,B
      C=SQRT(A*A+B*B)
      WRITE(6,*)'THE HYPOTENUSE IS ',C
      STOP
      END
```

chapter 2

Data Structures and Programming Structures

The digital computer stores all information, internally, in binary form. For example, a 16-bit memory word might contain the following:

$$0 \quad\quad 110 \quad\quad 000 \quad\quad 110 \quad\quad 001 \quad\quad 111$$
$$\uparrow \quad\quad\quad\quad\quad\quad\quad\quad\quad\quad\quad\quad\quad\quad\quad\quad\quad\quad\quad\quad \uparrow$$
$$\text{bit 15} \quad\quad\quad\quad\quad\quad\quad\quad\quad\quad\quad\quad\quad\quad\quad\quad\quad \text{bit 0}$$

This binary number could represent either a data word or an instruction word.

Assuming that a 16-bit binary number is a data word and that it represents an integer value, it can be converted to a decimal (base 10) integer through the power series:

$$\text{decimal value} = \sum_{N=0}^{15} B \cdot 2^N$$

where $B = 0$ or 1 depending on the binary digit. For the rightmost bit $N = 0$ and for the leftmost bit $N = 15$. For example, the binary number 0110 0001 1100 1111 would be

$$0 \cdot 2^{15} + 1 \cdot 2^{14} + 1 \cdot 2^{13} + 0 \cdot 2^{12} + 0 \cdot 2^{11} + 0 \cdot 2^{10} + 0 \cdot 2^{9}$$
$$+ 1 \cdot 2^{8} + 1 \cdot 2^{7} + 1 \cdot 2^{6} + 0 \cdot 2^{5} + 0 \cdot 2^{4} + 1 \cdot 2^{3} + 1 \cdot 2^{2} + 1 \cdot 2^{1} +$$
$$1 \cdot 2^{0} = 24975$$

Conversion of a binary number is simply accomplished when you recognize that each binary digit, starting from right to left, represents a power of two.

The conversion from decimal to binary reverses the previous operation. It requires successive division by two. A useful technique for this conversion is to integer divide the decimal value by two, keeping track of the remainder, until the decimal value has been reduced to zero. For example, the decimal value 473 would be processed as follows:

		remainder
2)	473	
2)	236	1
2)	118	0
2)	59	0
2)	29	1
2)	14	1
2)	7	0
2)	3	1
2)	1	1
	0	1

The binary number is the remainder written in reverse order, 111011001.

The following material deals with data words and how they are represented externally (base 10 and character) and internally (base 2), plus the way data words are used to form data structures. An understanding of how data are processed by the computer is necessary for an appreciation of its FORTRAN capabilities.

2.1   NUMERIC DATA

Numeric data, in external form, are numbers. Numeric data are used to count, label and compute. The five numeric data types of interest to the FORTRAN programmer are: integer, real or floating-point, double precision, logical and complex.

Integer data represent whole numbers that contain no fractional part. Numbers such as

$$10 \qquad 105 \qquad 32767 \qquad -50 \qquad 0$$

are integers. Integers are stored internally as signed binary numbers and require one memory word. Figure 2.1 shows the internal representation of integer data for 16-bit and 32-bit data words, where S is the sign bit (1 = negative, 0 = positive). The leftmost bit is the sign and the remaining bits represent the value part. Zero is a positive number with all 16 or 32 bits set to 0. The range of integers for a 16-bit word is

$$2^{15} - 1 \text{ to } -(2^{15}) \text{ or } 32767 \text{ to } -32768$$

The range of integers for a 32-bit word is

$$2^{31} - 1 \text{ to } -(2^{31}) \text{ or } 2147483647 \text{ to } -2147483648$$

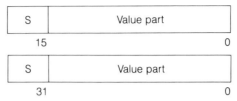

Figure 2.1   Internal representation of integer data

Binary arithmetic is performed in a way similar to decimal arithmetic if one keeps in mind that there are only two digits in the binary sequence as opposed to ten digits in the decimal sequence. To simplify the discussion of binary arithmetic, consider an eight-bit word where the leftmost bit is the sign. Remember that for an eight-bit word the range of integers would be $2^7 - 1$ to $-(2^7)$ or 127 to -128 decimal.

Using eight-bit words for illustration, the addition of two binary numbers becomes

$$25 \leftrightarrow 00011001$$
$$\underline{17 \leftrightarrow 00010001}$$
$$42 \leftrightarrow 00101010$$

Note that, as in decimal arithmetic, the process moves from right to left, column by column, with ones carried when necessary.

Most digital computers perform binary subtraction by adding the binary negative (the so-called 2's complement) of the subtrahend to the minuend. The 2's complement of a binary number is formed by complementing the binary number (replacing 1 with 0 and 0 with 1 in the sequence) and adding 1. Thus the 2's complement of 00010001 is 11101111, from $00010001 \xrightarrow{\text{complement}} 11101110 \xrightarrow{\text{add 1}} 11101111$. Note that there is a negative in the leftmost bit.

Consider the subtraction

$$\begin{array}{r} 00011001 \\ -\,00011001 \end{array} \xrightarrow{\text{2's complement}} \begin{array}{r} 00011001 \\ +\,\underline{11101111} \\ 00001000 \end{array}$$

The answer is 00001000 ($+8$ in decimal). Note that the addition in the leftmost bit results in a one carry to an imaginary ninth bit that does not register in an eight-bit word.

Now consider when the subtrahend is greater than the minuend.

$$\begin{array}{r} 00010001 \\ -\,00011001 \end{array} \xrightarrow{\text{2's complement}} \begin{array}{r} 00010001 \\ +\,\underline{11100111} \\ 11111000 \end{array}$$

The result is a binary number in 2's complement. The *magnitude* of this result can be found by exactly the same procedure used to generate a 2's complement. For example,

$$11111000 \xrightarrow{\text{complement}} 00000111 \xrightarrow{\text{add 1}} 00001000 \quad (-8 \text{ in decimal})$$

Positive integers are stored internally in binary form, whereas negative integers are stored in 2's complement. For example, assuming a 16-bit memory word,

$$1111111111111111 \text{ is } -1$$
$$0000000000000001 \text{ is } +1$$

It is important to remember that integers are signed binary numbers when operated on by the computer's arithmetic unit.

Real or *floating-point data* are represented by numbers that have decimal points. Numbers such as

$$-1.3 \quad 0.0 \quad 80000. \quad 6.023 \times 10^{23}$$

are real numbers. Real numbers are stored internally as binary numbers in scientific form and require 32 bits. Figure 2.2 illustrates one of several commonly used internal representations of real data, the IEEE standard for floating-point arithmetic. The 32 bits are divided into three fields:

1. Bit 31 is the sign bit of the mantissa or fractional part (1 = negative, 0 = positive).
2. Bits 23 through 30 are the exponent of two increased by 127 (i.e., exponent + 127).
3. Bits 0 through 22 are the magnitude of the mantissa or fractional part.

Real data then are encoded in a "normalized floating-point" form using this technique, and the decimal value is given by

$$(-1^S) \cdot 2^{E-127} \cdot (1.0 + F)$$

where S = sign bit (0 or 1), F is the 23-bit fractional part with an implicit leading 1, and E is the 8-bit exponent increased by 127. In a 16-bit word computer, real

Figure 2.2   Internal representation of real data

data occupy two adjacent memory words. In a 32-bit machine, only one memory word is required to store real data.

In order to illustrate this technique, consider the real number stored in computer memory in binary form:

$$0100\ 0001\ 1101\ 0000\ 0000\ 0000\ 0000\ 0000$$

↑   ↑   ↑

bit 31   bit 22   bit 0

This 32-bit real datum can be converted to its decimal equivalent as follows:

1. Bits 31, the sign, indicates a positive number: $(-1^0) = +1$.
2. Bits 23 through 30, the exponent, become

$$1 \cdot 2^7 + 0 \cdot 2^6 + 0 \cdot 2^5 + 0 \cdot 2^4 + 0 \cdot 2^3 + 0 \cdot 2^2 + 1 \cdot 2^1 + 1 \cdot 2^0 = 131.$$

3. Bits 0 through 22 are the fractional part evaluated as a power series of $1/2^N$ starting with bit 22 and proceeding to the right. The fractional part becomes:

$$1 \cdot 1/2 + 0 \cdot 1/4 + 1 \cdot 1/8 + 0 \cdot 1/16 + \ldots = 0.625$$

The decimal value can now be calculated from the formula as

$$(-1)^0 \cdot 2^{131-127} \cdot (1.625) = 26.0$$

Conversion from decimal to binary is complicated by the implicit leading 1. Consider the decimal value 20.0. To convert to internal floating-point binary form an exponent E must be selected such that

$$(-1)^S \cdot 2^{E-127} \cdot (1.0 + F) = 20.0$$

is satisfied, where F is a positive decimal fraction. The following table illustrates the use of a trial and error solution for E:

E	2^{E-127}	F
127	1	19
128	2	9
129	4	4
130	8	1.5
131	16	0.25
132	32	-0.375

where the correct value is $E = 131$ and $F = 0.25$. In binary form, the decimal value becomes

1. fractional part
   01000000000000000000000 = 0.25
2. exponent
   10000011 = 131
3. sign
   $S = 0$
   0100 0001 1010 0000 0000 0000 0000 0000
   ↑   ↑   ↑
   bit 31   bit 22   bit 0

Using this technique for storing real data in binary form, the magnitude of this data is from 2^{-128} to 2^{127} or $10^{\pm 38}$. Approximately seven significant digits (23-bit mantissa with an implicit leading 1) are available for arithmetic operations.

Double-precision data are represented internally using 64 bits. In double-precision arithmetic, the sign is still the leftmost bit, followed by an 11-bit exponent increased by 1023 and a 52-bit fractional part with an implicit leading 1. This gives a range of $10^{\pm 308}$. Approximately 15 significant digits are available for double-precision arithmetic operations.

Logical data are represented internally using one memory word (either 16 or 32 bits). Logical data are .TRUE. (all bits set to 1) or .FALSE. (all bits set to 0). Logical data result from testing the relationship between arithmetic values—for example, is A less than B?

Complex data are represented in memory as an ordered pair of floating-point numbers, the first number specifying the real part and the second number specifying the imaginary part. Each number is stored in binary form using 32 bits, as shown in Figure 2.3. The 64 bits are contiguous in memory and require four memory words for a 16-bit machine and two memory words for a 32-bit machine.

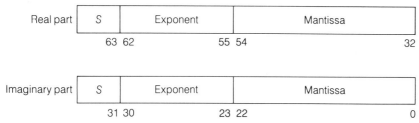

Figure 2.3 Internal representation of complex data

2.2 NONNUMERIC DATA

Nonnumeric data, in external form, consist of one or more characters strung together. Characters consist of the letters A through Z, the digits 0 through 9, and special characters such as + − * / , . ( ) = ′ $ and the blank space.

Nonnumeric or *character data* require eight bits to store a single character. Each character is represented by its own unique code. Two coding schemes are in common usage:

1. EBCDIC[1] code, used by IBM, is an eight-level code. A maximum of four characters may be packed in a 32-bit memory word.

2. ASCII[2] code, used by most other computing systems, is a seven-level code. A maximum of two characters may be packed in a 16-bit memory word. The leftmost bit is unused by this code.

Figure 2.4 shows the internal representation of character data.

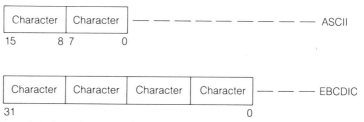

Figure 2.4 Internal representation of character data

The EBCDIC code uses eight bits and offers 256 possible character representations. The ASCII code uses only seven bits and has 128 possible character representations. A character datum is not numeric, but has a unique bit pattern for each character. Appendix A lists these patterns or codes. The eight bits used to represent a character are called a *byte* of memory (1 byte = 8 bits). It is not unusual to find the term *byte data* used interchangeably with *character data*. Computer memory is, in many cases, reported in bytes rather than words since words may be either 16- or 32-bit quantities.

2.3 CONSTANTS AND VARIABLES

In a high-level language such as FORTRAN, data are referenced as constants or as variables. A FORTRAN constant does not change in value during program exe-

---

[1]Extended Binary Coded Decimal Interchange Code.
[2]American Standard Code for Information Interchange.

cution. Constants in FORTRAN can be of the following types: integer, real, double-precision, logical, complex, or character. An *integer constant* is a number without a decimal point. A *real constant* has a decimal point and optionally may be written in scientific notation using the letter E for the power of ten. A *double-precision* constant must be expressed in scientific notation using the letter D for the power of ten. A *logical constant* is either true or false. A *complex constant* consists of two floating-point numbers, the first number being the real part and the second number being the imaginary part. A *character* or *non-numeric constant* is a string of one or more characters enclosed by apostrophes. Table 2.1 illustrates how typical constants appear in a FORTRAN program.

TABLE 2.1   FORTRAN Constants

Type	External form	FORTRAN representation
integer	13	13
real	$\begin{cases} -18.2 \\ 1.3 \times 10^{-16} \end{cases}$	−18.2 1.3E−16
double-precision	2.718281828	2.718281828D+00
logical	false	.FALSE.
complex	2.0 + 1.5i	(2.0,1.5)
character	HELLO	'HELLO'

Variables are names to which a value is assigned. Variables in FORTRAN may be of six types: integer, real, double-precision, logical, complex, or character. FORTRAN variable names consist of one to six alphabetic or numeric characters, the first of which must be alphabetic. Unless otherwise specified, a FORTRAN variable name defaults to type integer if it begins with the letters I through N or to type real if it begins with the letters A through H or O through Z. To override the default typing of a variable name, specification statements such as

- REAL AREA,LENGTH
- INTEGER COUNT
- LOGICAL TEST
- DOUBLE PRECISION PI
- COMPLEX VALUE
- CHARACTER*8 NAME

can be used to type the variables AREA and LENGTH as real, COUNT as integer, TEST as logical, PI as double-precision, VALUE as complex, and NAME consisting of eight characters. During compilation the compiler replaces variable names by memory addresses.

2.4 DATA STRUCTURES

Data structures are formed from data words and are of two kinds, *static* and *dynamic*. A static data structure is one in which the assigned area of memory is fixed; a dynamic data structure allows the assigned area of memory to change in size during program execution.

An *array* is a collection of several values of the same type. In most high-level languages, arrays are static data structures, referenced by an array name and consisting of one or more array elements. When the array elements are arranged in a single dimension (column), that is called a *one-dimensional* array. Arrays, being static structures, are named and sized. In FORTRAN, this is accomplished by specifying the array name followed by a set of parentheses enclosing the size of the array. For example,

DIMENSION X(10)

states that X is the array name and that the X array is made up of ten elements. DIMENSION X (10) reserves and labels an array in computer memory, as shown in Figure 2.5. Assuming that the X array is real, it requires 32 bits per element for a total of twenty 16-bit memory words. The array name points to the address in memory of the first element of the array. Array elements are accessed relative to this memory address through the array subscript. For example, if the first element of the X array is X(1), then X(3) is the third element. However, if the first element of the X array is X(−5), then X(3) will be the ninth element. An array element is always accessed by specifying the array name followed by a set of parentheses enclosing the subscript.

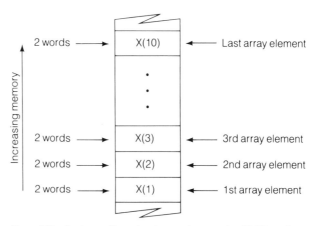

Figure 2.5 Real, one-dimensional array storage using 16-bit words

In a high-level language such as FORTRAN, arrays can be multidimensional, and two, three, or more dimensions may be specified. Computer memory is not multidimensional and these arrays must be mapped onto memory. Consider the integer, two-dimensional J array sized to three rows by four columns. Logically the array appears as follows:

$$J(1,1) \quad J(1,2) \quad J(1,3) \quad J(1,4)$$
$$J(2,1) \quad J(2,2) \quad J(2,3) \quad J(2,4)$$
$$J(3,1) \quad J(3,2) \quad J(3,3) \quad J(3,4)$$

where the first subscript represents the row and the second subscript, the column. The array will be mapped onto computer memory and stored column by column as shown in Figure 2.6.

The FORTRAN compiler generates appropriate binary code to calculate the correct memory location of any element, given its row and column, as an offset from the memory location of the first element. Three-dimensional arrays and beyond are processed in a similar manner. Arrays, in FORTRAN, may be of six types: integer, real, double precision, complex, logical, or byte (character).

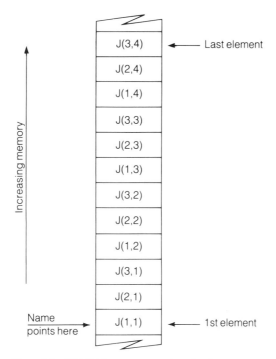

Figure 2.6   FORTRAN memory mapping of an integer, two-dimensional array

In FORTRAN, a string of characters is technically a byte array, where each character requires eight bits. The character constant is delimited by apostrophes; for example,

'HELLO'

is a character constant, five bytes long, and is stored in memory as shown in Figure 2.7.

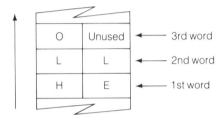

Figure 2.7   Character constant stored as a byte array using 16-bit words

The sixth byte, or the last half of the third word, is unused and not part of the five-character string. Most FORTRAN compilers pack two bytes per 16-bit memory word or four bytes per 32-bit memory word. The character variable, discussed in Chapter 8, is a variable name to which FORTRAN has assigned the property of a byte array. If NAME is defined to be a five-byte character variable, then

NAME = 'HELLO'

will store the string constant 'HELLO' in memory as shown in Figure 2.7, except that the first word can now be referenced by the character variable NAME.

Many modern digital computers allow *byte addressing*—that is, the computer hardware can access one or more bytes of information directly via special machine-level instructions. These special instructions significantly improve the speed with which character data can be processed. Thus the fundamental unit of information that can be accessed and operated on by the arithmetic-logic unit can be a byte when processing character data.

A *record* is a sequence of characters transferred as data from an external device to internal storage (input) or from internal storage to external device (output). The value associated with each datum within a record is called a *field*. For example, consider an input (or output) record containing three fields—100, 18.25, and THE END. Assume the record is 17 characters in length and that it is written as

0010018.25THE END

where the first field is five characters long and represents a datum of type integer; the second field is five characters long and represents a datum of type real; the third field is seven characters long and is of type character. This record is made up of three items of data and thus is a data structure. In high-level languages such as FORTRAN, input/output records are of fixed length and are static data structures.

A dynamic data structure is one in which the assigned area of memory can change in size. Dynamic data structures include stacks, queues, and lists. These data structures are available in system programming languages such as Pascal. The FORTRAN programming language does not support dynamic data structures.

2.5   PROGRAMMING STRUCTURES

Programming structures are techniques for processing data. A high-level language should offer statements that either lead to or are themselves programming structures. Five statement types are available in high-level programming languages:

- assignment
- input/output
- decision or control
- specification
- subprogram

The assignment statement is used to assign a value to a variable; for example,

$$A = 1$$

assigns the value 1 to A. The assignment statement can also be used to state an equation; for example,

$$AREA = 3.14159*DIAM**2/4.0$$

states that AREA is to be replaced by the computed value of the expression 3.14159 times DIAM squared divided by 4.

Input/output statements deal with data. Data (in) require input statements. Results (data out) use output statements. A block of contiguous assignment statements and/or input/output statements is the SEQUENCE programming structure.

Statements are executed sequentially, starting with the first statement and proceeding serially, unless a control statement changes the sequential execution order. A control statement tests some variable or expression and, based on this test, specifies the next statement to be executed. Typical programming structures that make use of control statements are the IFTHENELSE, DOWHILE, DOUNTIL, and CASE.

The IFTHENELSE programming structure represents a selection in that it tests for a condition that is either true or false. IF the condition is true THEN one or more FORTRAN statements that make up a true block will be executed, ELSE a different (false) block will be executed. The DOWHILE structure represents an iteration, that is, DO a block of FORTRAN statement, over and over again if necessary, WHILE a condition is true. The DOUNTIL structure is also an iteration in which a block of FORTRAN statements is repeated UNTIL a condition is true. The DOWHILE tests for the condition before execution of the block. The DOUNTIL tests after execution of the block. The CASE structure is a multiple selection, that is, select one of several cases, and it is implemented in FORTRAN as a multiple IFTHENELSE.

Specification statements deal with establishing data types and data structures and the formatting of input/output records. The subprogram statement is used to implement a predefined process or procedure—that is, a group of statements that perform a specified task. Assignment, control, input/output, and subprogram statements are used to develop programming structures.

A computer program consists of statements arranged in a logical order. A logical order implies the intelligent use of programming structures.

2.6   COMPUTATION ERRORS

Errors in computation are of two types: round-off errors and truncation errors resulting from finite approximations.

Round-off errors can arise from decimal-to-binary conversion. Certain decimal numbers of a fractional nature cannot be exactly represented in binary form. For example, decimal 0.125 can be exactly converted to binary 0.001. Decimal 0.1, however, has no exact binary equivalent and can be represented in binary by

$$0.0001100110011 . . .$$

which is decimal 0.09998. This conversion problem leads to difficulties when incrementing by fractional values in FORTRAN. Consider assigning 0.0 to A and then incrementing A by 0.1 ten times. The result will not be 1.0 but 0.99999 . . . . If the result were to be tested for "equal to 1.0," the test would be false. Another source of round-off error occurs when the initial data are in error due to the limitation imposed on real data by the number of significant digits. For example, in $\pi = 3.14159265 . . .$, the value used for π can have seven significant digits and would be 3.141592. If π appears in repetitive calculations, particularly those involving multiplication and division, the loss of digits beyond the seventh place may become significant.

Truncation errors resulting from finite approximations arise when functions are represented as infinite series. For example, the Taylor series expansion for e^x is given by

$$e^x = 1 + x + \frac{x^2}{2!} + \frac{x^3}{3!} + \frac{x^4}{4!} + \cdots$$

and the calculated value of e is the sum of all the terms. In a practical sense, only a finite number of terms can be summed. One common method of terminating the summation is to introduce an allowable error constant, ε, and then sum the terms of the series until the absolute value of the ratio of the last term used to the sum of the terms is less than ε. Or,

$$\left| \frac{i^{th}\ term}{series\ to\ i^{th}\ term} \right| < \varepsilon$$

Table 2.2 shows such a summation for $\varepsilon = 0.0005$.

TABLE 2.2   Calculation of *e* for an Error, $\varepsilon = 0.0005$

i	Term	Series to i	Error
1	1	1	1.0000000
2	1	2	0.5000000
3	0.5	2.5	0.2000000
4	0.1666666	2.6666666	0.0625000
5	0.0416666	2.7083333	0.0153846
6	0.0083333	2.7166666	0.0030675
7	0.0013888	2.7180555	0.0005200
8	0.0001984	2.7182539	0.0000730

2.7   SUMMARY

Data are stored in a computer in binary form. This internal representation of data and data structures establishes limits as to how those data can be processed. In the FORTRAN language, the way in which numeric data are stored in computer memory sets the magnitude and precision of that data while encoding schemes, such as the ASCII and EBCDIC codes, permit nonnumeric data to be processed. An array is a collection of values of the same data type, referenced by an array name and consisting of one or more array elements. Multidimensional arrays are stored column by column. Array elements are addressed starting with the first element of the array. Records represent data in the process of input or output. Programming structures are techniques for processing data and fall into five recognized categories: SEQUENCE, IFTHENELSE, DOWHILE, DOUNTIL, and CASE. Errors in the processing of data arise from either round-off or truncation. Round-off errors are directly related to the internal (binary) nature of the data. Truncation errors result from finite approximations.

EXERCISES

1. Convert these decimal numbers to binary.

372.65625	10020
1032	0.375
1777.75	100

2. Convert the eight-bit and 16-bit signed binary numbers to their decimal equivalents.

01000111	1111000010110110
00110110	0001100101110011
11011001	0100000000001111

3. Show the internal representation for each integer. Assume a 16-bit data word.

32767	100
0	-32768
-64	1600

4. What 32-bit binary numbers represent $2^{31} - 1$ and -2^{31}?

5. Perform the indicated decimal operations by converting each decimal value to a 16-bit signed binary number. Represent negative numbers as 2's complement. Express each answer in both binary and decimal form.

115	48	128
$+53$	-92	-123

6. Show the internal representation of the real datum -8.0.

7. Show the internal representation of the real datum 0.1.

8. Express π as a double-precision datum.

9. Show the internal representation of the complex datum $(1.0, 0.0)$.

10. What general rule or rules must be followed when selecting a FORTRAN variable name?

11. A real, one-dimensional A array has as its first element $A(-3)$ and as its last element $A(12)$. How many 32-bit memory words are required by this array? Which memory word references element $A(0)$?

12. Sketch how an integer, three-dimensional array would be stored in memory. Assume the array has as its first element K(0,0,0) and as its last element K(3,3,2).

13. The character variable METWO is assigned the value 'TOTAL'. Sketch how this five-byte array is stored in computer memory. Assume both a 16-bit and a 32-bit memory word. Place the appropriate EBCDIC code, which represents each character, in the appropriate memory word.

14. List the programming structures. Which programming structures are associated with control?

15. Which statement types deal exclusively with data?

16. How many binary digits to the right of the decimal point are necessary if 0.1 (base 10) is to be stored internally as 0.099999?

17. How many terms of the sine series must be summed in order to calculate $\sin(\pi/4)$, given $\varepsilon = 0.0001$.

18. What integer is represented by the following 16-bit word?

    0101010100110010

    What two ASCII characters does this word represent? (See Appendix A.)

19. If the number of bits in the exponent for a real datum was increased by one, how would this affect the limits on the magnitude of real data?

20. Write an appropriate FORTRAN constant for each of the following:

real	0.000167
integer	-803
double precision	1.666666666
character	THE END
complex	$6.0 - 8.0i$
logical	true
real	10^{-15}

21. How many default integer variable names are available to the FORTRAN programmer? How can the variable name TIMES be typed as integer?

22. Why is the largest positive integer value one less than the largest negative integer value?

chapter 3

Introduction to FORTRAN

FORTRAN is a high-level, problem-oriented language designed primarily for use in engineering and science. This language was developed by IBM and dates back to 1954. The FORTRAN language has undergone several revisions and modifications over the years. It was the first programming language to be standardized through the normal procedures of the American Standards Association (now the American National Standards Institute, or ANSI). These standards were approved in 1966 and the language was then denoted as standard FORTRAN IV. The 1966 standards were updated, revised, and approved as an American National Standard by ANSI on April 3, 1978. Since this work was completed in 1977, their new standard is designated as FORTRAN 77. The language discussed in this book is based on the new standards: American National Standard Programming Language FORTRAN, ANSI X3.9-1978.

FORTRAN is usually implemented on a computer as a compiler and the entire source program is read before it is translated into binary code. When implemented as a compiler, FORTRAN is not interactive; any programming errors detected by the compiler must be corrected and the program resubmitted for compilation.

A line in FORTRAN is a sequence of 72 characters where the valid FORTRAN characters are the 26 letters of the alphabet, the 10 digits (0–9), and special characters. There are 49 characters available in FORTRAN. The special characters are shown in Table 3.1.

Subscripts and superscripts, in an algebraic sense, are not permitted. The alphabetic characters must be in upper case. A comment line is any line that contains a C or * in column 1. Comment lines are used to explain the logic of the FORTRAN program. Characters following the C or * are treated as comments by the compiler and appear in the listing of the source program. A continuation line is any line that

TABLE 3.1   FORTRAN Special Characters

ƀ	blank	/	slash
=	equals	,	comma
+	plus	.	decimal point
−	minus	$	currency symbol
*	asterisk	'	apostrophe
(	left parenthesis	:	colon
)	right parenthesis		

contains a character other than a blank in column 6. A statement in FORTRAN is written in columns 7 through 72 and may be continued on more than one line, with a maximum of 19 continuation lines permitted. Columns 1 through 5 are reserved for the statement label. A statement label must be a unique, positive integer in the range 1 to 99999 inclusive. This label is used to identify the statement so that it can be referenced by another statement. Statement labels should be used only where necessary and they do not have to be assigned in any sequence. A statement label may appear anywhere within columns 1 through 5. Blanks and leading zeros are ignored.

A statement is an instruction, written in the FORTRAN language, explicitly stating what is to be done. Five statement types are permitted in FORTRAN:

- arithmetic (or assignment) statement
- input/output statements
- control statements
- specification statements
- subprogram statements

3.1   THE ARITHMETIC STATEMENT

The general form of the arithmetic statement is

$$v = \text{exp}$$

where v is the name of a variable and exp is an arithmetic expression. An arithmetic expression consists of a combination of variables, constants, and symbols.

A FORTRAN variable name can consist of one to six alphabetic or numeric characters, the first of which must be alphabetic. If the first character is I, J, K, L, M, or N, the data type is integer. When the first character of a variable name is A through H or O through Z, the data type is real. Table 3.2 shows some FORTRAN variables with their data types. In FORTRAN data type integer is stored internally

TABLE 3.2   FORTRAN Variables

FORTRAN variable	Data type
K3821	integer variable
A	real variable
LENGTH	integer variable
DIAMETER	invalid name (too many characters)

as a one-word signed binary number without a decimal point. The range of integer data depends on the number of binary digits or bits assigned to it. For example:

$$1 \text{ word} = 16 \text{ bits} \quad \text{range} = 2^{15} - 1 \text{ to } -(2^{15})$$
$$\text{or} \quad 32767 \text{ to } -32768$$
$$1 \text{ word} = 32 \text{ bits} \quad \text{range} = 2^{31} - 1 \text{ to } -(2^{31})$$
$$\text{or} \quad 2147483647 \text{ to } -2147483648$$

Real data are stored internally in binary form consisting of a mantissa and an exponent (power of 2). In external form real data appear as a signed number with a decimal point and can optionally be represented in scientific (power of 10) notation. The number of significant digits associated with real data is a function of the number of binary digits that make up the mantissa. For most computing systems a 23-bit or 24-bit mantissa is used. This yields seven significant digits for real data. The characteristic typically requires eight or nine bits, including the sign. The range of an eight-bit signed characteristic is $\pm 2^7 = \pm 128$. Thus the range of real data is $2^{\pm 128}$ or $10^{\pm 38}$.

A constant may also be either real or integer. An integer constant has no decimal point, whereas a real constant has a decimal point. Very large or very small constants can be represented in scientific notation as follows:

$$6.023(10^{23}) \quad .6023E + 24$$

The letter E follows the mantissa and precedes the power of 10. This is correct FORTRAN for writing a large constant. A plus sign is optional. Table 3.3 illustrates several FORTRAN constants.

To repeat, the arithmetic expression, exp, can be a constant, variable, or some combination of constants, variables, arithmetic operators, and parentheses. Thus a simple arithmetic expression would be exp = 1.0 or exp = DIAM. The five arithmetic operators are:

```
**   exponentiation
/    division
```

TABLE 3.3   FORTRAN Constants

FORTRAN constant	Data type
–32768	(negative) integer
100.0	(positive) real
0	(positive) integer
1.3E–8	(positive) real
11.5E820	invalid (power of 10 too large)

             *   multiplication
             –   subtraction or negation
             +   addition

More complex arithmetic expressions can now be formulated:

$$\text{exp} = A + B$$
$$\text{exp} = 0.3*DIAM$$
$$\text{exp} = W**2$$
$$\text{exp} = A + B*C/D*E + F$$

Evaluation of the expression $A + B*C/D*E + F$ requires knowledge of how FOR-TRAN will interpret this expression. All FORTRAN expressions are evaluated from left to right, starting with the innermost set of parentheses and working outward, according to the hierarchy.

         **   high
          */ $\downarrow$
       + –   low

Thus the expression $A + B*C/D*E + F$ will be evaluated stepwise as follows:

$$\text{step 1:} \quad b \cdot c$$

$$\text{step 2:} \quad \frac{(b \cdot c)}{d}$$

$$\text{step 3:} \quad \left(\frac{b \cdot c}{d}\right) \cdot e$$

$$\text{step 4:} \quad a + \left(\frac{b \cdot c}{d} \cdot e\right)$$

$$\text{step 5:} \quad \left(a + \frac{b \cdot c}{d} \cdot e\right) + f$$

Note the striking resemblance between the algebraic expression $a + \dfrac{b \cdot c}{d} \cdot e + f$
and the FORTRAN expression. The meaning of an expression can be altered through the use of parentheses. Thus (A + B*C)/(D*E + F) will be evaluated as:

$$
\begin{aligned}
&\text{step 1:} \quad b \cdot c \\
&\text{step 2:} \quad a + b \cdot c \\
&\text{step 3:} \quad d \cdot e \\
&\text{step 4:} \quad d \cdot e + f \\
&\text{step 5:} \quad \dfrac{a + b \cdot c}{d \cdot e + f}
\end{aligned}
$$

As a further example, consider the expressions:

$$-X**2 \qquad -(X**2) \qquad (-X)**2$$

The first and second expressions yield minus X squared, whereas the third expression yields X squared.

An added complication in FORTRAN occurs when real and integer data types are mixed within an arithmetic expression. This is termed *mixed-mode* arithmetic and real takes precedence over integer as shown in Table 3.4.

When raising to a power, care must be exercised. For example, A**4 and A**4.0 are not identical. When raising to an integer power, FORTRAN interprets this to mean successive multiplication, or A*A*A*A. If the power is real, logarithms are used, and the result will be the antilog (4.0 * log A). If A is zero or negative, the exponentiation fails, since the log of zero or a negative number does not exist.

As a general rule, mixed-mode arithmetic should be avoided. Use real data types for computation and integer data types for counting, wherever possible. When raising to a power always use an integer data type if possible.

TABLE 3.4 Mixed-Mode Arithmetic

Expression	Result
I*J	6
I/J	0 (truncates)
A*B	6.0
A/B	0.6666666
A*(I/J)	0.0 (truncates I/J)
I*A/J	1.333333
3*A	6.0
(3/2)*A	2.0 (truncates 3/2)
3*A/2	3.0

$a = 2, b = 3, i = 2, j = 3$

TABLE 3.5 Arithmetic Statements

Meaning	FORTRAN
$y = ax + b$	Y=A*X+B
$y = \dfrac{\pi d^2}{4}$	Y=3.14159*D**2/4.0
$\text{average} = \dfrac{\text{sum}}{n}$	AVE=SUM/N
$\text{volume} = (\text{length})^3$	VOL=RLEN**3
$\text{result} = \dfrac{a \cdot b}{c \cdot d}$	RESULT=(A*B)/(C*D)
$\text{answer} = x^{1.7} - 11$	ANSWER=X**1.7-11.0

The FORTRAN arithmetic (or assignment) statement can now be formulated. The symbol = means *assigned* and not equal when used in $v = $ exp. Thus statements of the type A = A + 1.0 are valid. This statement replaces A (on the left) with the old value of A (on the right) plus 1. Several arithmetic statements are shown in Table 3.5.

3.2 MEMORY CELLS AND ASSIGNMENT

A FORTRAN variable name points to an area in memory, called a *memory cell*, consisting of one or more memory words. The assignment statement references one or more memory cells in which the values of the variables are stored. Each memory cell should be thought of as containing a datum whose type is real, integer, character, logical, double precision, or complex. Thus the statement A = 3.0 assigns the label A to a memory cell in which 3.0 is stored. The contents of this memory cell can be changed during program execution, and the statement A = A + 1.0 stores 4.0 in memory cell A, replacing the old value of 3.0. Figure 3.1 illustrates this relationship

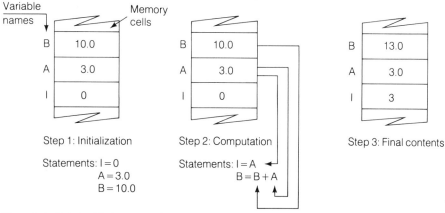

Figure 3.1 Relationship between variable names and memory cells

between a FORTRAN variable name and a memory cell. In step 1, values are assigned to I, A, and B. The variable name points to (references) the memory cell in which the value is stored: 0 for I, 3.0 for A, and 10.0 for B. Step 2 alters the contents of two of these memory cells through the assignment statements I = A and B = B + A. For the statement I = A, 3.0 is recalled from memory cell A, assigned to integer variable I, and stored as 3 in memory cell I, replacing the old value of 0. Recall from a memory cell does not change the contents of that memory cell. However, assignment to a memory cell destroys the old value by replacing the old value with the new value. The statement B = B + A recalls 3.0 from memory cell A and 10.0 from memory cell B, sums these values, and stores 13.0 in memory cell B, replacing the old value of 10.0. The relationship between memory cells and variable names is established during compilation.

3.3 THE WRITE STATEMENT

Output can be obtained from a FORTRAN program by using the WRITE statement, which is of the form

WRITE(logical unit number,*)list

for list-directed output. The logical unit number refers to an integer variable or integer constant whose value is the output unit (number) used for display. Each computer will have its own integer value for the logical unit number. For most systems, the logical unit number is 6. However, always check with your computer center for the correct integer. The asterisk specifies list-directed output. This means that the FORTRAN compiler will assign the format of your output, thus specifying the number of columns that will be used for displaying each list element. This will vary somewhat from computer to computer. Each WRITE statement begins output on a new line. A list is one or more arithmetic expressions or character constants separated by commas. A character constant is a string of characters enclosed by apostrophes. Thus

'THIS IS A CONSTANT'

is a valid character constant. A typical WRITE statement might be

WRITE(6,*)A,B,I/J

Assuming A = 10, B = −8.3, I = 5, and J = 2, the output would appear on one line as

ƀ10.0000ƀƀƀƀƀ − 8.30000ƀƀƀƀƀƀƀƀƀ2
|← A →||← B →|| I/J |

TABLE 3.6 FORTRAN Output

Statement	Output
`WRITE(6,*)A,B`	ƀ3.00000ƀƀƀƀƀƀ2.00000
`WRITE(6,*)A/B,I,J`	ƀ1.50000ƀƀƀƀƀƀƀƀƀ2ƀƀƀƀƀƀ1
`WRITE(6,*)'A=',A,'B=',B`	A=ƀ3.00000ƀƀƀƀB=ƀ2.00000
`WRITE(6,*)'END'`	END

$a = 3, b = 2, i = 2, j = 1$; ƀ = blank column

Typically, real output occupies 12 columns (left-justified); integer output, 6 columns (right-justified); and character output (not shown), the length of the character constant. A blank column separates numeric values. Very large and very small real data will automatically be displayed in E (power of 10) form. Real output will be rounded to six significant figures. (The format for list-directed output is discussed in Chapter 7.) Table 3.6 shows several WRITE statements with the associated outputs. The foregoing discussion of computer output is representative of a 16-bit computer. *Remember that the exact format of list-directed output will vary somewhat from machine to machine.*

Optionally, output can be obtained using the statement:

$$PRINT *, list$$

This output statement does not require specifying a logical unit number, since it defaults to the principal output device: the terminal display or the line printer. The PRINT statement can be used interchangeably with the WRITE statement when output is to be displayed at the terminal or listed on the line printer. The WRITE statement, however, is more general in that it allows output to be redirected to other devices, such as magnetic tape and magnetic disk. The WRITE statement will be used for output in all FORTRAN programs in this text.

3.4 THE READ STATEMENT

Input is handled through the READ statement, which is of the form

$$READ(logical\ unit\ number, *)list$$

for list-directed input. For most systems, the logical unit number used for input is 5. A list is one or more variable names, separated by commas, to which values are to be assigned. A typical READ statement would be

$$READ(5,*)A,B,I,J$$

Four values must be supplied. The first value will be assigned to A, the second value to B, the third value to I, and the last value to J. Input will normally be entered from a terminal keyboard or from punched cards. Each READ statement requires a new input line or a new data card. Each input value must be separated from its neighbor by a blank column or a comma. Thus for

$$\text{READ}(5,*)A,B,I,J$$

the input values would be

$$1.0, 3.14159265, 18, -100$$

with the resulting assignments (where real data are truncated beyond the seventh significant place):

$$a = 1.0$$
$$b = 3.141592$$
$$i = 18$$
$$j = -100$$

When input is from a terminal keyboard, output will be displayed at the terminal. If input is on punched cards, output will normally appear on a high-speed line printer.

Optionally, input can be stated using the statement:

$$\text{READ *, list}$$

This input statement defaults to the principal input device: terminal keyboard or card reader. It may be used interchangeably with the READ (logical unit number, *) list statement when input is to be from the terminal keyboard or the card reader. The READ statement with a logical unit number will be used for input in all FORTRAN programs. This option allows input to be redirected from other devices, such as magnetic tape and magnetic disk.

3.5 MEMORY CELLS AND INPUT/OUTPUT

The READ and WRITE statements also access memory cells during input and output operations. In Figure 3.2 the contents of the memory cell are 10.0 for X, -5.0 for Y, and 100 for I. These values are assigned through the statement

$$\text{READ}(5,*)X,Y,I$$

Figure 3.2 Input/output and memory cells

with data input

        10.0,-5.0,100

The statement

        WRITE(6,*)X*Y,I

displays

        -50.0000   100

3.6 CONTROL STATEMENTS

A FORTRAN program is a collection of FORTRAN statements arranged in a logical sequence. Execution of a FORTRAN program proceeds sequentially, starting with the first statement and continuing statement by statement unless the sequential flow of execution is altered by a control statement. A FORTRAN program should terminate on the control statement

                        STOP

STOP statements may appear anywhere in the program sequence and STOP is logically the final statement executed in a FORTRAN program.

The last statement (physically) in a FORTRAN program must be the control statement

END

This statement is a signal to the compiler that there are no more FORTRAN statements and that the program can now be translated into binary code. A feature of FORTRAN 77 is that the END statement can be used to terminate execution of a program. Older versions of FORTRAN require that a STOP statement precede END.

3.7 INTRINSIC FUNCTIONS

There is a class of mathematical functions used so often in problem solving that FORTRAN has provided the computation of these intrinsic functions as part of the language. These intrinsic functions are also called *library* functions. A complete discussion of intrinsic functions will be reserved for Chapter 9. A short discussion at this point, however, may prove useful.

The trigonometric sine of an angle is given by the infinite series

$$\sin x = x - \frac{x^3}{3!} + \frac{x^5}{5!} - \frac{x^7}{7!} + \frac{x^9}{9!} - \cdots$$

where x is the angle measured in radians. Rather than have to program the series summation every time the sine of x is to be computed, FORTRAN provides an intrinsic function, SIN(X) where X is real and measured in radians. Indeed, the argument of the sine function can be any valid real FORTRAN expression. Table 3.7 shows some of the more common intrinsic functions. The arguments of the trigonometric functions SIN and COS are in radians. For example, the arithmetic statement Y = 3.0*COS(ABS(B)) assigns to Y the calculated value of 3 times the cosine of the absolute value of B, where B is in radians. The sample program shows the use of several intrinsic functions.

```
C     SAMPLE PROGRAM
C     CODING INTRINSIC FUNCTIONS
C
      N=-50
      X=4.3
      Y=-7.5
      WRITE(6,*)ABS(X*Y),EXP(X+Y),LOG(ABS(X+Y)),IABS(N)
      STOP
      END
```

Output:

col. 1
↓
  32.2500   .407622E-01 1.6315   50

TABLE 3.7   Intrinsic Functions

Function name	Type of argument	Value of function	Type of result
SIN(X)	real	trigonometric sine	real
COS(X)	real	trigonometric cosine	real
ABS(X)	real	absolute value	real
IABS(N)	integer	absolute value	integer
SQRT(X)	real	square root	real
EXP(X)	real	exponential, e^x	real
LOG(X)	real	natural logarithm	real

3.8   SAMPLE PROGRAMS

The following sample programs illustrate FORTRAN programming. Program 1 adds constants simply by the output of their sums as an expression. Program 2 is a modification of the first program where variables are used in place of constants and an input statement is added, thus making the program general in nature. Program 3 outputs the area of a circle, given its radius. The output is labeled through the use of the character constant 'AREA='. Program 4 computes a function $\phi(x)$, given any value for x. Comment lines appear within the source program as a form of documentation. Input is prompted by a WRITE statement. Program 5 illustrates a simple algebraic computation. Intrinsic functions and their calculations are shown in program 6.

PROGRAM 1: A simple adder

```
WRITE(6,*)3+5,8+9
STOP
END
```

Output:

col. 1
↓
    8   17

PROGRAM 2: A simple adder with input

Option 1:

```
READ(5,*)A,B,C
WRITE(6,*)A+B,A+C
STOP
END
```

Option 2:

```
READ(5,*)A,B,C
ANS1=A+B
ANS2=A+C
WRITE(6,*)ANS1,ANS2
STOP
END
```

Input:

col. 1
↓
```
13.6,12.5,6.754
```

Output:

col. 1
↓
```
 26.1000      20.3540
```

PROGRAM 3: Area of a circle

```
READ(5,*)RADIUS
AREA=3.14159*RADIUS**2
WRITE(6,*)'AREA=',AREA
STOP
END
```

Input:

```
10.0
```

Output:

col. 1
↓
```
AREA= 314.159
```

PROGRAM 4: Evaluation of a polynomial

Let $\phi(x) = 11x^3 - 12x^2 + 66$

```
C       SAMPLE PROGRAM 4
        WRITE(6,*)'ENTER X '
        READ(5,*)X
        PHI=11.0*X**3-12.0*X*X+66.0
C       OUTPUT PHI
        WRITE(6,*)PHI
        STOP
        END
```

Input:

col. 1
↓
ENTER X 1.0

Output:

col. 1
↓
 65.0000

PROGRAM 5: The determinant of a 2 × 2 square matrix

Let the determinant of a square matrix A be given by:

$A = a_{11} * a_{22} - a_{12} * a_{21}$

```
C       CALCULATION OF THE DETERMINANT
        WRITE(6,*)'ENTER ROW 1 '
        READ(5,*)A11,A12
        WRITE(6,*)'ENTER ROW 2 '
        READ(5,*)A21,A22
C       CALCULATE DETERMINANT
        DET=A11*A22-A12*A21
        WRITE(6,*)'DET A = ',DET
        STOP
        END
```

Input:

col 1
↓
```
ENTER ROW 1 2.0,3.0
ENTER ROW 2 4.0,1.0
```

Output:

col 1
↓
```
DET A = -10.0000
```

PROGRAM 6: Calculation of the trigonometric sine, cosine, and tangent

```
C      ANGLE IS IN DEGREES
       WRITE(6,*)'ENTER ANGLE IN DEGREES '
       READ(5,*)ANGLE
C      CONVERT DEGREES TO RADIANS
       RAD=3.141593*ANGLE/180.0
       WRITE(6,*)'SINE =',SIN(RAD)
       WRITE(6,*)'COSINE =',COS(RAD)
       WRITE(6,*)'TANGENT =',SIN(RAD)/COS(RAD)
       STOP
       END
```

Input:

col 1
↓
```
ENTER ANGLE IN DEGREES 45.0
```

Output:

col 1
↓
```
SINE = 0.707107
COSINE = 0.707107
TANGENT = 1.00000
```

3.9   SUMMARY

FORTRAN, a high-level, problem-oriented language, is designed to solve problems that arise in engineering and science. High-level languages offer five statement types: assignment, input/output, control, specification, and subprogram. The assignment or arithmetic statement is used to code formulas and equations. Input and output are managed through the FORTRAN statements READ and WRITE. Simple control makes use of the STOP and END statements. Intrinsic functions permit basic algebraic and trigonometric operations to be performed simply by requesting the operation by name. The intrinsic functions form part of the library of permanently stored programs. The statements discussed in this chapter permit simple problem solutions, consisting of a sequence of steps, to be programmed in FORTRAN.

EXERCISES

1.   Circle the valid FORTRAN real variable names.

A3	K02	BOOT	3Z
APPLE	ABCD	1VALUE	VOLUMES
REALANS	LEN	ANS2	NONE

2.   Write a valid FORTRAN arithmetic expression for each of the following:

$$\frac{a+b}{c+d} \qquad \sqrt{x^2+y^2+z^2} \qquad \text{alpha} \cdot x^{1/3} \qquad a+\frac{b}{c}+d$$

$$m \cdot n^b \qquad \frac{\pi d^3}{6} \qquad \sqrt[3]{a^2-b^2} \qquad -b^2+4ac$$

3.   Correct any syntax error in the following FORTRAN statements. Do not change statements whose syntax is correct.

```
     Y=3.0*A÷B
     K=K-I/J
  10END
     3.14159=PI
     D=(A*A+B*B+C*C)**.5
     WRITE(IUNIT,*)A,B,JOBNO
     RADIUS = DIAMETER/2.0
     READ(5,*)A,B,I,J
  10 D=(SIDEA-5.0)(SIDEB-2.0)
```

4. Correct all logic and syntax errors in the following FORTRAN program.

```
C THE ROOTS OF A
  QUADRATIC EQUATION
C WITH COEFFICIENTS
  A,B,C
C
  READ(6,*)A;B;C
  DISCRM-B*B-4A*C
  1ROOT=(-B+SQRT(DISCRM)/2*A
  2ROOT=(-B-SQRT(DISCRM)/2A
  WRITE(5,*)1ROOT;2ROOT
  STOP
```

5. Correct all logic and syntax errors in the following FORTRAN program.

```
C     THE DISTANCE BETWEEN
C     TWO POINTS IN SPACE.
C     COORDINATES ARE (X1,Y1,Z1)(X2,Y2,Z2)
      DISTANCE=SQRT(X2-X1)**2+(Y2-Y1)**2+(Z2-Z1)**2
      INPUT DATA
      INPUT (X1,Y1,Z1),(X2,Y2,Z2)
      OUTPUT RESULT
      OUTPUT 'DISTANCE IS ',DISTANCE
      END
      STOP
```

6. What will be the printed output for each of the following WRITE statements, given that

$$a = 100, b = 30, i = 10, j = -3$$

(a) WRITE(6,*)B,I,J   (c)WRITE(6,*)A/B*A

(b) WRITE(6,*)A/B,I/J   (d)WRITE(6,*)J/I*B

7. What will be the printed output? Check your answer by executing the following program:

```
A=10.0
B=3.0
I=3
J=2
WRITE(6,*)I/J,1.0/B,2.0/B
WRITE(6,*)I/(J*A)
```

```
WRITE(6,*)(I/J)*A
WRITE(6,*)I*A/J
C1=0.6666666666
C2=0.4444444444
C3=1.0E7/11.0
WRITE(6,*)C1,C2,C3
STOP
END
```

8. Given the following FORTRAN program:

```
A=10.0
B=50.0
I=3
J=9
C=A+B
A=B/C
J=J/I
STOP
END
```

what values will be stored in memory cells A, B, C, I, and J after execution of this program?

Variable name	Memory cells
C	
J	
I	
B	
A	

9. For the FORTRAN program

```
READ(5,*)X,Y,I,J
Z=ABS(Y-X)
WRITE(6,*)I*J,Z
STOP
END
```

and the input

```
100.0,-500.0,14,5
```

what will be the printed output and the final contents of memory cells X, Y, Z, I, and J?

Variable name	Memory cells
Z	
J	
I	
Y	
X	

10. What is the largest integer (positive and negative) that can be processed by your computer? Explain how you arrived at your answer.

11. How many significant digits are there in real data on your computer? What is the range of real data on your computer?

12. Is the FORTRAN language implemented as a compiler on your computer? How does this implementation affect the preparation and translation of your (source) program?

13. Correct all logic and syntax errors in the following FORTRAN program.

```
C      VOLUME OF A CONE
C      DIAM=DIAMETER OF THE BASE
       ALT=ALTITUDE
       READ(IUNIT,*)DIAM,ALT
       AREA=π*DIAM**2/4.0
       VOLUME=(1/3)*AREA*ALT
       WRITE(6,*)VOLUME
       STOP
       END
```

14. Write a FORTRAN program to calculate the diagonal of a rectangular parallelepiped, given its three sides x, y, and z.

$$\text{diagonal} = \sqrt{x^2 + y^2 + z^2}$$

Test your program for $x = 2$, $y = 5$, and $z = 3$.

15. The roots of the quadratic equation

$$ax^2 + bx + c = 0$$

are given by

$$\frac{-b \pm \sqrt{b^2 - 4ac}}{2a}$$

Is it possible to write and execute a FORTRAN program for any values of a, b, and c?

16. Prepare, compile, and execute the following FORTRAN program, whose purpose is to output the calculated value of y for any value of x, where

$$y = 11x^3 - 18$$

```
C       POLYNOMIAL PROGRAM
        READ(5,*)X
        WRITE(6,*)11.0*X**3.0-18.0
        STOP
        END
```

Execute this program twice, once for $x = 3$ and a second time for $x = -3$. Comment on the results.

17. The equivalent resistance R for the electrical circuit shown is

$$R = \frac{R_1 \cdot R_2}{R_1 + R_2} + R_3$$

Write a FORTRAN program that will output the equivalent resistance R. Input is to be R1, R2, and R3. Use a character constant to label your output. Test your program using

$$R_1 = 100 \text{ ohms}$$
$$R_2 = 200 \text{ ohms}$$
$$R_3 = 200 \text{ ohms}$$

18. The general gas law for isentropic compression is given by

$$P_2 = P_1 \left(\frac{T_2}{T_1}\right)^{k/(k-1)}$$

where P_1 = initial pressure in atmospheres
P_2 = final pressure in atmospheres
T_1 = initial temperature in degrees Kelvin
T_2 = final temperature in degrees Kelvin
k = specific heat ratio = 1.4 for air

Degrees Kelvin = $\frac{5}{9}$(°F − 32) + 273. If a cylinder of air is compressed from 1 atmosphere and 40°F, write a program that will convert degrees Fahrenheit (°F) to degrees Kelvin and then compute the pressure required to achieve a final temperature of 200°F. Use as variable names:

P1 = initial pressure
P2 = final pressure
T1 = initial temperature
T2 = final temperature

Output is to be the calculated value for P2 in atmospheres.

19. A jet engine consumes 1 pound of fuel for 25 pounds of air. The hot gases are discharged from the tailpipe at a velocity u of 1600 feet per second relative to the airplane. The equation of efficiency is

$$e = 1/\left[1 + \frac{0.5(1 + r)(u/v - 1)^2}{(1 + r)(u/v) - 1}\right]$$

where r = pounds of fuel per pound of air and v = absolute velocity of the airplane in feet per second. Program this equation so as to input r, u, and v. Output, with a suitable label, the efficiency e. Test your program by executing it several times, using as input data:

$$v = 1000 \text{ feet per second}$$
$$v = 700 \text{ feet per second}$$
$$v = 200 \text{ feet per second}$$

20. The present value of an annuity of one is

$$\frac{1 - (1 + i)^{-n}}{i}$$

where i is the interest rate and n is the number of time periods for the given interest rate. Write a FORTRAN program to evaluate the present value for any i and n.

21.   The hypotenuse of a right triangle is given by

$$c = \sqrt{a^2 + b^2}$$

Write a program to calculate c for any a and b. Test your program for $a = 3$ and $b = 4$. Use the intrinsic SQRT(X). Output is labeled and of the form

FOR A = 3.0 AND B = 4.0
THE HYPOTENUSE IS 5.0

22.   Write a FORTRAN program to calculate and output the value of y, given

$$y = 1.5x^3 + 3x^2 + 6x^{1.5} + 18$$

Test your program for $x = 3$. What output would you expect for negative values of x?

23.   The modal heat capacity of ethylene at atmospheric pressure is given by

$$C_p = 2.706 + 0.29T - 90.6(10^{-7})T^2$$

where T is in degrees Kelvin. Write a program to calculate C_p for any given value of T. Test your program for $T = 273$ degrees Kelvin.

24.   Write a FORTRAN program to solve two simultaneous linear equations of the form

$$ax + by = c$$
$$ex + fy = g$$

for x and y. Use as test data $a = 1$, $b = 3$, $c = 19$, $e = 1$, $f = -1$ and $g = -1$.

25.   The period of a simple pendulum of length L is given by

$$T = 2\pi \sqrt{\frac{L}{g}}$$

where g, the acceleration of gravity, is 9.8 meters per second squared. Write a FORTRAN program that outputs T given a length L in meters. Test your program for $L = 1$ meter and $L = 5$ meters. What program changes would be needed if the length were in feet?

26. A box slides down a frictionless plane inclined at an angle of theta with the horizontal. The acceleration *a* of the box is given by

$$a = g \sin (\text{theta})$$

where *g* is the acceleration of gravity, 32.2 feet per second squared. Write a FORTRAN program to output acceleration for any angle theta. Test your program for theta = 20, 30, and 45 degrees.

chapter 4

Problem Solving and Flowcharting

Many beginning students of computer programming think that the program is nothing more than a set of coded statements that will instruct the computer to accept input, perform certain operations, and output the results. Nothing could be further from the truth. It is, unfortunately, true that a computer does not do what we want but only what it is told, and the "telling" must be clear and unambiguous. For simple problems the problem solver can code a series of instructions, clearly and unambiguously, and achieve a usable solution as output from the coded program. In other words, the problem solver may, with little difficulty, write out the steps of the program while "thinking through" the solution. Thus, in computing the sum of a set of numbers, for example, one can simply write the program as a series of steps that would normally be followed to arrive at the sum.

One might become more sophisticated by introducing into the code a so-called *loop* to repeatedly read in the numbers before summing takes place and, perhaps, sum any number of numbers. Sophistication at this level, however, is still relatively easy to achieve by the "thinking-through" process.

In more complex problems the "thinking through" becomes difficult and the direct coding can lead to inefficiencies and actual logic errors. Hence we come to the central question, "Is there some process by which we can make the complicated task of programming more manageable?" We believe there is!

4.1 A GENERAL PROCEDURE FOR PROBLEM SOLVING

A computer program, as we will think of it, is the entire process of computer problem solving. It consists of three parts:

- analysis
- algorithm and flowchart
- code

The *analysis* consists of defining the problem and outlining in general terms its solution. Problem analysis is often thought to be a trivial step; in fact, the proper definition and analysis of a problem is central to problem solving. Besides the general outline the analysis also includes the identification of input and required output as well as the definition of variables. The definition of variables should be considered carefully. Whenever possible, the FORTRAN variable name should be similar to the algebraic variable being named.

For example, the area of a circle is area $= \pi r^2$. In defining the FORTRAN variables one could say area $=$ A, radius $=$ R, and pi $=$ P, but it is not easy to think of A $=$ P*R*R as the area of a circle. Rather, if area $=$ AREA, radius $=$ RADIUS, and pi $=$ PI, then AREA $=$ PI*RADIUS**2 is more clearly seen as the area of a circle. True, the time spent typing such code is greater but the clarity of the program outweighs this disadvantage. If useful, the analysis should include sample calculations made in the solution of the problem. The sample calculations will come in handy in checking the correctness of your computer output.

The *algorithm* is a step-by-step "recipe" for carrying out the analysis. It clearly sets forth the logical sequence of steps necessary for the successful implementation of the program. Algorithm design can be a highly mathematical procedure. However, design of the algorithm in a more verbal sense will be used in this book. The *flowchart* is the pictorial display of the algorithm. It gives a graphic and symbolic description of the input and output, the flow of the logic, decisions to be made and calculations prescribed in the algorithm. Indeed, many programmers actually design the algorithm in flowchart form. Once the flowchart is refined and completed, the translation into FORTRAN code is greatly facilitated. Indeed, it is in the construction of the flowchart that the skills of the programmer are tested. In construction of the flowchart, *think modularly*. For example, think of input and output as processes to be defined later. Essentially say, "I may not quite know how I'll get the data in or the answers out, but I'll think about that later." If somewhere in your program you have to sum a set of variables, think of it as a process and figure out how later. Don't be afraid to *think modularly*. Also don't be ashamed to *iterate*. That is, go back, insert, correct, add, or delete in order to refine your flowchart. Beware of anyone who claims to solve an interesting problem by constructing a finished flowchart, without correction, from scratch.

Experienced programmers might minimize the value of the flowchart for understanding the logic of the problem solution, but it is highly recommended for the novice. Figure 4.1 shows the symbols used in drawing a flowchart.

The *code* is the sequence of statements, written in a particular programming language, that will instruct the computer how to successfully carry out the logic of the algorithm and flowchart.

Selection of test data follows the coding. The development of this data is crucial. Always have test data that will truly *test* your program. For example, if your program is designed to print a message when an answer is negative, make sure you enter data that will result in positive as well as negative results, to make sure that the program

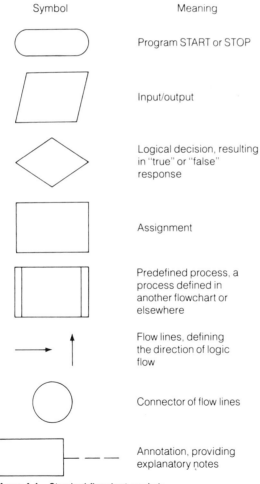

Symbol	Meaning
	Program START or STOP
	Input/output
	Logical decision, resulting in "true" or "false" response
	Assignment
	Predefined process, a process defined in another flowchart or elsewhere
	Flow lines, defining the direction of logic flow
	Connector of flow lines
	Annotation, providing explanatory notes

Figure 4.1   Standard flowchart symbols

will not output the negative message when the answer is positive. If there are limits on your program, find data that will exceed the limits to see what will happen. In short, always provide data that will test all possible outcomes of your program. If an error occurs during testing, then the program *debugging* starts. One of the simplest ways of finding errors in programs is to liberally sprinkle output statements throughout in order to see what's going on. These statements can always be removed later.

Finally, a word should be said about the documentation of the program. The purpose of the documentation is to provide information about the program. Every problem solver has experienced the frustration of trying to follow a program written by someone else (or even written by him- or herself some time earlier).

There are two types of documentation: internal and external. Internal documentation consists of special statements, directly included in the coding, that describe the purpose of the program, define the variables used, and note any special procedures followed. The analysis and a set of flowcharts provide the external documentation.

All programs should include the analysis, a set of flowcharts, and the code.

Before proceeding to specific examples of computer problem solving, let us consider the algorithm and flowchart logic in more detail. All flowcharts can be designed from a few basic forms called *programming structures*. They are:

SEQUENCE   IFTHENELSE   DOUNTIL   DOWHILE   CASE

Figure 4.2 shows the five basic programming structures in abstracted form.

4.2 EXAMPLES OF PROGRAMMING STRUCTURES

Figures 4.3 through 4.7 illustrate four different algorithms with their associated flowcharts for adding a set of numbers. These flowcharts illustrate the programming structures shown in Figure 4.2. These algorithms are designed to input a set of numbers, add them together, and output the sum. The algorithms also demonstrate the effect that different constraints have on the problem-solving logic.

Figure 4.3 sums five numbers and outputs the result. This is adequate when the set of numbers is not large. With a large set of numbers, assigning each number to its own variable would result in a most cumbersome program.

To remove the constraint on the size of the set of numbers, Figure 4.4 introduces the idea of a counter (ctr). Provided the size of the set of numbers is known (k), the counter (ctr) keeps track of the number of inputs, n (where n is the input value), and the program will output the sum when the counter (ctr) exceeds the size of the set (k).

Now suppose the size of the set of numbers is not known, then the set size, k, cannot be established at the beginning of the program. In that case $k = 0$ may be

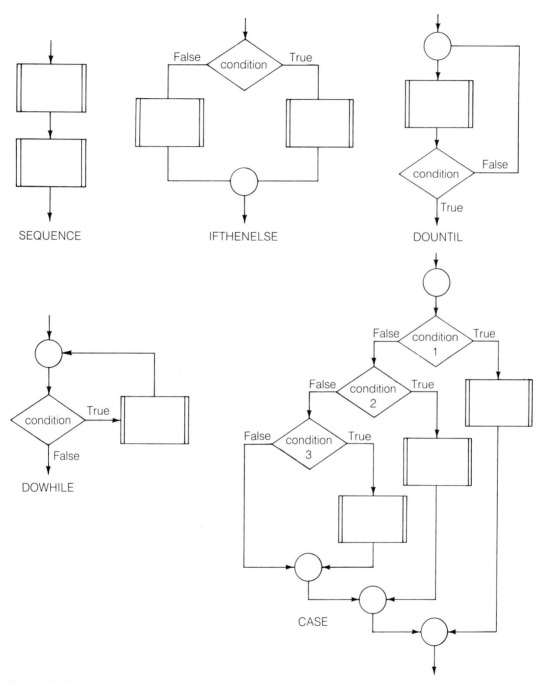

Figure 4.2 Five basic programming structures

The algorithm

1. Input five values n_1, n_2, n_3, n_4, n_5
2. Compute the sum of the five values,
   $\text{sum} = n_1 + n_2 + n_3 + n_4 + n_5$
3. Output the sum
4. STOP

The flowchart

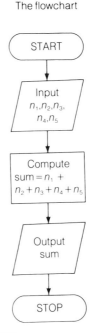

Figure 4.3   Summing five numbers with a SEQUENCE

used as a "flag" to inform the computer that all data (the set of numbers) have been entered. Figure 4.5 illustrates this point.

Figure 4.6 combines the concept of the flag at the end of an indefinite set of inputs (*n*) with a decision to separately add positive and negative numbers.

If an input value is to be used to terminate data entry, that is, input *n* and sum while $n > 0$, an anticipatory input is needed. The required steps are: (1) initialize sum, (2) input *n* (the anticipatory input), (3) while data remains, add *n* to sum and input *n*, and (4) output the sum. The flowchart and algorithm for this technique is shown in Figure 4.7.

4.3   A FURTHER EXAMPLE OF PROGRAMMING WITH STRUCTURE

Consider the problem of calculating the surface area or volume of a cylinder given its height and radius. Whether the area or volume is to be calculated depends on a code number that forms part of the input data. Let it be required to calculate and output the surface area if the code number is 1 or output the volume if the code number is not 1. Figure 4.8 is a typical flowchart for this problem.

The algorithm

1. Input number of values, k
2. Initialize sum = 0
3. Initialize counter, ctr = 1
4. DOWHILE ctr ≤ k
   (a) Input n
   (b) Add n to sum
   (c) Increment ctr = ctr + 1
5. Output sum
6. STOP

The flowchart

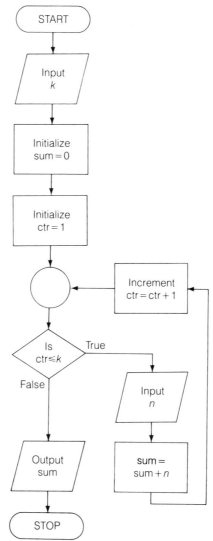

Figure 4.4   Summing a specified number of values with a DOWHILE

A careful study of Figure 4.8 reveals that the computation and output process is a SEQUENCE structure. It is simply a series of consecutive operations to be performed. The part of the flowchart that calculates the area or volume depending on the code is an IFTHENELSE structure. The condition "is code = 1" is tested, and if true the "true" branch is executed or if false the "false" branch is executed and

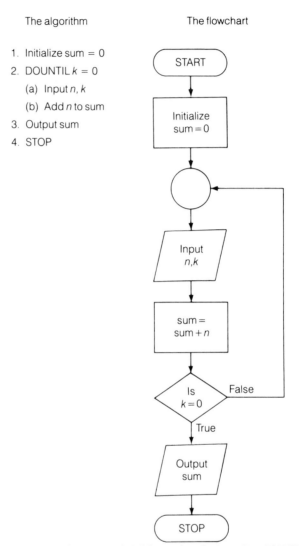

The algorithm

1. Initialize sum = 0
2. DOUNTIL $k = 0$
   (a) Input n, k
   (b) Add n to sum
3. Output sum
4. STOP

The flowchart

START

Initialize
sum = 0

Input
n,k

sum =
sum + n

Is
k = 0 — False

True

Output
sum

STOP

Figure 4.5 Summing an indefinite number of values with a DOUNTIL

the program proceeds. The entire program is a DOUNTIL programming structure. To see this more clearly, let us simplify the flowchart by abstracting out the IFTHENELSE structure as shown in Figure 4.9. This simplified flowchart shows that the process will continue UNTIL the test condition "are all data read" is true, after which the program proceeds.

The algorithm

The flowchart

1. Initialize sum(+) = 0
   and sum(−) = 0

2. DOUNTIL k = 0

   (a) Input n,k

   (b) Is n < 0?

   IF true THEN sum negative
   values, sum(−) = sum(−) + n

   ELSE sum positive values,
   sum(+) = sum(+) + n

3. Output sum(−) and sum(+)

4. STOP

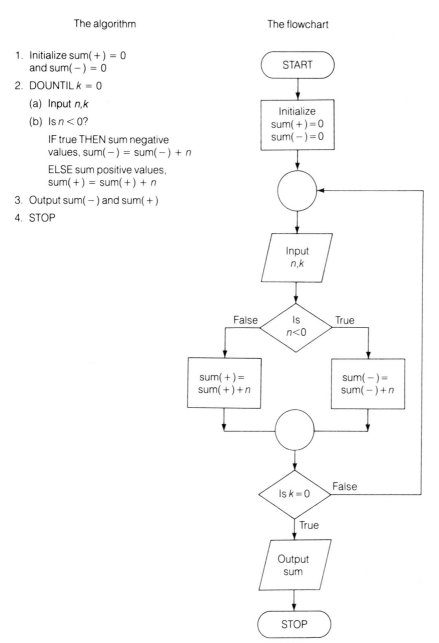

Figure 4.6   Summing positive and negative numbers with a DOUNTIL and IFTHENELSE

The Flowchart

The algorithm

1. Initialize sum = 0.
2. input n.
3. DOWHILE $n \neq 0$
   (a) add n to sum.
   (b) input n.
4. output sum.
5. STOP

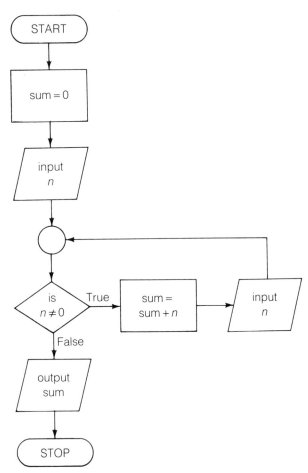

Figure 4.7 Summing an indefinite number of values with a DOWHILE

If a test condition "are there more data to be read" were placed before the input statement, the programming structure would be a DOWHILE, as shown in Figure 4.10. The DOWHILE structure continues the process WHILE there are still data to be read. One can see that the statement of the test condition in the DOWHILE is the reverse of that in the DOUNTIL.

The fifth basic programming structure is the CASE, symbolically drawn in Figure 4.2. The CASE permits *multiple* decision making within a single structure. Essentially the CASE is a multiple IFTHENELSE in the sense that a series of "true/false"

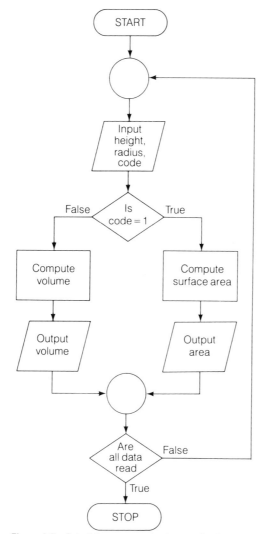

Figure 4.8 Calculating areas and volumes of cylinders

decisions are made, each one depending on the outcome of the previous test. This series of decisions occurs within the same block in the programming structure. In short, there is one entry point to the CASE block and any number of branches.

The CASE programming structure can be used effectively to generalize the flow-chart for the current problem of the cylinder. Suppose we wish to include the calculation of the volume and surface area of a cone in the flowchart. This is done

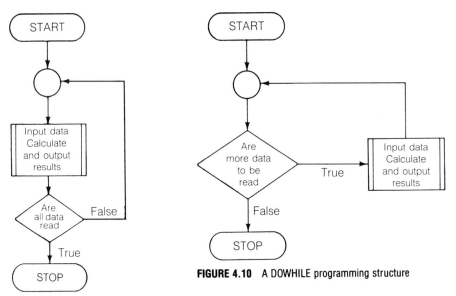

Figure 4.9   A DOUNTIL
programming structure

FIGURE 4.10   A DOWHILE programming structure

by assigning four code numbers to the four desired conditions: codes 1 and 2 for the surface area and volume, respectively, of the cylinder and codes 3 and 4 for the surface area and volume of the cone. Figure 4.11 is a flowchart showing the CASE programming structure.

4.4   SAMPLE PROBLEMS

The following illustrative problems should be studied carefully for proper problem-solving methodology. In studying the flowcharts particular attention should be paid to the programming structures involved.

For example, in the algorithm of problem 1, steps 1, 2, and 3 form a SEQUENCE programming structure. Steps 4 through 4c form a DOWHILE structure. Note that the operations within the DOWHILE loop are executed *while k* is less than or equal to $n - 1$. Within the loop there is one IFTHENELSE structure at 4b. The IFTHENELSE is associated with the test condition "is x less than sm." Figure 4.12 shows the flowchart for problem 1.

In the algorithm of problem 2, step 4 forms a DOWHILE loop. Within step 4 is an IFTHENELSE programming structure. Figure 4.13 shows the flowchart for problem 2.

You should now try to identify the programming structures for problems 3 and 4.

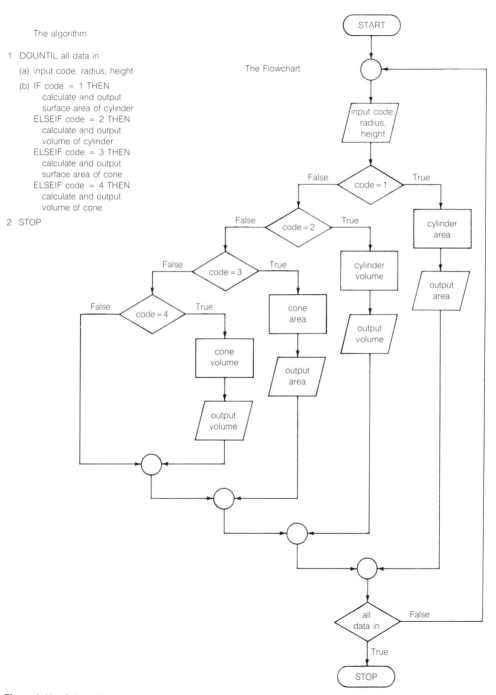

The algorithm

1. DOUNTIL all data in
   (a) input code, radius, height
   (b) IF code = 1 THEN
       calculate and output
       surface area of cylinder
       ELSEIF code = 2 THEN
       calculate and output
       volume of cylinder
       ELSEIF code = 3 THEN
       calculate and output
       surface area of cone
       ELSEIF code = 4 THEN
       calculate and output
       volume of cone.
2. STOP

The Flowchart

Figure 4.11　Calculating areas and volumes of cylinders and cones

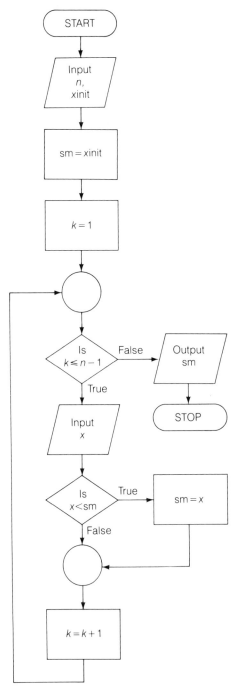

Figure 4.12 Flowchart for sample problem 1

PROBLEM 1: Identify the smallest of a set of numbers.

The analysis

1. Given a set of n numbers, find and output the smallest number.

2. Input the first number and assume it to be the "smallest."

3. Input the next number and compare it to the "smallest." If it is smaller, call this number "smallest." If it is equal to or larger than the "smallest," do nothing.

4. Proceed number by number for all n numbers of the set.

5. Define the variables.
    (a) Let x be any input number.
    (b) Let $x$init be the first number.
    (c) Let n be the size of the set of numbers.
    (d) Let sm be the "smallest."
    (e) Let k be a counter of the input numbers.

The algorithm

1. Input n and $x$init.

2. Let sm = $x$init.

3. Initialize the counter, $k = 1$.

4. DOWHILE $k \leqslant n - 1$.
    (a) Input x.
    (b) Is $x <$ sm?
         IF true THEN let sm = x ELSE proceed.
    (c) Increment counter, $k = k + 1$.

5. Output sm and STOP.

PROBLEM 2: Test whether a number is a prime number.

The analysis

1. Input the number to be tested for prime or not prime.

2. If a number is to be prime it must yield a remainder when divided by all integers between (but not including) the integer 1 and the number itself.

3. If step 2 is satisfied, output the message "prime"; if not, output the message "not prime."

4. Define the variables.
    (a) Let n be the number to be tested.
    (b) Let k be the divisor between 1 and n.
    (c) Let flag be either the message "prime" or the message "not prime."

The Flowchart

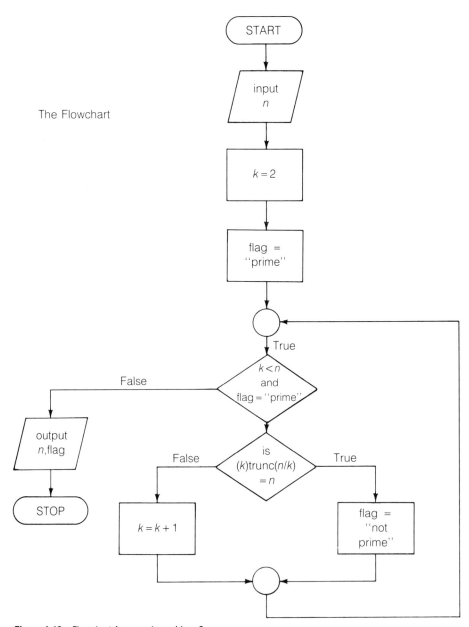

Figure 4.13 Flowchart for sample problem 2

The algorithm

1. Input n.

2. Initialize the divisor, $k = 2$.

3. Initialize flag, flag = "prime."

4. DOWHILE ($k < n$ and flag = "prime")

> IF truncated value of (n/k) times $k = n$ THEN flag = "not prime"
> ELSE $k = k + 1$.

5. Output n, flag.

6. STOP.

PROBLEM 3: Rank a sequence of integers in ascending order.

The analysis

1. Given a sequence of the five integers 5, 3, 4, 1, 2, it is required to rank and output the integers in ascending order.

2. Compare the integer in position 1 with each integer in positions 2 through 5. Whenever the integer in position 1 is greater than the integer in the comparison position, interchange the integers. Whenever it is not, do nothing. This puts the smallest integer in position 1.

3. To place the next smallest integer in position 2, compare the integer in position 2 with each integer in positions 3 through 5 and interchange the integer whenever the integer in position 2 is greater than the one in comparison position.

4. Continue until ranking is achieved.

5. Define variables.
   (a) Let the integers be x_i.
   (b) Let the position identifiers be i and k. Thus x_i is the integer in the ith position and x_k is the integer being tested.
   (c) Let the total number of integers be n.

Figure 4.14 shows the sequence of the comparisons and interchanges.

The algorithm

1. Input n integers, x_i.

2. Initialize counter, $i = 1$.

3. DOWHILE $i \leq n - 1$.
   (a) Initialize counter $k = i + 1$.

Interchange	5	3	4	1	2
Do nothing	3	5	4	1	2
Interchange	3	5	4	1	2
Do nothing	1	5	4	3	2
Interchange	1	5	4	3	2
Interchange	1	4	5	3	2
Interchange	1	3	5	4	2
Interchange	1	2	5	4	3
Interchange	1	2	4	5	3
Interchange	1	2	3	5	4
	1	2	3	4	5

Figure 4.14   A schematic representation of the ranking analysis

(b) DOUNTIL $k > n$.
  (i)   Is $x_i \leqslant x_k$?
        IF true THEN proceed
        ELSE interchange x_i and x_k and proceed.
  (ii) Increment counter $k = k + 1$.
(c) Increment counter $i = i + 1$.

4. Output ranked integers and STOP.

Part A

Part B

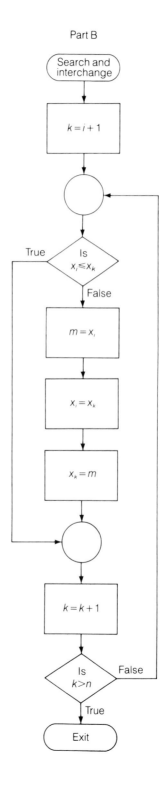

Figure 4.15 Flowcharts for the ranking problem

The flowchart

We will draw the flowchart in two parts. Part A will be the logic flow controlling the search and interchange process. This is represented by the four logic blocks in the numeric table of the analysis. Part B will be the logic of the search and interchange procedure itself. Figure 4.15 presents the set of flowcharts for the ranking problem.

PROBLEM 4: Calculate the factorial of *N*.

The analysis

1. Given N, calculate its factorial.

2. The factorial of N is given by $N(N - 1)(N - 2) \ldots (1)$

3. Output the factorial of N.

4. Define the variables.
    (a) Let N be any non-negative, whole number.
    (b) Let *fac* be the factorial of N.
    (c) Let *i* be a counter whose range is 1 to N.

The algorithm

1. Input N.

2. Let *fac* = 1.0

3. Initialize the counter, *i* = 1.

4. DOWHILE $i <= N$
    (a) *fac* = *fac*∗*i*
    (b) *i* = *i* + 1

5. Output *fac*.

6. STOP.

4.5   SUMMARY

Computer problem solving is more than writing code. There are, in general, three steps in the process of computer problem solving: analysis, algorithms and flowcharts, and code. Documentation completes the task. Structure in computer problem solving is very important and helps logical thinking. The flowchart is a pictorial aid in this process of logical thinking. The use of recognized structures such as SEQUENCE, IFTHENELSE, DOWHILE, DOUNTIL, and CASE leads to a logical and disciplined style of programming.

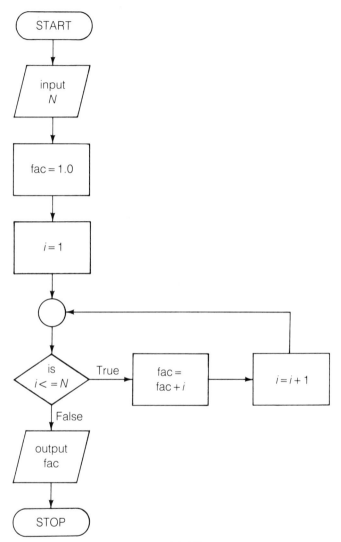

Figure 4.16 Flowchart for the factorial of *N*

EXERCISES

1. Draw a flowchart that will output the total monthly commission a salesperson is paid, based on the following monthly rate:

    (a) Base commission of $175, plus

    (b) Five percent of all sales over $12,000.

2. Draw a flowchart that will compute the percentage of males and females in a class of 200, and the average age of the class. The coding will be the digit 1 for male and 2 for female. The data should be accepted one set at a time, each set to include the student's age and male or female code number.

3. Draw a flowchart that will sum the series:

$$1 + \frac{1}{2} + \frac{1}{4} + \frac{1}{8} + \frac{1}{16} + \cdots \frac{1}{2^N} \text{ for 25 terms}$$

4. Do exercise 3 if, instead of 25 terms, the summation is terminated when $1/2^N$ is less than 0.0001.

5. You invest $100 per month for four years. The interest is compounded monthly at ½ percent per month. Draw a flowchart that will output the amount invested after four years.

6. Draw the flowchart for exercise 2 if, instead of 200 students, the flowchart should process any number of students.

7. Prepare a flowchart that will accept a worker's gross pay, pension contribution, tax deduction, and hospitalization contribution. The output should show gross pay, total deductions, and net pay. There are 500 workers to be processed. Input the data one set at a time.

8. Prepare a flowchart that will yield the real roots of the quadratic equation $ax^2 + bx + c = 0$ for an indefinite number of values a, b, c. If $b^2 - 4ac$ is greater than or equal to zero, the output should be the two roots of the equation $x_1, x_2 = (-b \pm \sqrt{b^2 - 4ac})/2a$. If $b^2 - 4ac$ is less than zero, the output should be the message "roots not real."

9. The hypotenuse of a right triangle is given by the equation $c^2 = a^2 + b^2$ where a, b are the perpendicular sides. Draw a flowchart that will accept 50 values of a, b, c and test whether a right triangle is formed.

10. The cosine of an angle in radians can be approximated by the series

$$\cos x = 1 - \frac{x^2}{2} + \frac{x^4}{24} - \frac{x^6}{720} + \frac{x^8}{40320}$$

Prepare a flowchart that will compute the cosine of 0°, 60°, 90°.

11. Draw a flowchart that will output the arithmetic average of an n element x array. The average is obtained by summing the array elements and dividing by n, where

$$\text{average} = \frac{x_1 + x_2 + \cdots + x_n}{n} = \frac{\sum\limits_{i=1}^{n} x_i}{n}$$

12. The exponential of x can be approximated by the series:

$$e^x = 1 + x + \frac{x^2}{2!} + \frac{x^3}{3!} + \cdots$$

Prepare a flowchart and algorithm to evaluate the exponential of x using this series. Calculate e^x to five significant digits. Output x, exponential of x, and the number of terms.

13. Repeat exercise 12, but sum the first 10 terms of the series. Output x and the exponential of x.

14. What, if anything, is wrong with this algorithm?

1. Initialize sum $= 0$.

2. Input n.

3. If $n <= 0$ THEN
    GOTO step 5
    ELSE
    sum = sum + n

4. GOTO step 2.

5. Output sum.

6. STOP.

15. Assume that a predefined process such as $n!$ is available to calculate a factorial. Draw a flowchart that calculates and outputs the number of permutations of n objects taken r at a time. The formula for the number of permutations is

$$_nP_r = \frac{n!}{(n - r)!}$$

chapter 5

Control Statements

If the capability of the computer were restricted to performing only a once-through sequence of operations, no matter how complicated, its usefulness as a problem-solving tool would be limited. It is precisely the capability of decision making (IFTHENELSE), looping (DOWHILE, DOUNTIL), and branching, all at electronic speeds, that makes the computer the powerful problem-solving aid it is. In summing a series of a large number of terms (say, the infinite series for the sine or cosine), the repeated calculation of the general term and the adding of this term to the previous sum requires the programming of statements that will test whether the sum is sufficiently precise and then transfer control to that part of the program that will either output the results or repeat the calculations.

In the problem of ranking (or sorting) a sequence of integers, as diagrammed in Figure 4.14, a decision must be made whether or not to interchange a smaller for a larger integer in the sequence. In another situation, such as exercise 19 of Chapter 3, a set of data is read into the program, calculations are made, and the program outputs the results and terminates. This program would have to be rerun with the second set of data were it not for the capability of the computer to programmatically transfer control back to the READ statement for the second set of data (and then for the third set) without terminating the program run.

FORTRAN 77 provides the necessary capability to control the logical process of a program through *control statements*. For example, to output a table of x and some function of x, the flowchart is as shown in Figure 5.1.

This flowchart illustrates the use of a control statement that tests for $x > 10$, thus permitting a block of statements to be repeated a predetermined number of times. This capability to reuse statements is called a *loop*. It is but one of several ways in which control statements can be used; in general, these statements instruct the computer when and how to make decisions, where to transfer control to, how many times to repeat a certain block of statements, and so forth. The two types of control statements are *unconditional* and *conditional*.

76

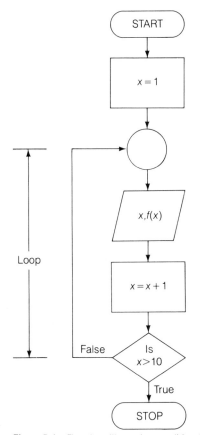

Figure 5.1   Flowchart illustrating conditional control

5.1   UNCONDITIONAL CONTROL

Two of the unconditional control statements have already been encountered: the
STOP and END statements. This chapter will discuss other control statements
found in FORTRAN 77.

The unconditional GO TO statement is of the form

GO TO s

where s is the label of an executable statement to which control is to be transferred.
Remember that a statement label must be a unique positive integer in the range 1
to 99999. After transfer of control, execution continues sequentially beginning with
statement s. For example, to output a table of square roots, the FORTRAN program
would read

```
      A=1.0
  10  WRITE(6,*)A,SQRT(A)
      A=A+1.0
      GO TO 10
      STOP
      END
```

The flowchart shown in Figure 5.2 clearly shows the flaw associated with this program. There is no way to terminate it! The STOP statement is never executed. The logical IF statement can be used to correct this flaw.

5.2 CONDITIONAL CONTROL: THE LOGICAL IF STATEMENT

The form of the logical IF statement is

$$IF(exp) \text{ statement}$$

where exp is a *logical expression* and statement is any executable statement except another IF statement or a DO statement. The DO statement will be considered later. If the logical expression, exp, is true, control is passed to the statement given

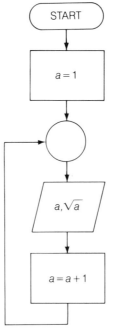

Figure 5.2 Flowchart illustrating unconditional control

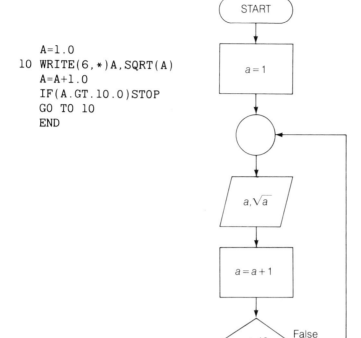

```
      A=1.0
  10  WRITE(6,*)A,SQRT(A)
      A=A+1.0
      IF(A.GT.10.0)STOP
      GO TO 10
      END
```

Figure 5.3 Square-root table using the IF statement

in the IF(exp) statement. If the logical expression, exp, is false, control is passed to the statement immediately following the logical IF statement and execution continues as though the IF statement were not present.

The logical expression, exp, is of the form

$$\text{exp}_1 \text{ relop } \text{exp}_2$$

where exp_1 and exp_2 are arithmetic expressions and relop is a relational operator. The valid relational operators are:

.LT.	less than
.LE.	less than or equal to
.EQ.	equal to
.NE.	not equal to
.GT.	greater than
.GE.	greater than or equal to

The logical expression exp_1 relop exp_2 is evaluated as being either true or false. For example, if exp is A.NE.B then exp is true when A is not equal to B, otherwise exp is false. If exp is Q.LT.10.0 then exp is true when Q is less than 10.0. If Q is greater than or equal to 10.0 then exp is false. The FORTRAN program for the square-root table, whose revised flowchart and code are shown in Figure 5.3, can now be written using a logical IF statement. Output will be a table of A and the square root of A for A = 1.0 to A = 10.0 in steps of 1.0.

The logical IF tests the condition for A greater than 10.0. In general it is good programming practice, when using real arithmetic, to set up the loop so as not to test for exact equality. For example, if incrementing by one-tenth, the decimal number 0.1 becomes 0.0999999 through binary conversion. Hence the relop .EQ. may never be realized.

Multiple testing can be performed using the logical IF where exp may be of the form

$$(exp_1 \text{ relop } exp_2).\text{AND.}(exp_3 \text{ relop } exp_4).\text{OR.}(exp_5 \text{ relop } exp_6)$$

and the logical operators

$$\text{.AND.} \qquad \text{.OR.} \qquad \text{.NOT.}$$

may be used to form this type of complex logical expression. For example, if exp is

$$\text{A.EQ.0.0.AND.B.EQ.0.0}$$

exp will be true when A is equal to 0.0 *and* B is equal to 0.0. Thus the statement

$$\text{IF(A.EQ.0.0.AND.B.EQ.0.0.AND.C.EQ.0.0)STOP}$$

will terminate a program when A and B and C are all zero. The statement

$$\text{IF(A.EQ.0.0.OR.B.EQ.0.0.OR.C.EQ.0.0)STOP}$$

will terminate a program when A or B or C is zero. A new hierarchy of operations now applies to statements that contain the logical expression, exp. This hierarchy is, from high to low:

$$**$$
$$*/$$
$$+ -$$
any relational
NOT
AND
OR

Parentheses may be used as needed to alter this hierarchy.

5.3 CONDITIONAL CONTROL: THE BLOCK IF STATEMENT

The form of the block IF statement is

IF(exp) THEN
block of statements
ENDIF

where exp is a logical expression. Following the IFTHEN may be one or more statements that compose the THEN block that will be executed when exp is true. The statements composing the THEN block must terminate with the ENDIF statement. The sole purpose of the ENDIF statement is to end the THEN block. For example, given

IF(D.GE.0.0)THEN
X1 = (− B + SQRT(D))/(2.0*A)
X2 = (− B − SQRT(D))/(2.0*A)
ENDIF

When D is greater than or equal to zero, X1 and X2 will be calculated as shown. When D is less than zero then execution will continue with the statement immediately following the ENDIF statement.

The block IF statement also allows the use of the ELSE statement

IF(exp) THEN
block 1
ELSE
block 2
ENDIF

If exp is true, block 1, the THEN block, is executed and block 2, the ELSE block, is skipped. Execution continues at the statement immediately following the ENDIF. When exp is false, block 1 is skipped and block 2 is executed, with execution continuing at the statement immediately following the ENDIF. This variation of the block IF statement is a true IFTHENELSE programming structure.

The block IF can be illustrated by considering the solution of the quadratic equation

$$ax^2 + bx + c = 0$$

whose roots are

$$x_1 = \frac{-b + \sqrt{b^2 - 4ac}}{2a}$$

$$x_2 = \frac{-b - \sqrt{b^2 - 4ac}}{2a}$$

Let the discriminant $d = b^2 - 4ac$. For $d \geq 0$, the roots x_1 and x_2 are real and can be calculated from the given equations. However, when $d < 0$ the roots are complex and for now will be set equal to zero. We can use zero for complex root designation because if, in fact, there were double roots at zero, the solution would be trivial.

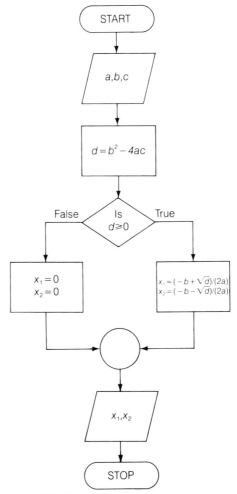

Figure 5.4 The solution of a quadratic equation

The flowchart of Figure 5.4 shows the necessary logic. The FORTRAN program would be

```
C       QUADRATIC EQUATION
        READ(5,*)A,B,C
C       CALCULATE DISCRIMINANT
        D=B**2-4.0*A*C
C       TEST
        IF(D.GE.0.0)THEN
            X1=(-B+SQRT(D))/(2.0*A)
            X2=(-B-SQRT(D))/(2.0*A)
        ELSE
            X1=0.0
            X2=0.0
```

```
         ENDIF
C        OUTPUT ROOTS
         WRITE(6,*)'ROOTS ARE:',X1,X2
         STOP
         END
```

Transfer of control into a THEN block or an ELSE block from outside that block is prohibited.

To program with structure, the DOWHILE and DOUNTIL structures should be used for looping whenever possible. The DOWHILE and DOUNTIL structures are shown in Figures 5.5 and 5.6, respectively. They can be implemented in FORTRAN through the use of a block IF statement.

The programming structures, DOWHILE, DOUNTIL, and IFTHENELSE, are accepted techniques for problem analysis and programming in any computer lan-

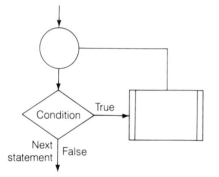

```
s   IF(condition)THEN
        statements within loop
        GO TO s
    ENDIF
    next statement
```

Figure 5.5   The DOWHILE structure

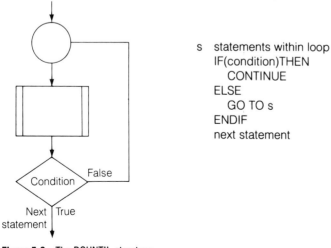

```
s   statements within loop
    IF(condition)THEN
        CONTINUE
    ELSE
        GO TO s
    ENDIF
    next statement
```

Figure 5.6   The DOUNTIL structure

guage. Their use is to be encouraged since they lead to a disciplined style and logical formulation of a computer program. Sample program 2, at the end of this chapter, illustrates the DOWHILE structure.

5.4 THE DO LOOP

The DO statement is used to specify a DO loop and is of the form

$$DO\ s\ i = \exp_1, \exp_2, \exp_3$$

where s is the label of an executable statement used to terminate the DO loop. This terminal statement may be a CONTINUE statement or any other executable statement other than another DO, IF, STOP, END, or RETURN statement. (The RETURN statement will be discussed in Chapter 9.) All statements from the DO statement up to and including the terminal statement are said to be in the range of the DO loop. The DO *variable*, i, is the name of a real or integer variable. The expressions $\exp_1$, $\exp_2$, and $\exp_3$ may be integer or real. The *initial parameter*, m_1, the *terminal parameter*, m_2, and the *incrementation* (or *decrementation*) *parameter*, m_3 are established by evaluating $\exp_1$, $\exp_2$, and $\exp_3$, respectively. The DO loop can best be understood by examining the flowcharts shown in Figures 5.7 and 5.8, which present the logic associated with m_3 positive (incrementation) and m_3 negative (decrementation). Transfer of control into the range of a DO loop from outside the range is prohibited. If $\exp_3$ is omitted, it is assigned the value of 1. Note also that

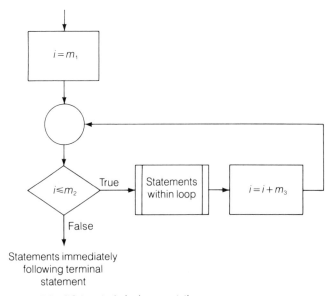

Figure 5.7 DO-loop logic for incrementation

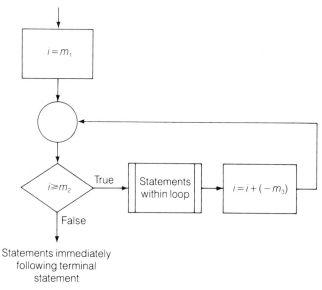

Figure 5.8   DO-loop logic for decrementation

i will be greater than (or less than) the terminal parameter by the value of the incrementation (or decrementation) parameter upon completion of the DO loop. The DO loop is implemented as a DOWHILE programming structure.

The program for a DO loop with incrementation parameter positive would be:

```
      ISUM=0
      DO 10 I=1,5
      ISUM=ISUM+I
      WRITE(6,*)I,ISUM
   10 CONTINUE
      WRITE(6,*)I
      STOP
      END
```

Output:

col. 1
↓

```
      1       1
      2       3
      3       6
      4      10
      5      15
      6
```

The program for a DO loop with incrementation parameter negative would be:

```
      ISUM=0
      DO 10 I=5,1,-1
      ISUM=ISUM+I
      WRITE(6,*)I,ISUM
   10 CONTINUE
      WRITE(6,*)I
      STOP
      END
```

Output:

col. 1
↓

```
      5        5
      4        9
      3        12
      2        14
      1        15
      0
```

Note that in both programs the final value of i is not equal to the terminal parameter but is incremented (or decremented) by 1. Some older versions of FORTRAN implement the DO loop as a DOUNTIL programming structure, where one pass is made through the loop, regardless of the values assigned to the DO parameters. For example, consider the partial program:

```
      NVALUE=0
      DO 200 I=1,10
      JVALUE=I
      DO 100 K=5,1
      LVALUE=K
  100 NVALUE=NVALUE+1
  200 CONTINUE
```

After execution of the statements, I = 11, JVALUE = 10, K = 5, NVALUE = 0, and LVALUE is undefined in FORTRAN 77 (DOWHILE). The DOUNTIL control structure gives I = 11, JVALUE = 10, K = 6, NVALUE = 10, and LVALUE = 5.

DO loops may be "nested"—that is, they may be successively included in other DO loops. However, the range of the individual DO loops must not overlap. Hence,

```
      DO 100 I=1,5
      DO 100 K=1,4
      DO 100 J=1,2
      IVAL=I+K+J
  100 CONTINUE
```

is a valid set of DO loops nested three deep, but

```
      DO 200 I=1,5
      DO 100 K=1,4
      DO 200 J=1,2
      IVAL=I+K+J
  100 CONTINUE
  200 CONTINUE
```

is invalid.

Figure 5.9 shows the appropriate flowchart for DO loops, nested two deep.

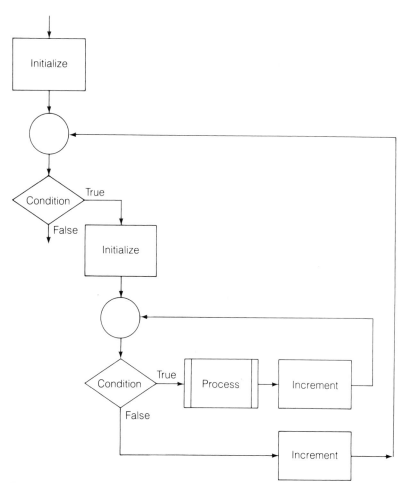

Figure 5.9   Nested DO loops

5.5 OTHER CONDITIONAL CONTROL STATEMENTS

Other control statements available in FORTRAN 77 are the arithmetic IF statement, the computed GO TO statement, and the ELSEIF statement. The WHILEDO statement, a nonstandard extension to FORTRAN 77, is available on some computer systems. A brief discussion of this statement is included.

The arithmetic IF statement is of the form

$$IF(exp)s_1, s_2, s_3$$

where exp may be any integer or real arithmetic expression. Remember, an arithmetic expression may be a constant, variable, or combination of constants, variables, arithmetic operators, and parentheses. Upon execution of the arithmetic IF statement, control will be transferred to the statement whose label is

$$s_1 \text{ when exp} < 0$$
$$s_2 \text{ when exp} = 0$$
$$s_3 \text{ when exp} > 0$$

After transferring control to the appropriate statement, execution continues at that statement.

The program for the square-root table, whose flowchart is shown in Figure 5.3, can alternatively be written as

```
      A=1.0
   10 WRITE(6,*)A,SQRT(A)
      A=A+1.0
      IF(A-10.0)10,10,20
   20 STOP
      END
```

In this program, the arithmetic IF statement tests to determine whether ten values of A have been processed.

The form of the computed GO TO statement is

$$GO\ TO\ (s_1, s_2, s_3, \ldots, s_n), i$$

where $s_1, s_2, s_3, \ldots s_n$ are executable statement labels and i is an integer variable name. Control will be transferred to statement s_1 when $i = 1$, to statement s_2 when $i = 2$, to statement s_3 when $i = 3$, and so forth. If i is less than 1 or i is greater than n, the computed GO TO statement is ignored and execution continues at the statement immediately following the computed GO TO. This statement offers multiple logic paths and is, essentially, the coding for the CASE programming structure discussed in Chapter 4. For example, consider the evaluation of the function $\phi(x)$ for values of $x = 1, 2, 3, 4, 5, \ldots$ where

$$\phi(x) = 0 \qquad ,x \le 0$$
$$\phi(x) = x^2 \qquad ,x = 1$$
$$\phi(x) = x^{1.7} \qquad ,x = 2$$
$$\phi(x) = x - 1.5 ,x = 3$$
$$\phi(x) = 0 \qquad ,x > 3$$

A partial FORTRAN program would be read as

```
      READ(5,*)X
      I=X
      GO TO(10,20,30),I
      PHI=0.0
      .        .
      .        .
      .        .
      GO TO 40
   10 PHI=X**2
      .        .
      .        .
      .        .
      GO TO 40
   20 PHI=X**1.7
      .        .
      .        .
      .        .
      GO TO 40
   30 PHI=X-1.5
      .        .
      .        .
      .        .
   40 CONTINUE
```

The flowchart for this partial program is shown in Figure 5.10 on the next page.

The ELSEIF statement can be used to implement the CASE programming structure. This statement is of the form

```
IF (exp1) THEN
    block 1 statements
ELSE IF (exp2) THEN
        block 2 statements
      ELSE IF (exp3) THEN
            block 3 statements
          .              .
          .              .
          .              .
ENDIF
```

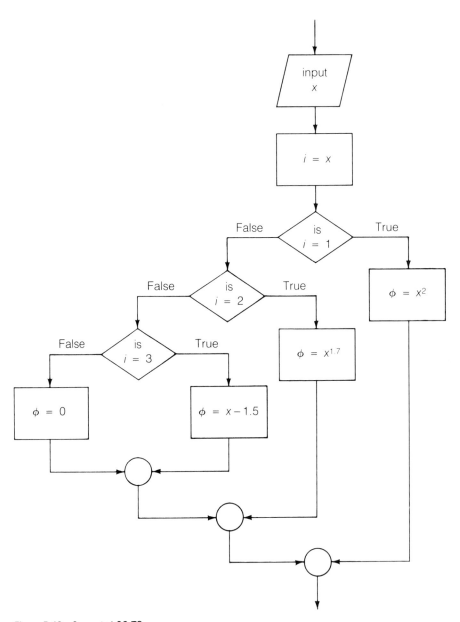

Figure 5.10 Computed GO TO

where exp is a logical expression. In flowchart form this statement becomes

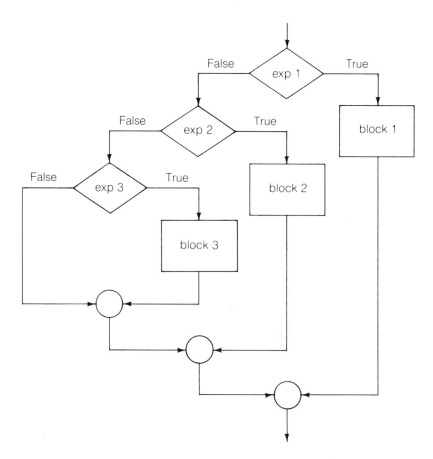

This use of the ENDIF statement assumes that there is no transfer of control statements, such as GOTOs, within the ELSEIF blocks. Furthermore, one block IF
statement can contain any number of ELSEIF blocks but only one ELSE block.
As an example of this implementation of the CASE or multiple selection structure,
consider the algorithm and flowchart for calculating the areas and volumes of cylinders and cones, as shown in Figure 4.11. The FORTRAN program becomes:

```
      PI=3.14159
5     WRITE(6,*)'ENTER DATA '
      READ(5,*)KODE,RADIUS,HT
      IF(KODE.EQ.1)THEN
        AREA=2.0*PI*RADIUS*HT
        WRITE(6,*)'AREA IS ',AREA
```

```
      ELSE IF(KODE.EQ.2)THEN
             VOL=PI*RADIUS**2*HT
             WRITE(6,*)'VOLUME IS',VOL
          ELSE IF(KODE.EQ.3)THEN
                 S=SQRT(RADIUS**2+HT**2)
                 AREA=PI*RADIUS*S
                 WRITE(6,*)'AREA IS',AREA
              ELSE IF(KODE.EQ.4)THEN
                     VOL=PI*RADIUS**2*HT/3.0
                     WRITE(6,*)'VOLUME IS',VOL
      ENDIF
      IF(KODE.LT.1.OR.KODE.GT.4)THEN
         CONTINUE
      ELSE
         GO TO 5
      ENDIF
      STOP
      END
```

Data is entered until "all data in," that is until KODE is outside the allowable range of 1 to 4, inclusive. The program can be modified so as to include the test for "all data in" within the block IF that implements the selection.

```
      IF(KODE.EQ.1)THEN
         .              .
         .              .

         .              .
      ELSE IF(KODE.EQ.4)THEN
             VOL=PI*RADIUS**2*HT/3.0
             WRITE(6,*)'VOLUME IS',VOL
          ELSE
             STOP
      ENDIF
         GO TO 5
      END
```

As an extension to the standard, many implementations of FORTRAN 77 offer a WHILEDO statement that is of the form

WHILE (exp) DO
    statements within the loop
ENDWHILE

where exp is a logical expression. This statement implements the DOWHILE programming structure. Any loop can easily be coded using this extension to FOR-

TRAN 77. For example, the DO loop program with a positive incrementation parameter becomes:

```
ISUM=0
I=1
WHILE(I.LE.5)DO
    ISUM=ISUM+I
    WRITE(6,*)ISUM
    I=I+1
ENDWHILE
WRITE(6,*)I
STOP
END
```

5.6 SAMPLE PROGRAMS

Following are several FORTRAN programs that illustrate the control statements discussed in this chapter. Program 1 illustrates the use of the DO loop in calculating the factorial of N. A logical IF statement tests for the special case of 0!. Program 2 finds the root of a function by a trial-and-error procedure. The block IF statement

$$IF(DELX.GE.0.001)THEN...ENDIF$$

is the DOWHILE control structure that ensures the estimated root is calculated to the nearest thousandth. The statement

$$IF(PHI.LT.0.0)GO\ TO\ 10$$

checks for $\phi < 0$ (continue—a root has not yet been found) or $\phi > 0$ (go back—the root has been passed). As an alternative, the arithmetic IF statement, with its three options, is ideal for this case since it permits the tests $\phi = 0$ (root found), $\phi < 0$ (continue), and $\phi > 0$ (go back). For those who want to use this arithmetic test, replace lines 6 and 7 as follows

$$IF(PHI)10,20,15$$
$$15\ X=X-DELX$$

where statement 20 is the WRITE statement. Program 3 calculates and outputs the arithmetic average of ten real numbers. Variable SUM acts as a running sum. The DO variable is an integer since it is used to count. Program 4, through the use of a real DO variable, supplies the value of x while stepping through the loop. This program outputs a table of x and $\phi(x)$. Program 5 illustrates the CASE programming structure.

PROGRAM 1: Computation of n factorial

$$n! = n(n - 1)(n - 2)(n - 3)\ldots(1)$$

where 0! is defined as 1. For example, $5! = (5)(4)(3)(2)(1) = 120$.

```
C       FACTORIAL PROGRAM
        READ(5,*)N
        FAC=1.0
        IF(N.EQ.0)GO TO 20
        DO 10 I=1,N
        FAC=FAC*I
    10  CONTINUE
    20  WRITE(6,*)FAC
        STOP
        END
```

Input:

5

Output:

```
 120.000
```

This program sets the factorial to 1, then checks for $n > 0$. If false the output for factorial n is 1. If n is greater than 0 (n must be an integer), a DO loop is used to compute the factorial. Real arithmetic is required since $n!$ can be a very large number. The test for $n = 0$ is added to reinforce the definition that $0! = 1$. It could be omitted since in FORTRAN 77, when $n \leq 0$, the DO loop is skipped and control immediately passes to the WRITE statement. This program is derived from the flowchart of sample problem 4 of Chapter 4. Note that the flowchart follows the DOWHILE programming structure.

PROGRAM 2: Estimation of the root of a function

$$\text{Let } \phi(x) = x^{1.7} - 13 = 0$$

The root of $\phi(x)$ can be estimated by starting at $x = 0$ and incrementing x by 1 until the sign of $\phi(x)$ changes. Repeat this procedure, each time narrowing by one-tenth the new increment, until the estimated root is close enough to the true root. The program will calculate the estimated root to the nearest thousandth.

(a) Using the block IF

```
      X=0.0
      DELX=1.0
  10  IF(DELX.GE.0.001)THEN
          X=X+DELX
          PHI=X**1.7-13.0
          IF(PHI.LT.0.0)GO TO 10
          X=X-DELX
          DELX=DELX/10.0
          GO TO 10
      ENDIF
      WRITE(6,*)X,PHI
      STOP
      END
```

Output:

```
4.52100        0.355148E-02
```

(b) Using the WHILEDO

```
      X=0.0
      DELX=1.0
      WHILE(DELX.GE.0.001)DO
        X=X+DELX
        PHI=X**1.7-13.0
        IF(PHI.GE.0.0)THEN
            X=X-DELX
            DELX=DELX/10.0
        ENDIF
      ENDWHILE
      WRITE(6,*)X,PHI
      STOP
      END
```

Output:

```
4.52100        0.355148E-02
```

PROGRAM 3: The arithmetic average of ten real numbers

$$\bar{x} = \text{average} = (x_1 + x_2 + x_3 + \ldots + x_{10})/10$$

```
C     AVERAGE PROGRAM
      SUM=0.0
      DO 10 I=1,10
      READ(5,*)X
      SUM=SUM+X
   10 CONTINUE
      WRITE(6,*)'AVE',SUM/10.0
      STOP
      END
```

Input:

```
1
2
3
4
5
6
7
8
9
10
```

Output:

```
AVE 5.50000
```

The real variable SUM is used to hold the running sum and as such is initialized to zero.

PROGRAM 4: Table of values of a polynomial

Given the polynomial $\phi(x) = 10x^3 - 18x^2 + 6x - 12$, output a table of values for $\phi(x)$ given $x = 1$ to $x = 2$ in steps of 0.1.

```
      DO 100 X=1.0,2.0,0.1
      PHI=10.0*X**3-18.0*X*X+6.0*X-12.0
  100 WRITE(6,*)X,PHI
      STOP
      END
```

Output:

```
1.00000       -14.0000
1.10000       -13.8700
1.20000       -13.4400
1.30000       -12.6500
1.40000       -11.4000
1.50000       -9.75000
1.60000       -7.52000
1.70000       -4.69000
1.80000       -1.20000
1.90000        3.00100
2.00000        8.00000
```

PROGRAM 5: Calculation of $f(x)$

Given that $f(x) = 5 + x$ for $0 < x < = 4$
             $f(x) = x^2$ for $4 < x < = 8$
             $f(x) = x^2 + x - 8$ for $8 < x$

Output $f(x)$ for any value of $x > 0$.

```
WRITE(6,*)'ENTER X '
READ(5,*)X
IF(X.GT.0.0.AND.X.LE.4.0)THEN
   FX=5.0+X
ELSE IF(X.GT.4.0.AND.X.LE.8.0)THEN
        FX=X*X
     ELSE IF(X.GT.8.0)THEN
             FX=X*X+X-8.0
ENDIF
WRITE(6,*)'FOR X=',X,'    FX=',FX
STOP
END
```

Input:

```
ENTER X 5.0
```

Output:

```
FOR X= 5.00000       FX= 25.0000
```

5.7 SUMMARY

Control statements, such as the unconditional GO TO and the conditional logical IF, block IF, and DO loop represent how decision making and looping are implemented in the FORTRAN language. Proper selection and arrangement of these statements within a program lead to the use of the recognized programming structures for control: IFTHENELSE, DOWHILE, and DOUNTIL. Programs that exhibit structure result from a logical formulation of the problem solution and a disciplined style of computer programming.

EXERCISES

1. What will be the printed output for the following program?

```
      ZRAY=0.0
      XRAY=1.0
   05 IF(XRAY-3.0)10,20,30
   10 XRAY=XRAY+1.0
      WRITE (6,*)XRAY,ZRAY
   20 ZRAY=XRAY**2
      IF(ZRAY.GE.10.0)GO TO 30
      WRITE(6,*)XRAY,ZRAY
      XRAY=XRAY+1.0
      GO TO 05
   30 STOP
      END
```

2. What will be the printed output for the following program?

```
      X=0.5
      N=1
  200 W=1.0
  100 W=W*X**2
      WRITE(6,*)W,X
      N=N+1
      X=X+0.5
      IF(X.LT.2.0)GO TO 100
      X=2.0*X
      IF(N.GT.4)STOP
      GO TO 200
      END
```

3. What will be the printed output for the following program?

```
      DO 100 I=1,5,2
      DO 50 J=1,3
      K=I+J
      WRITE(6,*)I,J,K
  50  CONTINUE
      WRITE(6,*)I,J,K
 100  CONTINUE
      WRITE(6,*)I,J,K
      STOP
      END
```

4. Correct the following IF statements to make them syntactically correct:

(a) IF(3*ABLE>=5)WRITE(6,*)ABLE

(b) IF N-4 6,3,3,

(c) IF(N−4.EQ.0)X.EQ.YRAY

(d) IF(N)GO TO 100

(e) IF(ABLE.EG.BAKER)GO TO 60

(f) IF XRAY.ELT.XJOB,STOP

(g) IF(X.NE.Y)READ ZTOP

(h) IF(ABS(PLUG)=PLUG)THEN STOP

(i) IF((A+B)R.GT.100)A=A+1,GO TO 40

(j) IF(ABS(L/N*M))70,80

5. Write the proper code to do the following:

(a) Write the value of X if X=0, square X, and store the result in Z if X>0, and store the absolute value of X in Y if X<0.

(b) If $b^2 - 4ac$ is less than zero, write "roots complex." If not, write "roots real."

(c) IF x = term, increment x by 1; if not, write x.

(d) Write the value of z if z^2 is greater than 100. If not, branch to an IF statement that will increment z by 1 if z is positive or zero or else decrement z by 1 if z is negative and return to the first IF.

6. Rewrite this program using a DO loop.

```
      N=12
      I=1
    5 IF(N-I)10,12,12
   12 WRITE(6,*)I*I
      I=I+1
      GO TO 5
   10 END
```

What will be the printed output?

7. Rewrite this program using a DO loop.

```
      N=12
      I=1
    5 IF(N-I)10,10,12
   12 WRITE(6,*)I*I
      I=I+1
      GO TO 5
   10 END
```

What will be the printed output?

8. What effect, if any, would be seen in sample program 4 if the termination parameter were set equal to 20? Check your answer by modifying and executing the program.

9. Write a FORTRAN program that calculates the arithmetic average of N real numbers. Test your program using as data: 11.3, −16.1, 5.0, 4.7, −7.3, 6.0, 0.0, 3.6 for a total of eight values.

10. Explain how the DO loop in FORTRAN 77 differs from that found in older versions of the language.

11. Write a FORTRAN program to determine if three given values represent the sides of a right triangle. Use as variable names A, B, and C, where C is hypotenuse and A and B the remaining sides. If A, B, and C represent a right triangle, output RIGHT TRIANGLE; otherwise, output NO RIGHT TRI-ANGLE.

12. Using the appropriate flowchart symbols, explain how the arithmetic IF and logical IF differ from the IFTHENELSE programming structure.

13. What is the largest factorial that can be calculated on your computer?

14. Modify sample program 2 so as to calculate the estimated root of

$$\phi(x) = x^3 + 27 = 0$$

15. The moment equations for a simply supported beam are given as

$$0 \leqslant x \leqslant 7 \text{ ft} \qquad M(x) = 300x \text{ (lb-ft)}$$
$$7 \leqslant x \leqslant 10 \text{ ft} \qquad M(x) = 7000 - 700x \text{ (lb-ft)}$$

Write a FORTRAN program to output a table of x in feet and $M(x)$ in pound-feet for $x = 0$ to $x = 10$ in increments of one foot. Place a suitable heading over the table.

16. The sine of x, where x is in radians, is given by the infinite series

$$\sin(x) = x - \frac{x^3}{3!} + \frac{x^5}{5!} - \frac{x^7}{7!} + \cdots$$

Write a FORTRAN program to output a table of angles (in degrees) and sines of those angles for 0, 15, 30, 45, 60, 75, and 90 degrees, accurate to four places.

17. Write a FORTRAN program to output the nth root of y. Test your program using the data shown below.

n	y	
2	16	
3	64	
4	16	
5	-3125	
0	0	(used to terminate)

Be sure to include any and all necessary tests and label the output.

18. Write a FORTRAN program to calculate 2^n using a DO loop and within the loop also use the statement

$$\text{VALUE} = \text{VALUE} * 2.0$$

where VALUE contains the current calculated power of 2. For example, if $n = 3$, the statement is executed three times.

VALUE = 1.0	value = 1
VALUE = VALUE * 2.0	value = 2
VALUE = VALUE * 2.0	value = 4
VALUE = VALUE * 2.0	value = 8

19. The number of combinations of n objects taken r at a time is given by

$$_nC_r = \frac{n!}{r!(n-r)!}$$

Write a FORTRAN program to calculate $_nC_r$ and test your program using $n = 10$ and $r = 3$.

20. One thousand dollars is to be invested for n years at an annual percentage interest rate of i, with interest compounded yearly. Write a FORTRAN program to calculate and output in tabular form the amount available after 1, 5, 20, and 50 years for interest rates of 4, 6, 8, and 10 percent.

21. Write a FORTRAN program that accepts as input a whole number and determines whether that number is odd or even. If odd, output ODD; otherwise output EVEN. Zero or negative input should terminate the program.

22. A force is represented by a vector. Given the magnitude of force and two points on the line of action of that force, write a FORTRAN program that will calculate and output the x, y, and z components of the force. As variable names, use

$$F = \text{magnitude of the force}$$
$$X1,Y1,Z1 = \text{coordinates of the first point on the line of action of the force}$$
$$X2,Y2,Z2 = \text{coordinates of the second point on the line of action of the force}$$

Label all output.

23. The gravitational potential energy of a suspended mass m is

$$U = mgl(1 - \cos\theta)$$

where θ is the angle the cord makes with the vertical, in radians, l is the length of the cord, and g is the acceleration of gravity. The cosine of any angle θ (in radians) can be estimated by the series expansion

$$\cos\theta = 1 - \frac{\theta^2}{2!} + \frac{\theta^4}{4!} - \cdots$$

If θ is small, the first two terms of this series may be used to approximate the cosine. Write a FORTRAN program that calculates $\cos\theta$ for two, four, and eight terms for a range of small values of θ. Output the results of these calculations in tabular form and comment on the accuracy of these results.

24. Resistors in parallel can be combined into a single resistance where the reciprocal of the equivalent resistance is the sum of the reciprocals of the separate parallel resistances. For example, given three resistors R_1, R_2, and R_3 in parallel, the equivalent resistance R is given by

$$\frac{1}{R} = \frac{1}{R_1} + \frac{1}{R_2} + \frac{1}{R_3}$$

Write a FORTRAN program that accepts as input the number of resistors in parallel and then incorporate a computed GO TO so as to branch to the appropriate statements that will input the parallel resistances and compute and output the equivalent resistance. Assume N lies between 1 and 5 inclusive. Test your program for:

(a) $N = 1$ $R_1 = 100$ ohms

(b) $N = 3$ $R_1 = 100$ ohms, $R_2 = 50$ ohms, $R_3 = 15$ ohms

(c) $N = 5$ $R_1 = 1000$ ohms, $R_2 = 2000$ ohms, $R_3 = 500$ ohms, $R_4 = 300$ ohms, $R_5 = 100$ ohms

25. Write a FORTRAN program that will estimate

$$\lim_{x \to 1} \frac{x^2 - 1}{x - 1}$$

by starting at $x = 0.9$ and slowly approaching $x = 1$ in increments of 0.001. Output your results as a table of x and the calculated value of the limit. Place a suitable heading over the table.

26. The equations

$$y = 3x + 9$$

$$y = x^{1.3}$$

have at least one common point of intersection. Write a FORTRAN program to calculate and output this point, accurate to five places.

27. The Van der Waals equation of state is given by the expression

$$(P + \frac{n^2 a}{V^2})(V - nb) = RT$$

where P = gas pressure, atmospheres (atm)
        V = volume, liters

$$T = \text{temperature, }°K$$
$$n = \text{number of moles}$$
$$R = \text{gas constant} = .08206 \, \frac{\text{liter} - \text{atm}}{\text{degree} - \text{mole}}$$
$$a, b = \text{constants } (a = 3.59, \; b = 0.0427)$$

If 0.25 moles of carbon dioxide gas at 373°K exerts a pressure of 26 atmospheres, write a FORTRAN program to calculate the volume of gas present.

28. For pin-ended, centrally loaded, structural steel columns, the working stress in psi is given by

working stress $= 17000 - 0.458(L/r)^2$
$$0 < L/r <= 30$$

working stress $= 16000 - 70(L/r)$
$$30 < L/r <= 120$$

working stress $= \dfrac{\pi^2 (30)10^6}{(L/r)^2}$
$$L/r > 120$$

where L/r is the slenderness ratio. Write a FORTRAN program to output a table of stress and slenderness ratios for $L/r = 10$ to $L/r = 150$ in steps of 10. Place a suitable heading over the table.

29. Write a FORTRAN program to output a table of x, 10^x, and log x for $x = 0$ to $x = 10$ in steps of 0.25. Comment on the output.

30. The exponential e^x can be approximated by the Taylor series $e^x = 1 + x + x^2/2! + x^3/3! + x^4/4! + \ldots$ Write a FORTRAN program to evaluate e^x by summing the series until e^x is correct to five significant places. Output x, e^x, EXP(X) and the number of terms.

31. Repeat the previous exercise summing the first 10 terms and output x, e^x and the relative error.

chapter 6

Arrays and Subscripted Variables

Very often, in problem solving, it is necessary to manipulate a set of data using a single variable name. For example, one might wish to find the arithmetic average or mean of a set of input values and then total the number of values above the average and the number of values below the average. If the set of values were large, assigning each input value to a different variable name would result in an extremely cumbersome program. Data of this type are commonly manipulated as an array. An *array* is a collection of values that have some common characteristic.

The elements of an array are arranged in sequence and differentiated from each other by an identifiable subscript. Values are assigned to the array elements.

If x is an array consisting of five elements, it can be represented as follows:

$$x_1$$
$$x_2$$
$$x_3$$
$$x_4$$
$$x_5$$

The first element of the x array is x_1 and the last or fifth element is x_5. Each element can be assigned a numeric value. Array elements are referenced as subscripted variables. For example, the subscripted variable x_j references the jth element of the x array. If $j = 4$, then the fourth element of the x array is referenced. An array that consists of a column of elements is termed a *one-dimensional* array. If the array has both rows and columns, it is called a *two-dimensional* array. For example,

$$c_{1,1} \quad c_{1,2} \quad c_{1,3}$$
$$c_{2,1} \quad c_{2,2} \quad c_{2,3}$$

is a two-dimensional array, having two rows and three columns. The subscripts of the array point to the specific array element. The first subscript is a row pointer and the second subscript is a column pointer. Thus $c_{1,3}$ is the element located at row 1 and column 3. The subscripted variable $c_{i,j}$ references the array element at row 2 and column 3 when $i = 2$ and $j = 3$.

Arrays are used in many areas of engineering and scientific calculations. For example, the arithmetic average of N elements of the x array can be obtained by summing the array elements and dividing by N, where

$$\text{mean} = \frac{x_1 + x_2 + \cdots + x_N}{N} = \frac{\sum\limits_{i=1}^{N} x_i}{N}$$

The symbol Σ specifies summation over the range stated—that is, from $i = 1$ to $i = N$. Arrays can also be used to store x, y data pairs for plotting and statistical analysis. Two-dimensional arrays are important in matrix algebra and the solution of simultaneous linear equations (see Chapter 10). Multidimensional arrays find application in optimum-seeking techniques, steady-state and transient analysis, and other engineering and economic calculations.

6.1 THE FORTRAN ARRAY

In a programming language such as FORTRAN 77, an *array* is a sequential collection of values of the same data type. An *array element* is one member of that collection. An *array name* can be any valid FORTRAN variable name. The first letter of an array name sets its type as to real or integer. An *array element name* or subscripted variable is simply the array name followed by a set of parentheses enclosing the array subscript. The *array subscript* must be an integer constant, variable, or expression whose calculated value points to an element of the array. A subscripted variable differs from the simple variable discussed in Chapters 3 and 5 in that a subscripted variable can reference any array element, whereas a simple variable has but a single value.

6.2 THE DIMENSION STATEMENT

Before an array can be used in a FORTRAN program, it must be declared. The *array declarator*

DIMENSION array name $(d[,d, \ldots])$

specifies the array name and certain properties of the array. The *dimension declarator* d states the size of the array—that is, the number of available array elements. The square brackets indicate that additional dimensional declarators beyond the first declarator are optional. The dimension declarator d must be a positive integer constant. For the real, one-dimensional, five-element X array, the array declarator would be

DIMENSION X(5)

This statement specifies that X is to be the name of the array and that the array is to consist of five elements. By default, the lower dimension bound is 1 and the upper dimension bound is d (5 for this array). The DIMENSION statement is a specification statement that changes the way a variable name is to be used and thus it must appear before any executable FORTRAN statement.

6.3 PROCESSING A ONE-DIMENSIONAL ARRAY

Consider the real, one-dimensional X array consisting of five elements, X(1) through X(5). A FORTRAN program is to be written to:

1. Fill the five element array
2. Determine the sum of the five-element array
3. Calculate and output the arithmetic average

To process this five-element X array, a DOWHILE control structure is used, as shown in the flowchart of Figure 6.1.

The DO loop implements this DOWHILE structure. Filling the array requires the statements

```
      DO 10 I=1,5
      READ(5,*)X(I)
   10 CONTINUE
```

The summation proceeds as

```
      SUM=0.0
      DO 20 I=1,5
      SUM=SUM+X(I)
   20 CONTINUE
```

The elements of the X array are referenced as the subscripted variable X(I). Output is obtained from the statement

```
      WRITE(6,*)'MEAN=',SUM/5.0
```

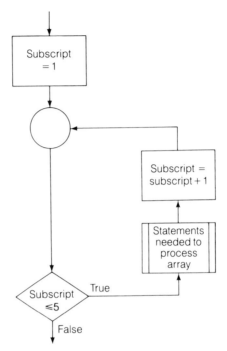

Figure 6.1 Processing a five-element array

The complete program is

```
      DIMENSION X(5)
      DO 10 I=1,5
      READ(5,*)X(I)
   10 CONTINUE
      SUM=0.0
      DO 20 I=1,5
      SUM=SUM+X(I)
   20 CONTINUE
      WRITE(6,*)'MEAN=',SUM/5.0
      STOP
      END
```

This program can be generalized to process an N element X array by modifying the DO loops to $I = 1, N$ instead of $I = 1, 5$ and selecting a dimension declarator large enough to include any projected value of N. The modified program would be

```
      DIMENSION X(100)
      READ(5,*)N
      IF(N.LT.1.OR.N.GT.100)STOP
      DO 10 I=1,N
  10  READ(5,*)X(I)
      SUM=0.0
      DO 20 I=1,N
  20  SUM=SUM+X(I)
      WRITE(6,*)'MEAN=',SUM/N
      STOP
      END
```

The dimension declarator was arbitrarily selected as 100. A READ statement to input a value for N and a test statement for $1 \leq N \leq 100$ was added. If input were

```
5
5
2
1
4
3
```

output would be

```
MEAN= 3.00000
```

This program can easily be extended to determine the number of values above the average and the number below the average by inserting the following statements before STOP:

```
      ABOVE=0.0
      BELOW=0.0
      DO 30 I=1,N
      IF(X(I).LT.SUM/N)THEN
         BELOW=BELOW+1.0
      ELSEIF(X(I).GT.SUM/N)THEN
            ABOVE=ABOVE+1.0
      ENDIF
  30  CONTINUE
      WRITE(6,*)ABOVE,BELOW
```

6.4 MULTIDIMENSIONAL ARRAYS

Arrays can be dimensioned by including several array names in a single DIMENSION statement. Thus

$$\text{DIMENSION } A(100), K(4,4,4), D(3,3)$$

is equivalent to the statements

$$\text{DIMENSION } A(100)$$
$$\text{DIMENSION } D(3,3)$$
$$\text{DIMENSION } K(4,4,4)$$

In either case, A is a real array of 100 elements, K is an integer array of 64 elements, and D is a real array of 9 elements. The A array is a real, one-dimensional array and can be thought of as a column of 100 elements:

$$
\begin{aligned}
\text{first element} \rightarrow\; &A(1)\\
&A(2)\\
&A(3)\\
&A(4)\\
&\quad\cdot\\
&\quad\cdot\\
&\quad\cdot\\
\text{last element} \rightarrow\; &A(100)
\end{aligned}
$$

Since an array element is accessed as a subscripted variable, A(10), A(I), A(J*2) all reference the tenth element of the A array given I = 10 and J = 5.

The D array is a real, two-dimensional array and it can be represented as a table consisting of rows (first subscript) and columns (second subscript):

$$
\begin{array}{lll}
\text{first element} \rightarrow D(1,1) & D(1,2) & D(1,3)\\
D(2,1) & D(2,2) & D(2,3)\\
D(3,1) & D(3,2) & D(3,3) \leftarrow \text{last element}
\end{array}
$$

The subscripted variables D(2,3), D(2,J), D(I,J) all reference the eighth element, located in row 2 and column 3 of the D array given I = 2 and J = 3.

K is an integer, three-dimensional array and it can be represented as shown in Figure 6.2. K(1,1,1) is the first element of the array and K(4,4,4) is the last element.

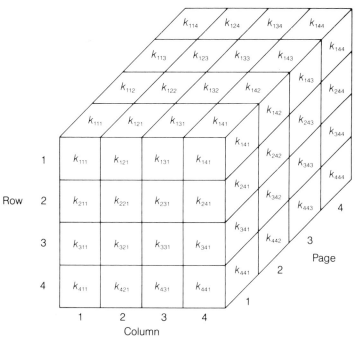

Figure 6.2   Representation of an integer, three-dimensional array

Figure 6.3   Relationship between array elements and memory cells

6.5 MEMORY ASSIGNMENT

The elements of an array are assigned to memory cells, starting with the first element and proceeding serially to the last. The array name points to the memory cells of the first element and array elements are accessed as an offset of the first element. Figure 6.3 shows the relationship between a real, one-dimensional array and memory cells during execution of the DO loop

```
      DO 10 I=1,5
      READ(5,*)X(I)
   10 CONTINUE
```

Two-dimensional arrays are processed in a similar manner. Consider filling the 3 row by 3 column D array with zeros. The nested DO loops

```
      DO 20 IR=1,3
      DO 20 IC=1,3
      D(IR,IC)=0.0
   20 CONTINUE
```

are used. Zeroing the D array, Figure 6.4 shows this array as it is stored, column by column, in computer memory. The array consists of nine memory cells and its initial contents are undefined. For IR = 1, IC varies from 1 to 3 and elements 1, 4,

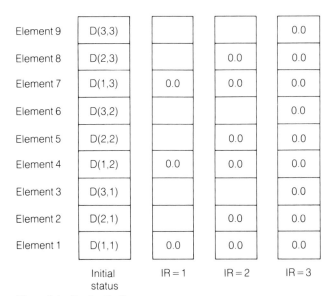

Figure 6.4 Zeroing the D array

and 7 are zeroed. For IR = 2, elements 2, 5, and 8 are zeroed; and for IR = 3, elements 3, 6, and 9 are zeroed. Although the D array is stored serially in computer memory, column by column, the D array appears to the FORTRAN programmer as a table, 3 rows by 3 columns, and it is filled row by row.

6.6   SUBSCRIPT EXPRESSIONS

The integer subscript expression may contain array elements and function references. Thus

$$A(5) \qquad A(J) \qquad A(20*K-1) \qquad A(K(3,1,2)) \qquad A(IABS(W))$$

are valid subscripted variables. The calculated value of the integer subscript expression must not reference an array element outside the dimensioned bounds of the array, since undesirable side effects may result. Some FORTRAN compilers do not check to determine whether this calculated value points to a valid array element, and it is possible, under these conditions, to access extraneous data outside the dimensioned bounds of the array. Because an array has been dimensioned to size d, this does not mean that all array elements must be assigned a value. It is necessary, however, to ensure that valid data have been stored in any array element that is referenced within an expression.

6.7   DIMENSION BOUNDS

FORTRAN 77 permits array dimensioning in the range 1 through 7. FORTRAN 77 also allows a lower dimension bound to be specified within the DIMENSION specification statement. A more general form of this statement is

$$DIMENSION \ array \ name \ ([d_1:]d_2. \ . \ .)$$

where d_1 is the lower dimension bound, which defaults to 1 if not stated, and d_2 is the upper dimension bound. The upper dimension bound d_2 must be greater than d_1. The dimension declarator d has been replaced by $[d_1:]d_2$. For the specification

$$DIMENSION \ M(-5:5), A(100), B(0:5,5)$$

the integer, one-dimensional M array consists of 11 elements from $M(-5)$ to $M(5)$ arranged in the following order:

$$
\begin{array}{r}
\text{first element} \rightarrow M(-5) \\
M(-4) \\
M(-3) \\
M(-2) \\
M(-1) \\
M(0) \\
M(1) \\
M(2) \\
M(3) \\
M(4) \\
\text{last element} \rightarrow M(5)
\end{array}
$$

The real, two-dimensional B array contains 30 elements, B(0,1) to B(5,5). Additional specification statements that can be used to declare an array will be discussed in Chapter 8.

6.8   A PROGRAM USING ARRAYS

Array usage can be demonstrated through a sample program. It is desired to calculate the arithmetic average and mean deviation of N elements of the real X array, where

$$
\text{arithmetic average} = \overline{X} = \frac{\sum\limits_{i=1}^{N} X_i}{N} \qquad \text{mean deviation} = \frac{\sum\limits_{i=1}^{N} |X_i - \overline{X}|}{N}
$$

The analysis

1. Fill the N element X array.
2. Sum the elements.
3. Calculate the average.
4. Sum the absolute value of the difference between each element and the average.
5. Calculate the mean deviation.
6. Output the results.
7. Define the variables:

X	array name
$\overline{X}$	arithmetic average
MD	mean deviation
SUM	sum
N	number of elements
i	subscript and counter

The algorithm

1. Accept N.
2. Fill the X array.
3. Set SUM $= 0$, $i = 1$.
4. DOWHILE $i < = N$
      SUM $=$ SUM $+ X_i$
      $i = i + 1$
5. $\overline{X} =$ SUM/N.
6. Set SUM $= 0$, $i = 1$.
7. DOWHILE $i < = N$
      SUM $=$ SUM $+ |X_i - \overline{X}|$
      $i = i + 1$.
8. MD $=$ SUM/N.
9. Output $\overline{X}$,MD.
10. STOP.

The flowchart for this sample program is given in Figure 6.5. The FORTRAN code is

```
C      CALCULATE AVERAGE AND DEVIATION
C
C      X    ARRAY NAME
C      XBAR AVERAGE
C      DEV  MEAN DEVIATION
C      SUM  SUM
C      N    NUMBER OF ELEMENTS
C      I    COUNTER
C
       DIMENSION X(100)
       READ(5,*)N
C      INPUT THE X ARRAY
       DO 10 I=1,N
    10 READ(5,*)X(I)
C      CALCULATE THE AVERAGE
       SUM=0.0
       DO 20 I=1,N
    20 SUM=SUM+X(I)
       XBAR=SUM/N
C      CALCULATE THE MEAN DEVIATION
       SUM=0.0
       DO 30 I=1,N
    30 SUM=SUM+ABS(X(I)-XBAR)
       DEV=SUM/N
C      OUTPUT RESULTS
       WRITE(6,*)'ANSWERS ARE',XBAR,DEV
       STOP
       END
```

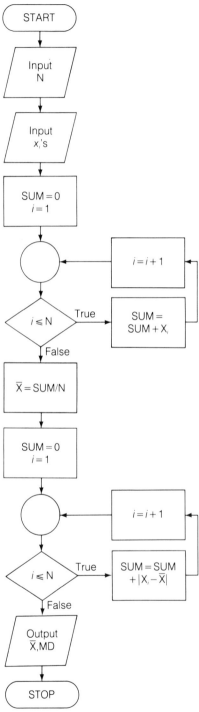

Figure 6.5 Flowchart for a sample program using arrays

6.9 ARRAY INPUT/OUTPUT

In FORTRAN 77 an array cannot be manipulated as a unit except in READ and WRITE statements. If an array name appears in a READ or WRITE statement, it is assumed by FORTRAN that the entire dimensioned array (all the elements) is to be processed. For example, given

```
DIMENSION X(100),Y(4,4)
```

and the input statement

```
READ(5,*)X
```

100 values for X, one for X(1), one for X(2), . . . , one for X(100) must be entered. Similarly, the statement

```
WRITE(6,*)X
```

outputs 100 values. The statements

```
READ(5,*)Y
WRITE(6,*)Y
```

input and output all 16 elements of the Y array, column by column. For example, if the elements of the Y array contained the values

1.	5.	9.	13.
2.	6.	10.	14.
3.	7.	11.	15.
4.	8.	12.	16.

the statement WRITE(6,*)Y would output the array column by column as follows:

```
1.00000   2.00000   3.00000   4.00000   5.00000   6.00000
7.00000   8.00000   9.00000   10.0000   11.0000   12.0000
13.0000   14.0000   15.0000   16.0000
```

Although this output illustrates writing a two-dimensional array by name, this column-by-column output is rarely used.

Array input and output can also be managed through the use of *implied DO loops*. They are of the form

READ(5,*) implied loop
WRITE(6,*) implied loop

For example, to input and output N elements of the X array, the statements

```
READ(5,*)(X(I),I=1,N)
WRITE(6,*)(X(I),I=1,N)
```

are used. These statements are equivalent to but not identical to the normal DO loops

```
      DO 10 I=1,N
   10 READ(5,*)X(I)
```

and

```
      DO 20 I=1,N
   20 WRITE(6,*)X(I)
```

The implied loops execute the READ and WRITE statements once, whereas the normal DO loops execute these statements N times. Consider an example when N = 3. The input and output for the implied loops would be

Input:

```
 3.0,-11.5,2.5
```

Output:

```
 3.00000    -11.5000    2.50000
```

For the normal loops input and ouput would be

Input:

```
3.0
-11.5
2.5
```

Output:

```
 3.00000
-11.5000
 2.50000
```

In either case the following assignments are made via the READ statement:

$$X(1) = 3.0$$
$$X(2) = -11.5$$
$$X(3) = 2.5$$

Nested implied DO loops can be used with multidimensional arrays. Processing starts at the innermost loops and proceeds outward. Consider the two-dimensional Y array. The implied loop

```
WRITE(6,*)((Y(I,J),J=1,3),I=1,2)
```

executes the WRITE statement and will output six values on one line, such as

$Y(1,1)$ $Y(1,2)$ $Y(1,3)$ $Y(2,1)$ $Y(2,2)$ $Y(2,3)$

By comparison, the normal DO loops

```
   DO 20 I=1,2
   DO 20 J=1,3
20 WRITE(6,*)Y(I,J)
```

execute the WRITE statement six times and will output one value per line, such as

$Y(1,1)$
$Y(1,2)$
$Y(1,3)$
$Y(2,1)$
$Y(2,2)$
$Y(2,3)$

If elements of the Y array are to be output row by row, use a combination of implied loops and normal DO loops. Thus

```
   DO 20 I=1,2
20 WRITE(6,*)(Y(I,J),J=1,3)
```

will output values for

$Y(1,1)$ $Y(1,2)$ $Y(1,3)$
$Y(2,1)$ $Y(2,2)$ $Y(2,3)$

For a column-by-column display, the statements

```
        DO 30 J=1,3
     30 WRITE(6,*)(Y(I,J),I=1,2)
```

will output values for

Y(1,1)	Y(2,1)
Y(1,2)	Y(2,2)
Y(1,3)	Y(2,3)

By an appropriate combination of implied DO loops and normal DO loops, input and output of multidimensional arrays can be arranged in any convenient format. *Remember*: Implied DO loops can be used only with READ and WRITE statements.

6.10 SAMPLE PROGRAMS

The following sample programs illustrate array processing. Program 1 calculates the sum of an integer, one-dimensional array. Program 2 calculates row and column sums for an integer, two-dimensional array. Program 3 ranks five numbers in ascending order, as analyzed in Chapter 4. In this third sample program, the values 5, 3, 4, 1, 2 are assigned to the elements of the one-dimensional NUM array so that $NUM_1 = 5$, $NUM_2 = 3$, $NUM_3 = 4$, $NUM_4 = 1$, $NUM_5 = 2$. Refer to the flowchart of Figure 4.15 for the logic involved in this ranking program. Implied DO loops are used throughout the sample programs for array input. Program 4 calculates and stores a function of x in a real, one-dimensional array. The subscript is generated from a real DO variable.

PROGRAM 1: Sum N elements of an integer, one-dimensional array

```
C       CALCULATE THE COLUMN SUM
C
C       NUM       ARRAY NAME
C       I         ROW POINTER
C       ISUM      COLUMN SUM
C       N         NUMBER OF ROWS
C
        DIMENSION NUM(100)
        READ(5,*)N
        READ(5,*)(NUM(I),I=1,N)
        ISUM=0
        DO 10 I=1,N
     10 ISUM=ISUM+NUM(I)
        WRITE(6,*)'SUM IS',ISUM
        STOP
        END
```

Input:

```
5
1,3,6,2,8
```

Output:

```
SUM IS 20
```

PROGRAM 2: Row and column sums of an integer, two-dimensional array

```
C      CALCULATE SUMS
C      NUM       ARRAY NAME
C      IR        ROW POINTER
C      JC        COLUMN POINTER
C      ISUM      COLUMN SUM
C      JSUM      ROW SUM
C      NR        NUMBER OF ROWS
C      NC        NUMBER OF COLUMNS
C
       DIMENSION NUM(100,100)
       READ(5,*)NR,NC
       DO 10 IR=1,NR
    10 READ(5,*)(NUM(IR,JC),JC=1,NC)
C      CALCULATE ROW SUMS
       DO 30 IR=1,NR
       JSUM=0
       DO 20 JC=1,NC
    20 JSUM=JSUM+NUM(IR,JC)
    30 WRITE(6,*)'FOR ROW',IR,' SUM IS',JSUM
C      CALCULATE COLUMN SUMS
       DO 50 JC=1,NC
       ISUM=0
       DO 40 IR=1,NR
    40 ISUM=ISUM+NUM(IR,JC)
    50 WRITE(6,*)'FOR COL',JC,' SUM IS',ISUM
       STOP
       END
```

Input:

```
3,2
1,2
3,5
6,1
```

Output:

```
FOR ROW     1 SUM IS     3
FOR ROW     2 SUM IS     8
FOR ROW     3 SUM IS     7
FOR COL     1 SUM IS    10
FOR COL     2 SUM IS     8
```

PROGRAM 3: Ranking N integers in ascending order

```
C     RANKING A SET OF INTEGERS
      DIMENSION IX(50)
      WRITE(6,*)'ENTER N '
      READ(5,*)N
C     FILL THE INTEGER IX ARRAY
      WRITE(6,*)'ENTER INTEGERS '
      READ(5,*)(IX(I),I=1,N)
C     SORT THE IX ARRAY IN ASCENDING ORDER
      DO 50 I=1,N-1
      K=I+1
   25 IF(IX(I).LE.IX(K))THEN
        CONTINUE
      ELSE
        IHOLD=IX(I)
        IX(I)=IX(K)
        IX(K)=IHOLD
      ENDIF
      K=K+1
      IF(K.LE.N)GO TO 25
   50 CONTINUE
C     OUTPUT THE RANKED ARRAY
      WRITE(6,*)'RANKED ARRAY IS '
      WRITE(6,*)
      WRITE(6,*)(IX(I),I=1,N)
      END
```

Input:

```
ENTER N 5
ENTER INTEGERS 5,3,4,1,2
```

Output:

```
 RANKED ARRAY IS

       1     2     3     4     5
```

PROGRAM 4: Tabulate a function of x

Given $f(x) = (x - 2)^2$, calculate and store $f(x)$ in a real, one-dimensional array for $x = -5.0$ to $x = 5.0$ in increments of 0.5.

```
C      CALCULATE AND STORE F(X)
C
       DIMENSION FX(-10:10)
C      FILL THE FX ARRAY
       DO 10 X=-5.0,5.0,0.5
       INDEX=2.0*X
       FX(INDEX)=(X-2.0)**2
    10 CONTINUE
       END
```

The subscript INDEX is generated by evaluating the real, arithmetic expression 2.0*X. Care must be taken with this approach so as to ensure that the calculated value, in this case 2.0*X, gives the subscript when truncated. For this example, the incrementation parameter 0.5 has an exact binary equivalent and the proper subscript is generated. However, if X were to vary from -1.0 to 1.0 in increments of 0.1, then INDEX = 10.0*X would yield an invalid subscript, since 0.1 does not have an exact binary equivalent.

6.11   SUMMARY

Arrays and subscripted variables allow data to be manipulated as a set of values, assigned to a single variable name. All arrays must be dimensioned. Valid array subscripts can be an integer constant, variable, or expression. Arrays cannot be referenced by name only, except for input and output statements. Furthermore, the implied DO loop can only be used with READ and WRITE statements. Arrays and subscripted variables, in general, can be used in any engineering or scientific calculation that involves processing large quantities of data with one or more common characteristics.

EXERCISES

1. Circle the valid array element names.

X(300)	Y(B)	K(I)
Q(16.)	A(K(J))	D3(K/J)
WOO(69)	M(A)	X(I+J)
VALUE(SQRT(36.0))	P(A*I)	N(ABS(W))

2. How many elements are there in each of the following arrays?

```
DIMENSION A(150),B(-1:8)
DIMENSION K(10,-10:10),D(5,5,3,3)
DIMENSION VAL(5,5,-3:2,5,4)
```

3. Given

DIMENSION Y(-50:40)
I $= 5$
J $= 10$

which array element is being referenced by each of the following subscripted variables?

Y(J)	Y(I$*$J/10)
Y(J/10)	Y(J $-$ 50)
Y(I $-$ J)	Y(J$*$10)

4. What will be the printed output for the following FORTRAN program?

```
    DIMENSION X(20)
    DO 10 J=1,20
10  X(J)=J
    DO 20 L=5,1,-1
20  WRITE(6,*)(X(4*L-J),J=0,3)
    STOP
    END
```

5. Given that

$$JOB(M,N) = \begin{array}{rrrr} 2 & -3 & 5 & 7 \\ 8 & 6 & 4 & 1 \\ -1 & 0 & -1 & -3 \end{array}$$

is stored in memory, what will the following WRITE statements output if M $= 1$, N $= 2$?

```
WRITE(6,*)JOB(M+N,N)
WRITE(6,*)JOB(2-M,N/M)
WRITE(6,*)JOB(M/N+2,M*N)
WRITE(6,*)JOB(4*M,4*N)
```

6. Rewrite the following program using a DO loop.

```
DIMENSION A(10)
N=8
K=1
```

```
10 IF(K.GT.N)STOP
   A(K)=3*K
   K=K+1
   GO TO 10
   END
```

7. Rewrite the following program using a DO loop.

```
   DIMENSION XRAY(20)
   K=1
10 IF(K.GE.20)STOP
   XRAY(K)=K*K
   K=K+2
   GO TO 10
   END
```

What will be stored in XRAY(15), XRAY(9), XRAY(12)?

8. Using DO loops rewrite the following program in a more structured form.

```
   DIMENSION A(10,10)
   N=6
   I=1
25 J=1
35 A(I,J)=I+J
   IF(J.EQ.N)GO TO 50
   J=J+1
   GO TO 35
50 IF(I.EQ.N)STOP
   I=I+1
   GO TO 25
   END
```

9. Rewrite the following program in a more structured form using DO loops.

```
   DIMENSION ABLE(13,15)
   I=1
25 J=1
30 ABLE(I,J)=I*J
   IF(J.GE.15)GO TO 50
   J=J+2
   GO TO 30
50 IF(I.GT.12)STOP
   I=I+3
   GO TO 25
   END
```

What will be stored in ABLE(4,3), ABLE(10,11) and ABLE(4,6)?

10. Using DO loops rewrite the following program in a more structured form.

```
    DIMENSION A(10,10)
    N=6
    I=1
25  J=1
30  IF(J-N)35,35,40
35  A(I,J)=I+J
    J=J+1
    GO TO 30
40  I=I+1
    IF(I-N)25,25,45
45  STOP
    END
```

11. An array of positive integers is to be searched for the largest and smallest elements. Write a FORTRAN program to find these elements and their location (value of the subscript) within the array. Output should be labeled. The program should be able to process at least 100 integers.

12. The standard deviation of a set of observations is given by

$$\text{standard deviation} = \frac{\sqrt{\Sigma(\overline{X} - X_i)^2}}{N - 1}$$

where X_i = ith element of the X array
$\overline{X}$ = arithmetic average of N array elements
N = number of array elements

Using implied DO loops, write and test a FORTRAN program to calculate the standard deviation. Label all output and use as test data the ten-element array

$$1.0, 2.0, 3.0, 4.0, 5.0, 6.0, 7.0, 8.0, 9.0, 10.0$$

13. Write a FORTRAN program that will sort an array of real numbers into descending sequence. Output the array before and after sorting. Use as test data the array

$$33.0, 1.0, 396.0, 8.5, -11.0, 2.85, 0.0$$

14. The distance between any two points in the xy plane is given by

$$\text{distance} = \sqrt{(x_i - x_j)^2 + (y_i - y_j)^2}$$

Given the points whose (x,y) coordinates are

(5.0,3.3)
(9.0,2.0)

(3.0,6.0)
(4.0,4.0)
(10.,2.0)

write a FORTRAN program that outputs the greatest distance between any two of the points. Output the coordinates of these two points.

15. Write a FORTRAN program to accept four test grades for each of ten students and output with suitable headings:

(a) average grade for each student

(b) class average for each test

16. Write a FORTRAN program that evaluates the scalar product of two vectors A and B, where the scalar product is given by

$$AB = A_x B_x + A_y B_y + A_z B_z$$

where $A = A_x i + A_y j + A_z k$
$B = B_x i + B_y j + B_z k$

Test your program for all possible combinations of the following vectors

$$100i + 100j + 100k$$
$$50i - 100j + 100k$$
$$200i - 50j - 100k$$

17. Using real, two-dimensional arrays, write a FORTRAN program to add two matrices. Matrix addition proceeds as follows:

$$\text{matrix } C = \text{matrix } A + \text{matrix } B$$

where each element of the C matrix is calculated using the formula

$$c_{ij} = a_{ij} + b_{ij}$$

where i is the row and j is the column. Test your program using

$$\text{matrix A} = \begin{bmatrix} 1 & 5 \\ 2 & 7 \\ 3 & -2 \end{bmatrix}$$

$$\text{matrix B} = \begin{bmatrix} 1 & 0 \\ 8 & 3 \\ -11 & 6 \end{bmatrix}$$

Output all three arrays in matrix form.

18. A cynical college professor suspects that there is some unauthorized collaboration during his final exam. To test his thesis he compares the test grades between adjacent students. If the grades differ by three points or fewer in more than 40 percent of the comparisons, he will assume widespread dishonesty and take early retirement.

    Draw a flowchart and code a FORTRAN program that will do the professor's comparisons for him. Data are to be READ into a two-dimensional square array row by row. You should provide storage for up to a 25×25 array. Your output should give the row and column of each pair of students whose test grades are within three points of each other. Finally, your output should give the percent of the total comparisons that are within three points.

19. A FORTRAN program uses the input statement

    $$READ(5,*)JUNK$$

    to fill a four-dimensional integer array dimensioned by

    $$DIMENSIONJUNK(2,2,2,2)$$

    Show how values are assigned to this array if input were

    $$1, 3, 7, 19, 11, 0, 32, 8, 9, 14, 2, 50, 33, 15, 6, 16$$

20. Write a FORTRAN program to normalize a 20-element real array. Output the original array and the normalized array. Use only one array in your program. Thus the original array is to be replaced by the normalized array. An element of the normalized array is found by dividing the corresponding element of the original array by the largest element of the original array.

21. Write a FORTRAN program to input an m $\times$ m (m multiplied by m) real array up to $m = 25$. Test for the row-by-row difference between successive columns. If the difference $a_{i,j}$ minus $a_{i,j+1}$ is negative, output the message DIFFERENCE IS NEGATIVE; if the difference is zero, output DIFFERENCE IS ZERO; and if the difference is positive, output DIFFERENCE IS POSITIVE.

22. The following table shows the number of hours worked by four different crafts on five different jobs. Prepare a FORTRAN program to input the hours worked into a two-dimensional array XJOB(M,N) and using the pay rates given for each craft, output the total payroll for each of the five jobs and each of the four crafts. Also output the total payroll for all crafts on all jobs.

Craft Job No.	Carpenters	Plumbers	Painters	Electricians
1	3.15	12.5	20.0	15.5
2	20.5	20.0	18.5	25.5
3	24.0	15.5	21.0	17.0
4	30.0	17.5	22.0	20.0
5	18.5	11.0	18.0	12.0

Payrates:

Carpenters	$7.57
Plumbers	7.57
Painters	7.20
Electricians	7.75

23. Write a FORTRAN program that will fill a one-dimensional integer array of up to 25 elements and output two one-dimensional integer arrays consisting of the positive elements and the negative elements.

24. Redo exercise 21 comparing for each column the difference between successive rows.

25. Write a FORTRAN program to input an m × n real array and output the location (row/column) of the largest and smallest values.

26. Write a FORTRAN program to zero an m × m array and then replace the zeros in the first and last rows and columns with ones.

27. Redo exercise 26, replacing the two diagonals by ones.

28. Write a FORTRAN program to input an m × n (multiply m by n) array and output a k × 1 array where the second array is formed from the odd columns and the odd rows of the first array. Label the output.

29. Write a FORTRAN program to fill an integer, one-dimensional array, consisting of up to 200 integers, with positive and negative numbers. Use zero to terminate data input. Output the data with suitable headings, one column of negative numbers, and one column of positive numbers.

30. Write a FORTRAN program to transpose an n × n integer array in place (that is, using only one array). Output the original array and the transposed array. Label the output.

31. Write a FORTRAN program that sets each element of a two-dimensional integer array $x_{m,n} = m^2 + n^2$ and outputs the resulting array. Label your output.

32. Write a FORTRAN program that will fill a 10×10 array with zeros and then replace the zeros by ones for every element where the subscript adds up to 11 or more. Label your output.

33. Modify sample program 4 to output the FX array in tabular form.

```
INDEX     X           FX
 -10    -5.00000    49.0000
   .        .           .
   .        .           .
   .        .           .
```

34. All of the elements of a real, one-dimensional array specified by DIMENSION $Q(-5:5)$ are to be transformed element by element, into a real, one-dimensional array specified by DIMENSION $T(11)$, using the following scheme

$$T_1 = Q_{-5}$$
$$T_2 = 4*Q_{-4}$$
$$T_3 = 9*Q_{-3}$$
$$T_4 = 16*Q_{-2}$$
$$.$$
$$.$$
$$.$$
$$T_{11} = 121*Q_5$$

Write a FORTRAN program to accomplish this transformation. Output both arrays after the transformation is complete. Use as test data the Q array

$$0, 4, 2, -1, 9, 13, -11, 5, -3, 7, 8$$

chapter 7

Formatting

The READ and WRITE statements transfer data from external devices to internal storage or from internal storage to external devices. These input/output statements process information as a sequence of characters. Such a sequence is termed a *record*. In the case of list-directed input/output, each execution of a READ or WRITE statement results in the transfer of a single record. List-directed formatting requires that the sequence of values associated with a record be separated from each other by a value separator such as a blank or a comma. For example, READ(5, *)A,B requires two values for input. Each value consists of a sequence of characters, and the values must be separated by a value separator such as a comma. If $A = 3.0$ and $B = -18.3$, the input record is

$$3.0, -18.3$$

This record consists of a sequence of nine characters and it contains two values, one value for A and one value for B, plus the value separator (comma). Each value and the value separator occupies part of the input record. Each individual part of the record is called a *field*. The input record $3.0, -18.3$ contains three fields. The first field has a *field width* of three and contains the value 3.0. The second field has a width of one and contains the value separator. The third field contains the value -18.3 and its field width is five.

The same analogy holds true for list-directed output. The statement WRITE(6, *)A,B produces the output record

Ƅ3.00000ƄƄƄƄƄ−18.3000ƄƄƄƄ

This output record consists of a sequence of 25 characters arranged in three fields of widths 12, 1, and 12. The first field contains the value 3.0, the second field consists of the value separator (blank, Ƅ), and the third field contains the value -18.3. Formatting of input/output records is predefined when using list-directed READ and WRITE statements. List-directed formatting was discussed in Chapter 3.

7.1 FORMATTED OUTPUT

In addition to list-directed output, the FORTRAN output statement can also be written as

WRITE (logical unit number, *s*) list for output

where *s* replaces the * associated with list-directed output. The symbol *s* must be a statement label that references a specification statement that provides information specifying the exact format of the output record. This specification statement is called the FORMAT statement and is of the form

s FORMAT(field descriptors)

The field descriptors consist of specifications that define the

- number of records to be processed
- number and type of fields in each record
- number and type of characters in each field

Some of the common field descriptors are

$$Iw \qquad Fw.d \qquad Ew.d \qquad wX$$

where *w* is the width of the field and *d* represents the number of numeric characters to be placed to the right of the decimal point. *I* specifies that the field contains a value of type integer, *F* a value of type real, *E* a value of type real but in scientific notation, and *X* a field of blanks. Thus I5 states that the field is five characters wide and its value will be of data type integer. Table 7.1 summarizes these field descriptors and their meanings.

TABLE 7.1   Some Field Descriptors and Their Meanings

Field descriptor	Meaning	Example
Iw	integer data field of width *w*	I5
Fw.d	real data field of width *w*, *d* numeric characters to the right of the decimal point	F10.4
Ew.d	real data field in scientific notation of width *w*, *d* numeric characters to the right of the decimal point	E12.4
wX	skip or blank field of *w* blank characters	5X

When several field descriptors appear within the same list, they are separated by either a comma or a slash. A comma is used as a separator when the field associated with the field descriptor is part of the current record (continuation of the same output record). A slash indicates a new record is to be processed.

Assume the following assignments

$$A = 10.0$$
$$B = -0.05$$
$$I = 100$$

The output record is to be formatted so that the value of A occupies six characters, of which two will be to the right of the decimal point. The field descriptor $Fw.d$ will be used, where $w = 6$ and $d = 2$. The value of B occupies eight characters, of which three will be to the right of the decimal point. The field descriptor F8.3 will be used. Three blank characters are inserted next, using the wX descriptor, where $w = 3$. The integer variable I is to have its value represented by the descriptor I4. The field descriptors become

F6.2,F8.3,3X,I4

Given this selection of field descriptors, the output record contains four fields of length six, eight, three, and four characters. The format statement becomes

FORMAT(F6.2,F8.3,3X,I4)

The WRITE statement that references (or uses) the FORMAT statement can now be formulated. The elements of the WRITE list use the field descriptors starting with the leftmost descriptor and proceeding to the right. If the output statement is

```
      WRITE(6,100)A,B,I
  100 FORMAT(F6.2,F8.3,3X,I4)
```

the output record will be

ƀ10.00ƀƀ−0.050ƀƀƀƀ100

The variable A uses the field descriptor F6.2, B uses the descriptor F8.3, 3X requires no value, a field of three blanks is the output, and I the field descriptor I4. WRITE/FORMAT states the following: write on logical unit 6 according to the format specified in statement 100, the value of A, the value of B, and the value of I. If the output statement were

```
      WRITE(6,100)B,A,I
```

and given the preceding FORMAT statement, the output record would be

ƀ–0.05ƀƀ10.000ƀƀƀƀ100

Real output is rounded so that the number of decimal digits is equal to the *d* portion of the field descriptor. The partial program

```
    A=10.06
    B=329.2
    WRITE(6,50)A,B
 50 FORMAT(F5.1,F5.0)
```

outputs the record

ƀ10.1ƀ329.

Numeric output is right-justified—that is, it is pushed to the right of the field. Leading zeros[1] and the plus sign are replaced by blanks. A minus sign is always displayed. For example, the field descriptor F5.2 manages real data in the range 99.99 to −9.99, whereas the descriptor I4 represents integer data in the range 9999 to −999.

The *Ew.d* field descriptor specifies scientific notation of the form mantissa followed by E± power of 10, where power of 10 requires two numeric characters. If the value 1080.0 is to be the output using the descriptor E10.3, the field will be ten characters wide, with three to the right of the decimal point. The output for E10.3 would be

ƀ0.108E+04

A leading zero is placed to the left of the decimal point and the mantissa appears to the right of the decimal point. The leftmost character contains the sign with the plus sign replaced by a blank. When using the *Ew.d* field descriptor, seven characters are reserved for the sign, the leading zero, the decimal point, the letter E, and the signed power of 10.

7.2 CARRIAGE CONTROL AND REPLICATION

On output the first character of each output record is taken for *carriage control*. The carriage-control character is *not* displayed and each output record begins its display

---

[1]For *Fw.d* output and values less then 1, some versions of FORTRAN place a leading zero to the left of the decimal point. This option will be used here.

TABLE 7.2   Carriage Control

First character of the output record	Printer	Terminal
blank	new line	new line
0	skip a line	skip a line
1	new page	new page or clear screen[a]
+	suppress line feed	suppress line feed

[a]May generate only a carriage return and line feed (new line) on some terminals.

starting with the second character (the first print column). The valid carriage-control characters and their functions are shown in Table 7.2.

If the carriage-control character is not one of the four shown in the table, the standards do not specify the action taken. The output for the partial program

```
      A=10.06
      B=329.2
      WRITE(6,50)A,B
   50 FORMAT(F5.1,F5.0)
```

is

col. 1
↓

```
10.1ƀ329.
```

where the first character of the output record is not displayed.

When a slash separates field descriptors, a new record is specified. If in the previous example the FORMAT statement were

```
   50 FORMAT(F5.1/F5.0)
```

the output would be

col. 1
↓

```
10.1
329.
```

Character constants can be included in the FORMAT statement as if they were field descriptors. In this way not only can output be labeled but also carriage-control characters can be defined. The partial program

```
      A=33.5
      B=-18.0
      I=100
      J=20
      WRITE(6,500)A,B,I/J
  500 FORMAT('1A=',F6.1,3X,'B=',F6.1,5X,I2)
```

outputs the record

A=ƀƀ33.5ƀƀƀB=ƀ-18.0ƀƀƀƀƀƀ5

at the top of a new page.

Numeric field descriptors can be *replicated* by placing a positive integer constant *n* in front of the field descriptor. This is equivalent to writing the descriptor *n* times. Thus 3F6.0 is equivalent to F6.0, F6.0, F6.0.

7.3 SAMPLE OUTPUT

Figure 7.1 illustrates output using several FORMAT statements. Example A, second field descriptor, shows the use of replication. Note that when F5.0 is the first field of the record only four columns are available for printing. Example A, the third field descriptor, shows the result of not allowing for the nonprinting carriage-control column in the first field. Example A, the fourth field descriptor, shows the use of the slash (/) to line feed and the carriage-control characters. Example A, the sixth field descriptor, illustrates a common method of accounting for carriage control, 1X. Example B, the second field descriptor, illustrates what happens when there are too few field descriptors to satisfy the output list. In this case, when there are not enough descriptors, they are reused starting with the leftmost descriptor. It is strongly recommended that the carriage-control character be specified by a separate field descriptor such as a "ƀ" or 1X for a new line, "0" for skipping a line, "+" for suppressing the line feed, and "1" for a new page. If all the field descriptors in a FORMAT statement are not used, the unused descriptors are ignored and the next READ or WRITE statement referencing that FORMAT statement will begin processing data starting with the leftmost descriptor.

7.4 FORMATTED INPUT

The READ statement references the FORMAT statement in a manner much the same as the WRITE statement except that the input record is read starting with the first character since there is no carriage control on input. Another difference is that

Given: A = 300.0, B = −20.0, C = 0.333, I = 1000, J = 10

Example A: WRITE(6,100)A,B,I,J
                        100 FORMAT(field descriptors)

Field descriptors	Output
F5.0,F5.0,I5,I5	300.ƀ−20.ƀ1000ƀƀƀ10
2F5.0,2I5	300.ƀ−20.ƀ1000ƀƀƀ10
F5.1,2X,F5.0,2I5	00.0ƀƀƀ−20.ƀ1000ƀƀƀ10
2F5.0/2I5	300.ƀ−20.
	1000ƀƀƀ10
'ƀ',2F5.0/'0',2I5	ƀ300.ƀ−20.
	blank line
	ƀ1000ƀƀƀ10
1X,2F5.0/1X,2I5	ƀ300.ƀ−20.
	ƀ1000ƀƀƀ10

Example B: WRITE(6,200)A,A/B,C
                        200 FORMAT(field descriptors)

Field descriptors	Output
'1ANSWERSƀARE'/1X,3E10.3	ANSWERSƀARE (on a new page)
	ƀ0.300E+03−0.150E+02ƀ0.333E+00
F10.2	ƀƀƀ300.00
	ƀƀƀ−15.00
	ƀƀƀƀƀ0.33
1X,F6.0,F6.2	ƀƀ300.−15.00
	ƀƀƀƀ0.
1X,E10.3/	ƀ0.300E+03
	blank line
	−0.150E+02
	blank line
	ƀ0.333E+00
	blank line

Figure 7.1 Examples of formatted output

on input of a real number the decimal point allows the field descriptor to be overridden. The statements

```
      READ(5,100)A,B,K
  100 FORMAT(F5.0,F5.1,I5)
```

specify an input record of 15 characters arranged in three fields, each five characters
wide. The following inputs assign A = 3.0, B = −2.5, K = 30.

                    input 1: ƀƀƀƀ3ƀƀ−25ƀƀƀ30
                    input 2: 3.0ƀƀ−2.5ƀƀƀƀ30
                    input 3: ƀƀ3.0ƀ−2.5ƀƀƀ30

```
                    READ(5,160)A,B,I,J
              160 FORMAT(field descriptors)
```

Field descriptors	Input	Assignment
2F6.0,2I4	100.ƀƀ18.2ƀƀ−100ƀƀ10	A = 100.0, B = 18.2 I = −100, J = 10
2F5.0/2I5	ƀƀ100ƀƀ260 −18ƀƀƀƀƀƀ1	A = 100.0, B = 260.0 I = −1800, J = 1
2F5.0/2I4	100.ƀ26.0ƀƀ ƀƀ−18ƀƀƀƀ1	A = 100.0, B = 26.0 I = −1, J = 8000
F10.0/F10.0/I5/I5/	blank line −36.92 ƀ1000 blank line	A = 0.0, B = −36.92 I = 1000, J = 0
2F10.0,I2,2X,I2	ƀƀƀ1.5E+05ƀƀƀ33.E+1ƀ1005ƀƀ	A = 1.5E05 B = 33.0E10 I = 10, J = 0

Figure 7.2 Examples of formatted input

For input 1, the *F* descriptors supply the decimal points since they were not specified as part of the input record. The I5 descriptor reads its five-character field exactly as specified. For inputs 2 and 3, the real numbers have a decimal point and the *F* specification is overridden. I5 again reads its five characters exactly as specified. If the input record were ƀƀƀ3.ƀ−2.530ƀƀƀ, A and B are correctly assigned but I would be assigned the value 30000. Figure 7.2 illustrates formatted input using the FORMAT statement. Note that in the third example the integer input of the digit 1 is outside the field specification and hence is ignored. In the fourth example a blank input line results in the assignment of zero to A and J. In the fifth example the fourth field is a skip field and hence the integer 5 is ignored. As shown in Figure 7.2, blank columns are treated as zero for numeric data types. This is particularly important when specifying *E* or *I* field descriptors. The *w*X field descriptor causes *w* characters of the input record to be skipped.

7.5 THE GENERALIZED FIELD DESCRIPTOR

The *Gw.d* field descriptor, which is used primarily for output, combines the *Fw.d* and *Ew.d* descriptors into one specification. If the magnitude of the output as specified by a *Gw.d* field descriptor exceeds the *F* format, then an *E* format will be used automatically. Consider the program that calculates and outputs a table of factorials.

```
      FAC=1.0
      DO 10 I=1,10
      FAC=FAC*I
   10 WRITE(6,20)I,FAC
   20 FORMAT(1X,I2,2X,G13.6)
      END
```

This program outputs

```
 1    1.00000
 2    2.00000
 3    6.00000
 4    24.0000
 5    120.000
 6    720.000
 7    5040.00
 8    40320.0
 9    362880.
10    0.362880E+07
```

The representation of the output depends on the magnitude of the result, coupled with the field descriptor's specification. While the magnitude is small, an F type output is used. When the value becomes larger and essentially does not fit within an F type format, E notation is used. When specifying the $Gw.d$ field descriptor, it is important to ensure that w is large enough to hold a possible E field output. The ANSI standard, for the $Gw.d$ field, specifies that blanks be placed to the *right* of the number when it is printed, that is, numeric output for the $Gw.d$ field is left-justified. This placement of blanks differs from the $Fw.d$ and $Ew.d$ field descriptors, where leading blanks are used and the output is right-justified. In some cases, the *exact* format of the $Gw.d$ field is machine (implementation) dependent. Typically, list-directed output uses the $Gw.d$ field descriptor for real data, Iw for integer data and $1X$ for the separator.

7.6 SOME FORMAT CONSIDERATIONS

Format specification statements can appear anywhere in the program, but they must appear before the END statement. A single FORMAT statement can be referenced by more than one input/output statement. The partial program

```
      READ(5,*)A,B
       .           .
       .           .
       .           .
```

```
          WRITE(6,500)A,B,A+B
      .           .
      .           .
      .           .
          WRITE(6,500)A,B,A-B
      .           .
      .           .
      .           .
   500 FORMAT(F6.0,F6.0,F8.0)
```

correctly references the FORMAT statement. List-directed input/output statements can be mixed with input/output statements that reference FORMAT statements.

When the output field specified by the numeric field descriptor is too small to hold the output value, then the FORTRAN program will, at execution, display an error message indicating that the field width is too small. If a real number is smaller than the descriptor, say 10^{-3} when using F5.1, the output will be 0.0.

Output, using FORMAT statements, requires some knowledge of the magnitude and significance of numeric output. The FORMAT statement does, however, allow much greater control over the output format. Tables of output are easily generated and the number of significant digits can be precisely defined. Input, using FORMAT statements, requires the exact placement of each input character of the record and it is used when data must be entered in a predefined format. Terminal users frequently combine the ease of list-directed input with output using the FORMAT statement. FORMAT statements are normally grouped together at the beginning or end of the program so they can be readily located.

7.7 SAMPLE PROGRAMS

The following programs illustrate formatting using the FORMAT statement. Program 1 revisits the estimation of the root of a function presented in Chapter 5. Program 2 inputs and outputs a real array. Program 3 calculates the average of N elements of the real X array. Note, in program 3, the effect of FORMAT statement 1000 on data input.

PROGRAM 1: Estimation of the root of a function

Estimate the root of $\phi(x) = x^{1.7} - 13 = 0$.

```
C      ROOT OF A FUNCTION
       X=0.0
       DELX=1.0
    10 IF(DELX.GE.0.001)THEN
          X=X+DELX
```

```
           PHI=X**1.7-13.0
           IF(PHI.LT.0.0)GO TO 10
           X=X-DELX
           DELX=DELX/10.0
           GO TO 10
       ENDIF
       WRITE(6,100)X,PHI
       STOP
   100 FORMAT(1X,'ROOT IS',F6.3,3X,'THE FUNCTION IS',F7.4)
       END
```

Output:

ROOTƀISƀ4.521ƀƀƀTHEƀFUNCTIONƀISƀ0.0036

PROGRAM 2: Real array input/output

```
C      ARR ARRAY NAME
C      IR  ROW POINTER
C      IC  COLUMN POINTER
       DIMENSION ARR(3,3)
C      INPUT ROW BY ROW
       DO 10 IR=1,3
    10 READ(5,*)(ARR(IR,IC),IC=1,3)
C      OUTPUT TO NEW PAGE
       WRITE(6,100)
C      OUTPUT ARRAY ROW BY ROW
       WRITE(6,200)((ARR(IR,IC),IC=1,3),IR=1,3)
       STOP
   100 FORMAT('1 THE ARRAY IS'/)
   200 FORMAT(1X,3G10.3)
       END
```

Input:

```
3.0,11.0,2.0
1.0,-2.0,3.0
0.0,20.0,9.0
```

Output (on a new page):

```
ƀTHE ARRAY IS
(blank line)
ƀƀƀƀƀ3.000ƀƀƀƀƀ11.000ƀƀƀƀƀ2.000
      1.000    -2.000     3.000
      0.000    20.000     9.000
```

PROGRAM 3: Calculation of the average of N elements of the real X array

```
C      X    ARRAY NAME
C      N    NUMBER OF ELEMENTS
C      I    POINTER
C      SUM RUNNING SUM
C      AVE AVERAGE
 1000 FORMAT(I3/(5F5.0))
 2000 FORMAT (' AVERAGE IS',E11.4)
      DIMENSION X(500)
      READ(5,1000)N,(X(I),I=1,N)
      SUM=0.0
      DO 10 I=1,N
   10 SUM=SUM+X(I)
      AVE=SUM/N
      WRITE(6,2000)AVE
      STOP
      END
```

Input:

ƀ10
ƀƀ1.0ƀƀ2.0ƀƀ3.0ƀƀ4.0ƀƀ5.0
ƀƀ6.0ƀƀ7.0ƀƀ8.0ƀƀ9.0ƀ10.0

Output:

AVERAGEƀISƀ0.5500E+01

7.8 SUMMARY

The FORMAT specification statement provides information specifying the exact format of the input or output record. The output record is made up of fields, and each field must be described using a field descriptor. The allowable descriptors are: Iw for integer numeric fields; $Fw.d$, $Ew.d$, and $Gw.d$ for real numeric fields; wX for a skip or blank field; character constant for a nonnumeric field. Output records require a carriage-control character as the first character of the output record. The carriage-control character is not printed. Field descriptors are separated by a comma (continue the input or output as part of the current record) or a slash (continue the input or output as a new record). Integer input must be right-justified in the Iw field. When the decimal point is included in the field, it overrides the decimal part of the field descriptor. Formatting allows the programmer to exercise total control over the form of input and output.

EXERCISES

1. Given

$$A = 1095.0$$
$$B = 25.38$$
$$C = -100.0$$
$$I = 100$$

what will be the printed output using the following FORTRAN statements?

    WRITE(6,statement number(A,B,C,I)

Statement number	FORMAT statement
100	FORMAT(IX,3F10.5,I5)
200	FORMAT(IX,3F10.5/I6)
300	FORMAT(IX,3G10.3,2X,I3)
400	FORMAT('0 ANSWERS'/1X,3F10.5/1X,I4)

2. Show the output exactly as it would be printed. Assume col. 1 is the first printed column and use the symbol b̷ to signify blanks.

```
       L=7
       X=7.3259
       Y=-4
       WRITE(6,10)X,L,Y
    10 FORMAT('b̷LENGTH=',F6.3,I3,'b̷WIDTH=',F5.1)
```

Output:

col. 1

↓

3. Show the output exactly as it would be printed. Assume col. 1 is the first printed column and use the symbol b̷ to signify blanks.

```
       I=2
       MUDD=10
       XJOB=.00015
       YJOB=27.682
       WRITE(6,20)I,XJOB,MUDD,YJOB
    20 FORMAT(1X,I2,E9.2,2X,I2,2X,F5.1)
```

Output:

col. 1

↓

4. Redo exercise 3 using the following FORMAT statement.

```
20 FORMAT(1X,I3,2X,E9.2)
```

Output:

col.1

↓

5. Given the following outputs, write the corresponding WRITE/FORMAT pairs:
$I = -45, J = 90, ABET = 375.828, BBET = 7.63294$.

col.1

↓

(a) -45ØØØ7.6329ØØØ375.828

col.1

↓

(b) Ø90ØØØ7.6329
     -45Ø375.8280

col.1

↓

(c) Ø90ØØØØØ-45
     ØØØ7.63ØØØØ375.83

col.1

↓

(d) THEØINTEGERSØAREØ-45ØØ90
     THEØREALØNOSØAREØ375.8ØØ7.6

col.1

↓

(e) INTEGERSØØØREALS
     ØØØ90ØØØØØØ375.8
     ØØ-45ØØØØØØØØ7.6

6. Given that $XI = -5.6679$, $YK = 1.32E-6$, $I = 9$, and $K = -12$ show the exact output that would be printed by each of the following FORMATs. (Use ƀ to signify blanks and assume the first printed column as col. 1):

```
WRITE(6,10)XI,I,YK,K
```

(a) 10 `FORMAT(3X,E10.3,I4,E10.3,I4)`

(b) 10 `FORMAT(3X,E10.3,I4)`

(c) 10 `FORMAT(3X,2(E10.3,I4))`

(d) 10 `FORMAT(2(3X,E10.3/I4))`

(e) 10 `FORMAT(1X,'ANSWERSƀARE'/(4X,2(E10.3,I5)))`

7. Given

$$A = 363.0$$
$$B = 11.95$$
$$I = -200$$

show the exact format of each input record so that these values are correctly assigned.

(a)   `READ(5,50)A,B,I`
     50 `FORMAT(2F10.0,I5)`

(b)   `READ(5,60)A,I,B`
     60 `FORMAT(F10.5/I5/F10.5)`

(c)   `READ(5,70)A,B,I`
     70 `FORMAT(2F5.0,5X,I10)`

(d)   `READ(5,80)I,A,B`
     80 `FORMAT(I5/2E12.4)`

8. Give the necessary WRITE/FORMAT statements that will print a zero in every 10th column across the page. In columns 25 and 75 print the digit 1. Assume col. 1 is the first output column.

9. Complete the following program that will print out the array IRRAY(10,10) row by row.

```
      DIMENSION IRRAY(10,10)
      DO 10 J=1,10
      DO 10 K=1,10
  10  IRRAY(J,K)=(J+K)**2
      DO
      WRITE(6,100)
```

```
      20   CONTINUE
           FORMAT
           STOP
           END
```

10. Complete the FORTRAN statements so as to print the indicated output.

```
      C        PRINT TABLE HEADINGS
               WRITE(6,*)
      C        CALCULATE SINES AND COSINES
               DO 10 IDEG=
               RAD=
               SINE=
               COSINE=
      C        OUTPUT FORMATTED RESULTS
      10       WRITE(6,100)
               STOP
      100      FORMAT
               END
```

Output:

```
    DEGbbbbbSINEbbbbCOSINE

     0bbbbbb0.00bbbbb1.00
    30         0.50       0.87
    60         0.87       0.50
    90         1.00       0.00
```

11. Complete the FORTRAN statements so as to output the indicated table. Do not add or delete statements.

```
          DO 10 I=
          DO 10 J=
          WRITE(6,100)I,J
      10
          STOP
      100 FORMAT
          END
```

Output is:

```
    1bb+1
    1bb+2
```

2⌀⌀+1
2⌀⌀+2
3⌀⌀+1
3⌀⌀+2

12. What will be the exact format of the printed output for the following FOR-
    TRAN program?

```
      DO 10 K=1,2
      DO 10 J=1,2
      C=3*(J+K)/2
   10 WRITE(6,60)K,J,C
      STOP
   60 FORMAT(1X,2I3,3X,'C=',F8.3)
      END
```

13. Write a FORTRAN program to calculate e^x to six significant digits.

$$e^x = 1 + x + \frac{x^2}{2!} + \frac{x^3}{3!} + \frac{x^4}{4!} + \cdots$$

Output should be of the form:

$$\text{EXP(value of X)} = \text{value of } e^x$$

For example, if $x = 1.0$, the output is

$$\text{EXP(⌀1.0⌀)⌀} = ⌀2.71828$$

Test your program for $x = 0$, $x = 1$, and $x = 10$.

14. Output a table of powers of 2 from 2^0 to 2^{31}. The output is to be in the
    following format:

```
   N          2**N
   0             1
   1             2
   .             .
   .             .
   .             .
```

Write a FORTRAN program to output this table. Comment on the results.

15. Write a FORTRAN program to output a table of areas of circles whose diam-
    eters range from 1 to 20 in steps of one. Use an appropriate $Fw.d$ field descrip-
    tor for all numeric output.

16. An integer array, four rows by four columns, is to be input row by row and output column by column. Write a FORTRAN program to accomplish this but use only one READ statement and one WRITE statement in the program.

17. Redo the table of factorials program found under 7.5 using an appropriate $Fw.d$ field descriptor. What, if any, output format problems are encountered?

18. Why is list-directed input a better choice than formatted input when a terminal is used for data entry?

19. Compile and execute the following FORTRAN program and comment on the numerical significance of the output.

```
      DO 10 I=1,20
      RI=I
   10 WRITE(6,50)RI,1.0/RI,EXP(RI)
      STOP
   50 FORMAT(1X,F4.0,3X,F4.1,3X,F6.0)
      END
```

20. Write a FORTRAN program to output the nth root of a real number. Use the $Gw.d$ field descriptor for all real output. Test your program by calculating the fifth root of 243, the second root of 100, and the tenth root of zero. Comment on the results.

chapter 8

Specification Statements

FORTRAN 77 contains a number of what are called *specification statements*. These statements are nonexecutable and must be stated at the beginning of the program. One exception to this rule is the FORMAT specification, which may appear anywhere within the program. The purpose of specification statements is to define the characteristics of data used in the program. One kind of specification statement has already been introduced—the DIMENSION statement. In this chapter, five other specification statements will be discussed:

- type statements
- IMPLICIT
- PARAMETER
- DATA
- CHARACTER

The COMMON specification statement will be discussed in Chapter 9.

8.1 TYPE STATEMENTS

The type statement is used to override or confirm implicit typing and may specify dimension information. The name of a variable or array that appears in a type statement specifies the data type for that name throughout the program. The form of the type statement is

$$\text{type } v_1, v_2, v_3, \ldots$$

where type is one of INTEGER, REAL, DOUBLE PRECISION, LOGICAL, or COMPLEX, and v_i is a variable name, array name, or array declarator.

The type statements

$$\text{REAL N,KARRAY(30),ARRAY(5,5)}$$
$$\text{INTEGER I,XRAY,ZJOB(10)}$$

written at the beginning of a program redefine specific integer variables as real variables and real as integer. Thus, throughout a program subject to these specification statements, N would be a real variable, KARRAY a real array of 30 elements, XRAY an integer variable, and ZJOB an integer array of 10 elements. The type real of ARRAY and type integer of variable I are simply confirmed. Remember that if an array declarator is included in an INTEGER/REAL type specification, that array must not be DIMENSIONed. On the other hand, if the array name only is typed, then the dimension must be declared.

The type statement

$$\text{DOUBLE PRECISION X,NEXT(10,10)}$$

defines the variables X and array named NEXT as real variables with precision to 15 significant figures. Remember that under normal circumstances (single precision), the real variable is precise to only seven significant figures. Again one must not dimension an array that has already been typed through an array declarator.

Double-precision constants are written much the same as real constants. The representation of double-precision constants in scientific notation (exponential form) is the same as real constants except that the E is replaced by D. Thus the real constant 106.7554E05 is written in double precision as 106.7554D05 and stored internally as $0.106755400000000 \times 10^8$ rather than stored as 0.1067554×10^8 in single precision. If a double-precision constant is assigned to a variable that has not been typed double precision, the constant is assigned according to the regular rules of real and integer assignment.

For input/output of double-precision values, the $Dw.d$ is used in a completely analogous manner to the $Ew.d$. It should be noted that, because double-precision values require twice the storage of real data, arithmetic with double precision will take twice as long to execute as single precision. Double precision should be used only when extreme precision is required.

The type statement

$$\text{LOGICAL ALPHA,BETA}$$

declares that the variable ALPHA and BETA are logical variables that can be assigned only the values .TRUE. or .FALSE. as logical constants. Thus, if a program segment is written as

```
C=44.0
D=58.9
BETA=D.GT.C
ALPHA=D.LE.C
```

the logical value .TRUE. would be stored in BETA and .FALSE. in ALPHA.

For input/output of logical values the *Lw* format specification is used. For input the constant .TRUE. will be assigned to the type logical variables if the leading nonblank character in the field is T, regardless of what characters follow in the field. If F is the leading nonblank character, the constant .FALSE. is assigned. On output the letter T or F will be printed right-justified in the field depending on the value of the logical variable as .TRUE. or .FALSE. For example, consider the preceding program sequence with

```
    WRITE(6,50)ALPHA,BETA
 50 FORMAT(1X,2L5)
    END
```

added at the end. On execution the printout would be

col. 1
↓
ƀƀƀƀFƀƀƀƀT

Note that for logical output the WRITE statement is formatted using an *Lw* specification.

Complex variables can be processed in FORTRAN through a type statement such as

COMPLEX A,INOTE,MUGG(2,2)

where A and INOTE are complex variables and MUGG(2,2) is an array of four complex numbers. All complex numbers are stored as a pair of *real* values, the first being the real part and the second the imaginary part.

As an illustration of the use of a COMPLEX type statement, consider the following program:

```
    COMPLEX IMAG,COMP
    WRITE(6,*)'ENTER DATA '
    READ(5,*)IMAG
    COMP=(9.2,-6.0)
    IMAG=IMAG+3.0*COMP
    WRITE(6,10)IMAG
 10 FORMAT('ƀREAL PART=',F5.1,5X,'IMAGINARY PART=',F5.1)
    STOP
    END
```

When this program is executed and the numbers 13.6 and 12.9 are supplied for the real and imaginary part of IMAG, the following occurs:

```
ENTER DATA 13.6,12.9
REAL PART= 41.2    IMAGINARY PART= -5.1
```

Note that when the output is complex, two *real* output fields must be supplied, one for the real part and one for the imaginary part.

As in the previous case of REAL data taking precedence over INTEGER data in an arithmetic expression, one can now establish a new precedence for all four arithmetic data types: COMPLEX over DOUBLE PRECISION over REAL over INTEGER. For example, if C is typed COMPLEX, I is typed INTEGER, and R is typed REAL, then the arithmetic expression C + I + R, when evaluated, will convert I to complex, add it to C, then convert R to complex and add it to the sum of C and I.

Later, in Chapter 9, the *intrinsic* functions will be introduced. These will type variables as real, integer, double precision, or complex, *but* only at the point when the variable is assigned, rather than throughout the program. Finally, note that arithmetic expressions can now consist of COMPLEX, DOUBLE PRECISION, REAL, or INTEGER data types.

8.2 THE IMPLICIT STATEMENT

The specification statement IMPLICIT is used to type a range of variables. The form of the IMPLICIT statement is

$$\text{IMPLICIT type } (a_1 - a_2), \text{ type } (a_3 - a_4), \ . \ . \ .$$

where type is one of INTEGER, REAL, DOUBLE PRECISION, LOGICAL, or COMPLEX, and a_i is a single letter in alphabetical order.

The IMPLICIT specification types a range of variables or arrays. For example,

$$\text{IMPLICIT INTEGER}(A - R), \text{COMPLEX}(X - Z)$$

tells the computer that unless specifically overridden by another type statement, all variables and arrays beginning with letters A through R are type integer, and those beginning with X through Z are type complex. Two major cautions should be noted when using the IMPLICIT specification statement:

1. IMPLICIT must appear in the program before all other specification statements, except PARAMETER (which is discussed later).

2. If more than one IMPLICIT statement is used, the same letter may not appear more than once in *all* the IMPLICIT statements in the program unit.

As an example of specification statements overriding the IMPLICIT, consider

IMPLICIT DOUBLE PRECISION(O – T,W),REAL(K – N)
INTEGER NUMBER, RADIUS

All variables (including arrays) that begin with the letters O through T and W will be typed double precision *except* RADIUS, which is specifically typed integer. In addition, all variables (including arrays) that begin with the letters K through N will be typed real *except* NUMBER, which is specifically typed integer.

8.3   THE PARAMETER STATEMENT

A PARAMETER specification statement is used to give a constant a symbolic name. The form of the statement is

$$\text{PARAMETER } (p_1 = e_1, \ p_2 = e_2, \ \ldots)$$

where p_i is a symbolic name, and e_i is a constant.

The main purpose of the PARAMETER statement is to economize computer time. For example, if a program statement requires the use of a constant multiplier (such as $\pi = 3.14159$) at various points in the program, one could write the following:

```
PI = 3.14159
SIN2X = 2. *SIN(PI*DEGREES/180.)*COS(PI*DEGREES/180.)
COS2X = (COS(PI*DEGREES/180.))**2 -
        (SIN(PI*DEGREES/180.))**2
```

During the execution of this program segment, the value of PI will be assigned to the real variable PI every time the arguments of the intrinsic functions are calculated and PI is referenced. This takes time! On the other hand, if the program segments were written as

```
PARAMETER (PI = 3.14159)
SIN2X = 2.*SIN(PI*DEGREES/180.)*COS(PI*DEGREES/180.)
COS2X = (COS(PI*DEGREES/180))**2 -
        (SIN(PI*DEGREES/180.))**2
```

then, when the program is compiled, the constant 3.14159 is substituted for PI everywhere in the program, *before* the program is executed. It must be remembered that the parameter PI cannot change value during program execution and hence must appear only within an expression.

8.4 THE DATA STATEMENT

The DATA specification statement is an alternative way of supplying data to a program. The form of the DATA statement is

DATA *n*list/*c*list/

where *n*list is a list of variable names, array names, or array element names, and *c*list is a list of constants or symbolic names of constants.

The number of constants in *c*list must be the same as the number of variables in *n*list. In other words, there must be a one-to-one correspondence between the items in *c*list and *n*list. The type of the *c*list constants should agree with the *n*list entity. If not, the *c*list constant is converted to the type given in the *n*list entity according to the rules of arithmetic conversion. If *c*list contains a set of identical constants, then the constants can be replicated by multiplying the constants by the number of replications. Thus

DATA SUM,XCOUNT,YCOUNT/3*1.0/

will assign the real constant 1.0 to each of the three real variables in the *n*list. This capability is useful in the initialization of variables or initially zeroing array elements.

FORTRAN 77 allows the DATA specification statement to include implied DO loops. In this case the form is

DATA (*d*list, $i = m_1, m_2$)/*c*list/

where *d*list is the array name, i is the DO variable, and m_1, m_2 represents the range of the DO variable. For example,

DATA(JOB(I),I = 1,6)/3*0,3*1/

will assign the integer constant zero to the first three elements of the array JOB and will assign the integer constant one to the last three elements.

The DATA statement is nonexecutable. It is used to assign values to variables, arrays, and array elements during compilation. It can appear anywhere after the other specification statements. This differs from the READ statement where data are assigned at execution. Since the DATA statement is nonexecutable, it cannot be called during execution. Hence, any variables in nlist that are redefined during execution cannot be reinitialized.

8.5 THE CHARACTER STATEMENT

Although FORTRAN is essentially a numeric programming language, it does have the capability of processing sequences of alphanumeric characters. These sequences of alphanumeric characters are called *character strings*. The string may consist of any character that can be represented in the processor. The blank character (b̸) is a valid character in the string. The length (len) of a character string is the number of characters in the string.

Character string constants, also called *literals*, were discussed in Chapter 3. Literals are generally used to identify numeric output or as column headings. For example, the program

```
      INTEGER SUM
      READ(5,*)N
      WRITE(6,75)
      SUM=0
      DO 50 I=1,N
      SUM=SUM+I*I
   50 WRITE(6,100)I,SUM
      WRITE(6,*)'END OF SUMS'
      STOP
   75 FORMAT(' I IS',3X,'SUM IS')
  100 FORMAT(1X,I3,3X,I5)
      END
```

will output a column of n successive integers and a column of successive sums of the squares of those integers, under the appropriate column heading. Note that because SUM was typed integer, the format specification for the output of SUM must be integer.

Often it is advantageous to manipulate character strings as variables, such as in alphabetizing or in billing procedures. The type statement that permits a string of alphabetic characters to be assigned to a variable or array is of the following form

$$\text{CHARACTER } v_1*\text{len}_1, v_2*\text{len}_2, \ldots$$

where v_i is a variable name, array name, or array declarator, and len_i is the number of characters in the variable or the number of characters in each element of the array. For example,

CHARACTER LAST*10,FIRST*10

is a CHARACTER type statement that instructs the computer to declare two character variables LAST and FIRST with a length of ten characters each. If the length is not specified, it is assumed by the computer to be one. If the character variables in the CHARACTER type statement are all of the same length, then a replicating form of the type statement can be used, such as

CHARACTER*10 LAST,NAME

The writing of the type statement this way means that all character variables after the length specification are to be of the same length, unless specifically typed of a different length. For example,

CHARACTER*10 LAST,NAME,MIDDLE*5

declares that the two character variables LAST and NAME can be up to ten characters long and MIDDLE can be up to five characters long.

Character expressions may be assigned to variables in much the same way as numeric expressions are assigned. The form of the assignment statement is

$$v = e$$

where v is a character variable, and e is a character expression.

Of course, the arithmetic operators $+$, $-$, $*$, $/$, $**$ have no meaning when applied to character expressions. However, there is one operator peculiar to operations on character variables and expressions. It is called *concatenation* and its symbol is $//$. Thus CH$=$'AB'$//$'CD' will store ABCD in the character variable CH. It should be noted that only as much of the right side of the assignment statement is used as is necessary to fill the typed length of the variable. If the character variable CH were typed CHARACTER CH*3, only ABC would be stored.

The character variable is padded with blanks at the right if the string assigned to it is less than the typed length. Conversely, if the string assigned to a character variable is greater than the typed length, the string will be truncated from the right.

Sometimes it is desirable to manipulate only a certain part of a character string, such as when searching a text for a particular word. Such a search program could be used by, say, a lawyer who wanted to obtain a list of all statutes pertaining to automobile liability. If all the statutes for Texas are stored as character strings in computer memory, the lawyer could use a line-by-line search program where the string "automobile liability" would be sought, and the statute number and line would be printed out every time "automobile liability" was encountered. To write such a program requires a knowledge of character substrings.

8.6 PROCESSING CHARACTER DATA

A character substring is a contiguous portion of a character string and, of course, is of type character. A character substring is identified by a substring name and may be assigned values and referenced. The character substring is of the form

$$v(e_1:e_2) \quad \text{or} \quad a(s)(e_1:e_2)$$

where v is a character variable name, $a(s)$ is a character array element, and e_i is an integer expression.

The value of e_1 specifies the leftmost character position of the substring and e_2 specifies the rightmost character position. Thus LAST(2:4) is a substring of the character variable LAST containing the characters of the variable in positions 2 through 4. If a character array element is given as BILL(5), then the substring BILL(5)(1:6) specifies characters 1 through 6 of the fifth element in the character array BILL.

The program sequence

```
CHARACTER*17 VAR1,VAR2,VAR3
VAR1=' THIS IS A STRING'
VAR2=VAR1(10:17)//VAR1(6:8)//VAR1(1:5)
INDEX=6
VAR3=VAR1((INDEX+4):17)
```

will store the string A STRING IS THIS in VAR2 and A STRING in VAR3.

Character expressions can be compared for equality or inequality in much the same way as numeric expressions. The form is even the same as in Chapter 5. It is

$$\text{IF(exp) statement}$$

where the logical expression, exp, is of the form

$$\text{exp}_1 \text{ relop } \text{exp}_2$$

In this case exp$_1$ and exp$_2$ are type character expressions but the relation operators (relop) are the same.

.LT.	less than
.LE.	less than or equal to
.EQ.	equal to
.NE.	not equal to
.GT.	greater than
.GE.	greater than or equal to

It is clear that, in the case of character expressions, two strings are equal if a character-by-character comparison shows the same characters. A question that immediately arises, however, is: How can a string of alphanumeric characters be considered "greater than" or "less than" another string of alphanumeric characters? To answer this question, something called the *collating sequence* is introduced. The collating sequence for a computer is the order in which characters are ranked. In other words, the collating sequence determines if the letter A is greater than R or less than 2. In this sense the digit 2 should be thought of as a character, just like A or + or /, not as a numeral. The collating sequence in FORTRAN is somewhat dependent on individual computer systems. Table 8.1 shows the FORTRAN 77 ASCII collating sequence.

The blank (b̷) is the lowest rank, followed by the special characters, then the digits in ascending order, two special characters, and finally the alphabetic characters increasing through the Z, which is the highest rank. Appendix A gives the decimal values of the ASCII character codes as well as the EBCDIC codes used in IBM computers.

By knowing the collating sequence of a specific computer, the logical IF statement can be used to rank character variables, as in alphabetizing a list of names. Consider the program

```
CHARACTER*10 WORD1,WORD2,HOLD
READ(5,*)WORD1,WORD2
IF(WORD1.GT.WORD2)THEN
   HOLD=WORD1
   WORD1=WORD2
   WORD2=HOLD
ENDIF
WRITE(6,*)WORD1
WRITE(6,*)WORD2
END
```

This sequence of statements will accept two words as character strings, alphabetize them and output the result. The IF statement compares the two words letter by letter from the left end of the string and ranks according to the collating sequence

TABLE 8.1   ASCII Collating Sequence

ƀ	$	'	(	)	*	+	,	−	.	/
0	1	2	3	4	5	6	7	8	9	:
=	A	B	C	D	E	F	G	H	I	J
K	L	M	N	O	P	Q	R	S	T	U
V	W	X	Y	Z						

of Table 8.1. As soon as a character in WORD1 is "less than or equal to" a character in WORD2, control is transferred to the WRITE. If a character in WORD1 is "greater than" the corresponding character in WORD2, the test passes and the two words are interchanged. When comparing character strings of unequal length, the shorter string is padded with trailing blanks before comparison. For example, if WORD1 = 'SWAMP' and WORD2 = 'SWAMPRAT', the string SWAMP would be padded with three trailing blanks and, because the blank is the lowest-ranked character, SWAMP would be considered "less than" SWAMPRAT.

8.7   CHARACTER INPUT/OUTPUT

The READ/WRITE statements that are used for numeric input and output apply also to character data.

For list-directed input the character string must be enclosed in apostrophes. If an apostrophe is to be one of the characters in the string, then it must be represented by a double apostrophe. When the length of the character string, as specified in the CHARACTER type statement, is greater than the actual length of the input string, the character string is assigned to the variable left-justified and the remaining character positions are padded with blanks. If the length, as specified, is less than the actual length, the character string is truncated from the right.

For list-directed output the actual length of the character string is produced as specified in the CHARACTER type statement. That is, there are no automatic field widths as in list-directed numeric output. Further, character constants are not preceded or followed by a value separator when output is list-directed.

For formatted character input/output the edit descriptor is Aw. If the Aw descriptor is used for input, the enclosing apostrophes are eliminated. When the field width w is specified, then the width of the field is w characters. If w is not specified, the number of characters in the field is equal to the length of the character input/output item specified in the CHARACTER type statement. List-directed input/output essentially uses the unspecified A edit descriptor.

For additional information on the relationship between character length and the Aw edit descriptor, see Section 13.5.11, American National Standard Programming Language FORTRAN, ANSI X3.9-1978.

8.8 SAMPLE PROGRAMS

The following sample programs illustrate the programming of the character variables and character arrays. Program 1 will read up to 100 words into a character array where each array element contains up to ten letters, and then output those words in which the third and fourth characters are "AR." Program 2 is designed to search five lines of text material and output the number of times the word "THE" appears. Program 3 calculates and outputs a table of complex square roots.

PROGRAM 1: Testing for a common character substring

```
      CHARACTER A*2,B(100)*10
      WRITE(6,*)'READ N '
      READ(5,*)N
      WRITE(6,*)'READ WORDS '
C
C     READ WORDS USING AN IMPLIED DO LOOP
C
      READ(5,*)(B(I),I=1,N)
      A='AR'
C
C     TEST FOR CHARACTER SUBSTRING=AR
C
      DO 50 I=1,N
      IF(B(I)(3:4).EQ.A)WRITE(6,*)B(I)
   50 CONTINUE
      STOP
      END
```

Input:

```
READ N 3
READ WORDS 'CHARTER','BARRISTER','CHARACTER'
```

Output:

```
CHARTER
CHARACTER
```

PROGRAM 2: Counting the number of THEs in a text

```
      INTEGER T
      CHARACTER TEXT(5)*40,THE*5
```

```
C
C      READ THE TEXT
C
       WRITE(6,*)'ENTER TEXT '
       WRITE(6,*)
       DO 50 I=1,5
   50 READ(5,*)TEXT(I)
       THE=' THE '
C
C      SEARCH TEXT LINE BY LINE USING
C      A FIVE CHARACTER SUBSTRING OF TEXT(I)
C
       T=0
       DO 100 I=1,5
       DO 100 J=1,36
       IF(TEXT(I)(J:J+4).EQ.THE)T=T+1
  100 CONTINUE
       WRITE(6,*)'NO. OF THE"S IS',T
       STOP
       END
```

Input:

```
ENTER TEXT
' WHEN THE THEATER IS FULL, '
' THE AUDIENCE MUST ARRIVE '
' EARLY. OTHERWISE THEY WILL '
' BE CLIMBING OVER THOSE ON THE '
' AISLE. '
```

Output:

```
NO. OF THE'S IS        3
```

PROGRAM 3: Calculation of the complex square root

```
       COMPLEX ROOT,VALUE
       WRITE(6,40)
       DO 20 I=-5,5
       VALUE=I
       ROOT=SQRT(VALUE)
   20 WRITE(6,60)I,ROOT
   40 FORMAT(' VALUE        ROOT'/)
   60 FORMAT(1X,I3,3X,2F8.4)
       STOP
       END
```

Output:

```
VALUE        ROOT
  -5     0.0000  2.2361
  -4     0.0000  2.0000
  -3     0.0000  1.7321
  -2     0.0000  1.4142
  -1     0.0000  1.0000
   0     0.0000  0.0000
   1     1.0000  0.0000
   2     1.4142  0.0000
   3     1.7321  0.0000
   4     2.0000  0.0000
   5     2.2361  0.0000
```

8.9 SUMMARY

Specification statements define the characteristics of the data used in a FORTRAN program. They are nonexecutable and include DIMENSION, FORMAT, INTEGER, REAL, DOUBLE PRECISION, LOGICAL, COMPLEX, IMPLICIT, PARAMETER, DATA, and CHARACTER. The ordering, or *hierarchy*, of specification statements is given in Figure 8.1.

Figure 8.1 Hierarchy of specification statements

EXERCISES

1. Write the necessary specification statements that will type the variable I as real, FORM and DUMB as integer, and J as double precision.

2. Write the necessary specification statements that will type all variables beginning with the letters A through E as integer and the integer array BEAT (20) as double precision.

3. Write the specification statements that will fill a real, one-dimensional array ION (10) alternately with five zeros and five ones.

4. Using the PARAMETER statement to define π, write a FORTRAN program that outputs a table of diameters and areas of circles from diameter = 1 to diameter = 10 in steps of 1. Compile and execute your program to output a table of real and double-precision areas. Output should be of the form

DIAMETER	AREA(REAL)	AREA(DOUBLE)
1.0	0.785398	0.7853981635
$\downarrow$	$\downarrow$	$\downarrow$
10.0		

5. The exponential of x can be calculated using the infinite series

    $$e^x = 1 + x + \frac{x^2}{2!} + \frac{x^3}{3!} + \cdots$$

    Write a FORTRAN program to evaluate exp(x) to ten significant digits and output x, exp(x), and number of terms summed. Can this infinite series be used to estimate the complex exponential of x by typing x as complex?

6. Write a FORTRAN program that calculates and outputs the double-precision roots of the polynomial

    $$(x - \tfrac{1}{3})(x + \tfrac{2}{3}) = 0$$

    Label all output.

7. A truth table is used to express the unique relationship between two logical variables A and B, where

A	B	A.AND.B	A.OR.B	.NOT.A
T	T	T	T	F
T	F	F	T	F
F	T	F	T	T
F	F	F	F	T

Write a FORTRAN program that accepts either true or false for the logical variables A and B, performs the logical test, and outputs, in suitable form, the correct table entry. For example, if A = .TRUE. and B = .FALSE., then the output is

A.AND.B IS FALSE
A.OR.B   IS TRUE
.NOT.A   IS FALSE

Test your program using all possible logical values for A and B.

8. It is desired to search an integer array for the largest and the smallest element. Write a FORTRAN program that will search this array and output

LARGEST ELEMENT IS (value)
SMALLEST ELEMENT IS (value)

Implicitly type *all* variables as integer. Initialize the integer array using the DATA statement. Use as test data the values

33   1   − 18   3   62   0   5   19

9. Write a FORTRAN program to find the roots of the quadratic equation $ax^2 + bx + c = 0$. If the roots are real (discriminant $> = 0$), printout the real roots; if the roots are complex (discriminant < 0), printout the real part and the imaginary part. Test your program with the following sets of (a, b, c):

a:	− 1	1	1
b:	3	0	− 2
c:	1	1	0

10. Write a FORTRAN program to input two string arrays consisting of up to 100 names and addresses in which the first string array consists of: last name (up to 10 characters) and first name (up to 6 characters), and the second string array is the address (up to 18 characters). The output should be alphabetized in the form of address labels. Use as data:

JONES,SUE   312 FRONT ST.
ABLE,KEN   493 MAIN ST.
PARKER,ZACK   805 FOURTH AVE.

Output:

```
KEN ABLE
493 MAIN ST.
```

```
SUE JONES
312 FRONT ST.

ZACK PARKER
805 FOURTH AVE.
```

11. Write a FORTRAN program to input name, social security number, address and to print this information in tabular form with the headings

	SOCIAL SECURITY	
NAME	NUMBER	ADDRESS

Use as test data:
STU DENT,203-29-8645,MARQUIS HALL,CAMPUS
JOE BLOE,999-67-9999,AXP,CAMPUS
MS FORTUNE,005-32-1010,ALLENTOWN,PA
I M FARAWAY,108-26-3212,NOME,ALASKA
END OF DATA
Terminate your program on END OF DATA.

12. Write a FORTRAN program that will READ and store up to 2,000 student names with graduating class dates and campus address. Your program must be able to identify and print out names and addresses for members of a given class and also be able to print out names and class numerals for all residents of a given dormitory. Use as test data:

APPLETON, CHARLES	1989	111 EASTON HALL
LONGLEY, STEVEN	1987	113 SOUTH COLLEGE
MATTHEWS, GEORGE	1988	437 SOUTH COLLEGE
OBERT, PETER	1989	213 EASTON HALL
PETERS, DONNA	1987	303 RUEF HALL
TOWNE, MARY	1987	121 RUEF HALL

13. Write a FORTRAN program that will prepare mailing labels for up to 2,000 names. Output should be of the form:

```
CHARLES APPLETON  85
111 EASTON HALL
```

Use the names from exercise 12 as test data.

14. A telephone company keeps a log of calls, including the zone called, for each of 500 subscribers. A call to zone 1 costs $1.50, zone 2 costs $2.25, zone 3 costs $3.75, and zone 4 or beyond costs $6.00. Write a FORTRAN program

that will read a given log and output the cost to each subscriber. Use as test data:

Business Name	Zone Called
Superco	1
AMF	2
AMEX	3
Superco	4
Craft	4
APEX	5
Superco	3
ABC	3
Craft	1

15. Write a FORTRAN program that will assign the character + or − to the elements of 10 × 10 matrix, MAT(I,J), depending on whether i + j is even or odd. Output the character matrix using A FORMAT.

16. Write a FORTRAN program that accepts as input a character constant of length 60. The purpose of the program is to search the constant for the appearance of the keyword 'NO' and, if this keyword appears, output

THE KEYWORD APPEARS n TIMES

or

THE KEYWORD DOES NOT APPEAR

where n is the number of times the keyword appears.

17. Given a list of ten names, JOE, SALLY, FRED, JOHN, PAUL, COSMO, JUDY, ALICE, ZELDA, PETE, write a FORTRAN program to read the names into a character array called NAMES. Sort the names into alphabetical order and store them in the same array. Output the array before and after sorting.

chapter 9

Functions and Subroutines

Functions are used to define unique relationships among variables. For example, the function $f(x) = \sqrt{x}$ is such a relationship. The function name is f, the dummy argument of the function is x, and the function definition is the square root of x. When $f(x)$ is called, the dummy argument is replaced by the actual argument and the calculated value of the function (using the actual argument in place of the dummy argument) is returned in place of the function. If $f(25.0)$ is the function call, then the value returned for the function is 5.0. In general, a function consists of

* function name
* dummy arguments
* function definition

A function is a procedure that returns the computed value of the function. A function can be a complicated relationship among several variables. For example,

$$g(x) = x^2 \qquad\qquad x < 0$$
$$g(x) = x^3 + x - 16 \qquad x \geqslant 0$$

is a valid function. The dummy argument is x and the function definition involves not only calculations but also the testing of x. Several dummy arguments are allowed. For the function

$$d(a,b,c) = b^2 - 4ac$$

the dummy arguments are a, b, and c. If the function call is $d(1.0,3.0,2.0)$, the value 1.0 is returned for the function.

FORTRAN 77 implements functions at three levels:

* intrinsic or built-in functions
* arithmetic-statement functions
* external functions specified as function subprograms

9.1 INTRINSIC FUNCTIONS

Several of the intrinsic functions were discussed in Chapter 3. A more complete list of these built-in functions is given in Table 9.1. The dummy argument X can be replaced by any real, double precision, or complex expression. The dummy argument is in radians for SIN, COS, and TAN. The ATAN function returns the angle in radians. These function names are generic names and the function type is set by the type of the argument. If X is real, SQRT(X) is a real function; if X is complex, SQRT(X) is a complex function.

The following program outputs a table of double-precision sines and cosines and illustrates the use of intrinsic functions.

```
C     TABLE OF SINES AND COSINES
C
C     R IS IN RADIANS
C
      DOUBLE PRECISION R
      DO 10 R=0,3.0,0.1
   10 WRITE(6,*)R,SIN(R),COS(R)
      STOP
      END
```

The intrinsic functions SIN and COS are type double precision because the actual argument R is double precision.

Note in Table 9.1 the difference between the data type specifications REAL X and INTEGER X described in Chapter 8 and the intrinsic functions REAL(X) and INT(X). The intrinsic function provides a type conversion only for the statement in which it is written. The type specification provides conversion of the variable type throughout the program unit. Appendix B lists the commonly used intrinsic functions available in FORTRAN 77.

TABLE 9.1   Intrinsic Functions

Function	FORTRAN	Meaning
trigonometric—dummy argument X can be any real, double precision, or complex expression	SIN(X)	sine of x
	COS(X)	cosine of x
	TAN(X)	tangent of x
	ATAN(X)	inverse tangent of x
algebraic—dummy argument X can be any real, double precision, or complex expression	EXP(X)	exponential of x
	LOG(X)	log to the base e of x
	SQRT(X)	square root of x
utility—dummy argument X can be any integer, real, double precision, or complex expression	ABS(X)	absolute value of x
	INT(X)	truncation to integer
	REAL(X)	conversion to real

9.2 ARITHMETIC-STATEMENT FUNCTIONS

The arithmetic-statement function is a function that can be written as a single statement. It is of the form

function name (dummy arguments) = function definition

This statement must appear before any executable statements but after type and DIMENSION statements. The function name can be any valid FORTRAN variable name (which sets the function type) and the dummy arguments must be simple variable names. The function definition is an arithmetic expression. Thus the arithmetic-statement function for $d(a,b,c) = b^2 - 4ac$ is

$$D(A,B,C) = B*B - 4.0*A*C$$

The dummy arguments A,B,C are replaced by actual arguments when the function is called. These actual arguments can be any valid FORTRAN arithmetic expression that agrees in type with the dummy arguments. Thus

$$D(1.0,3.0,2.0)$$
$$D(X,Y,Z)$$
$$D(ABS(D-W),SQRT(D),1.E5)$$

are valid function calls. The use of the arithmetic-statement function is illustrated in the following program.

```
C       SOLUTION OF QUADRATIC EQUATION
C       DEFINE THE FUNCTION
        D(A,B,C)=B*B-4.0*A*C
        READ(5,*)A,B,C
        IF(A.EQ.0.0)STOP
        IF(D(A,B,C).LT.0.0)THEN
          WRITE(6,*)'NO REAL ROOTS'
        ELSE
          R1=(-B+SQRT(D(A,B,C)))/(2.0*A)
          R2=(-B-SQRT(D(A,B,C)))/(2.0*A)
          WRITE(6,*)'ROOTS ARE',R1,R2
        ENDIF
        STOP
        END
```

The program calculates the real roots of the quadratic equation

$$f(x) = ax^2 + bx + c = 0$$

where d, the discriminant, is calculated using the function

$$d(a,b,c) = b^2 - 4ac$$

The name of the function is D, and thus it is a real function. The dummy arguments are A,B,C, and the function definition is $B*B - 4.0*A*C$. The function is called three times within the program. Each time, the dummy arguments are replaced by the actual arguments in the function call. The computed value of the function is returned and used in place of the function. This example clearly illustrates that the dummy arguments and actual arguments are related to each other on a one-to-one basis through the function call, even though they have the same names. The dummy arguments have meaning only within the function definition. When using functions, the following must be considered:

• function name and type
• dummy arguments, specifically
  —number of arguments
  —order of arguments
  —type of arguments

In the previous example, the function name is D and it is of type real. When the function is called, the actual arguments must agree in number, order, and type with the dummy arguments.

9.3 FUNCTION SUBPROGRAMS

Frequently it is necessary to reference functions that are not intrinsic and cannot be defined by a single statement. Such functions are written as a FORTRAN subprogram external to the program that calls the function. These external functions are procedures consisting of a procedure head that names and types the function and defines the dummy arguments. The body of the procedure is a FORTRAN program whose statements define the function. The function subprogram returns the computed value of the function and it is of the form

> FUNCTION name (dummy arguments)
> type and dimension statements
> executable statements
> RETURN
> END

The function name is any valid FORTRAN variable name. This name sets the function type, by default, unless a type specification statement precedes the word FUNCTION. The dummy arguments can be simple variables or array names. The

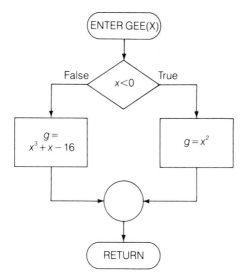

Figure 9.1 Flowchart for function *g(x)*

RETURN statement simply returns to the calling program the calculated value of the function. The function is assigned a value somewhere within the range of executable statements by writing

$$\text{function name} = \text{expression}$$

To illustrate the function subprogram, consider the following relationship:

$$g(x) = x^2 \qquad\qquad x < 0$$
$$g(x) = x^3 + x - 16 \qquad x \geqslant 0$$

The function name, in FORTRAN, will be GEE and the dummy argument is X. This function is type real. There is but one dummy argument and it is of type real. A flowchart for this function is shown in Figure 9.1. Note that since a subprogram does not START or STOP, the corresponding statements for the subprogram are ENTER and RETURN.

The function subprogram is

```
FUNCTION GEE(X)
IF(X.LT.0.0)THEN
   GEE=X*X
ELSE
   GEE=X**3+X-16.0
ENDIF
RETURN
END
```

When the RETURN statement is executed, control passes back to the calling program. RETURN can be placed anywhere within the range of executable statements. Thus the subprogram can also be written:

```
FUNCTION GEE(X)
IF(X.LT.0.0)THEN
   GEE=X*X
   RETURN
ELSE
   GEE=X**3+X-16.0
   RETURN
ENDIF
END
```

This function is called from a FORTRAN program in the following manner:

```
C      FORTRAN PROGRAM
       DO 10 A=-5.0,5.0,0.5
       WRITE(6,*)A,GEE(A)
    10 CONTINUE
       STOP
       END
```

Output would be a table of A and GEE(A) for A = − 5.0 to 5.0 in steps of 0.5. The actual argument A replaces the dummy argument X when the function is called. Upon execution of the RETURN statement, the calculated value of the function is returned.

The function name can appear anywhere within the subprogram. For example, the calculation of the factorial of N would proceed as follows:

```
C      FACTORIAL FUNCTION
C
C      FAC        FUNCTION NAME
C      N          DUMMY ARGUMENT
C
       FUNCTION FAC(N)
       FAC=1.0
C      RETURN 1.0 IF N.LE.0
       IF(N.LE.0)RETURN
C      DO LOOP CALCULATES FACTORIAL
       DO 20 J=1,N
    20 FAC=FAC*REAL(J)
C      RETURN THE FACTORIAL
       RETURN
       END
```

Real arithmetic is selected for the calculation of the factorial since N! can be a very large number. Integer arithmetic would soon result in an arithmetic overflow for even modest values of N.

9.4 SUBPROGRAMMING WITH ARRAYS

Arrays are processed in subprograms simply by referencing the array by name. For example, a function subprogram MEAN is to be written that returns the arithmetic average of N elements of the real X array. The dummy arguments of the function are N (number of elements) and X (array name). The function subprogram would be

```
      REAL FUNCTION MEAN(N,X)
      DIMENSION X(1)
      SUM=0.0
      DO 10 I=1,N
   10 SUM=SUM+X(I)
      MEAN=SUM/REAL(N)
      RETURN
      END
```

The X array must be dimensioned within the function since X is an array name. However, the calling program defines the actual array; hence the dimension declarator has no meaning in the subprogram. The X array is a dummy array and has no size. The DIMENSION specification statement states only that X is an array name. FORTRAN passes argument references by address—that is, the calling program passes to the function in place of N the address at which the actual argument (for N) is located. In place of the X array, FORTRAN passes the address of the first element of the array specified in the actual argument. Thus the only links between the calling program and the subprogram are the function name and the arguments of the function. All other arrays, variables, labels, and statements are local to either the subprogram *or* the calling program. Optionally, the dimension declarator of the dummy array can be set to an integer variable when that variable appears as a dummy argument. Thus the function subprogram can also be written as

```
      REAL FUNCTION MEAN(N,X)
      DIMENSION X(N)
      SUM=0.0
      DO 10 I=1,N
   10 SUM=SUM+X(I)
      MEAN=SUM/REAL(N)
      RETURN
      END
```

The calling program would be

```
C      MAIN PROGRAM
       REAL MEAN,A(100)
       READ(5,*)NUM
       READ(5,*)(A(I),I=1,NUM)
       WRITE(6,*)'MEAN IS',MEAN(NUM,A)
       STOP
       END
```

Again, the dummy arguments and actual arguments of the real function MEAN must agree in number, order, and type. If input is

```
5
1.0,2.0,3.0,4.0,5.0
```

output will be

```
MEAN IS 3.0000
```

9.5 SUBROUTINE SUBPROGRAMS

Function subprograms have a limitation in that they return a single value, the computed value of the function. However, if multiple values are to be returned, then the *subroutine* subprogram should be used. It is of the form

> SUBROUTINE name (dummy arguments)
> type and dimension statements
> executable statements
> RETURN
> END

The subroutine name is a label and it can be any valid FORTRAN variable name. However, there is no type associated with a subroutine name. Subroutines are called from a FORTRAN program by the new statement

> CALL name (actual arguments)

The dummy arguments of a subroutine must be simple variable or array names. The actual arguments can be any valid FORTRAN expression that agrees in number, order, and type with the dummy arguments.

Consider the calculation of the real roots of the function

$$f(x) = ax^2 + bx + c = 0, a \neq 0$$

A subroutine that implements this calculation is

```
SUBROUTINE ROOTS(A,B,C,ROOT1,ROOT2)
DISCR=B*B-4.0*A*C
IF(DISCR.LT.0.0) THEN
   ROOT1=0.0
   ROOT2=0.0
   WRITE(6,*)'NO REAL ROOTS - ZERO RETURNED'
ELSE
   ROOT1=(-B+SQRT(DISCR))/(2.0*A)
   ROOT2=(-B-SQRT(DISCR))/(2.0*A)
ENDIF
RETURN
END
```

The subroutine name is ROOTS and the dummy arguments are A, B, C, ROOT1, and ROOT2, all of which are real. All variables, statements, and labels, except the dummy arguments and the subroutine name, are local to the subroutine. Argument references are passed by address, as in the case of function subprograms. A FORTRAN program that calls this subroutine would be

```
C      MAIN PROGRAM
       CALL ROOTS(1.0,3.0,2.0,R1,R2)
       WRITE(6,*)'ROOTS ARE',R1,R2
       STOP
       END
```

Output from the program will be

```
ROOTS ARE -1.00000      -2.00000
```

A subroutine is a procedure, but is different from a function; a new flowchart symbol is used to represent a subroutine call. It consists of a rectangle with two vertical lines enclosing the subroutine name. The flowcharts for the roots of the function $f(x) = ax^2 + bx + c = 0$ are shown in Figure 9.2.

These programs can be easily modified so as to determine the complex roots of the function as follows:

```
C      MAIN PROGRAM
       COMPLEX R1,R2
       READ(5,*)A,B,C
       CALL CROOTS(A,B,C,R1,R2)
       WRITE(6,*)'ROOTS ARE',R1,R2
       STOP
       END
C
```

```
C       SUBPROGRAM
C
        SUBROUTINE CROOTS(A,B,C,ROOT1,ROOT2)
        COMPLEX ROOT1,ROOT2,DISCR
        DISCR=B*B-4.0*A*C
        ROOT1=(-B+SQRT(DISCR))/(2.0*A)
        ROOT2=(-B-SQRT(DISCR))/(2.0*A)
        RETURN
        END
```

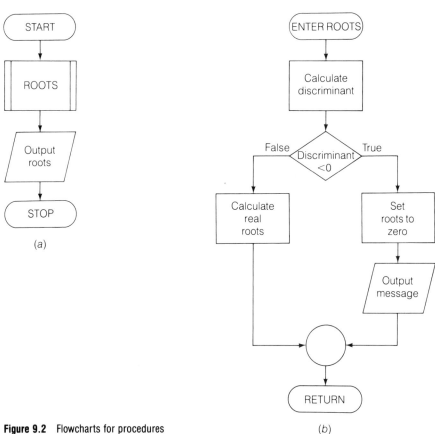

Figure 9.2 Flowcharts for procedures

9.6 MULTIPLE ENTRY POINTS

Entry into a subprogram normally occurs at the first executable statement. FOR-TRAN 77 permits multiple entry points into functions and subroutines. The statement

ENTRY name (dummy arguments)

causes execution of a subprogram to commence with the statement immediately following the ENTRY. The ENTRY statement can be placed anywhere in the subprogram but it must be located within the range of executable statements. A subprogram call using the entry name results in execution of the subprogram beginning at that ENTRY point. Consider, for example, a subroutine that calculates the sum of N elements of the real X array. The subroutine name, commonly referred to as the *primary entry-point name*, is NEWSUM and its dummy arguments are N,X,SUM. A call to NEWSUM calculates the sum of N elements of the X array where SUM is initialized to zero. The alternate, or *secondary*, entry-point name is OLDSUM, whose dummy arguments are N, X, and SUM. A call to OLDSUM calculates the sum of N elements of the X array without initializing SUM. The subroutine and calling program are

```
C       SUBPROGRAM
        SUBROUTINE NEWSUM(N,X,SUM)
        DIMENSION X(N)
        SUM=0.0
C       ENTRY POINT
        ENTRY OLDSUM(N,X,SUM)
        DO 10 I=1,N
   10   SUM=SUM+X(I)
        RETURN
        END
C
C       MAIN PROGRAM
C
        DIMENSION X(10)
        READ(5,*)(X(I),I=1,10)
        CALL NEWSUM(10,X,SUM)
        SAVEIT=SUM
        CALL OLDSUM(10,X,SUM)
        WRITE(6,*)SAVEIT,SUM
        STOP
        END
```

If input is

1,2,3,4,5,6,7,8,9,10

output is

 55.0000   110.000

The flowcharts for these programs are shown in Figure 9.3. The dummy arguments of the primary and the secondary entry-point names can differ.

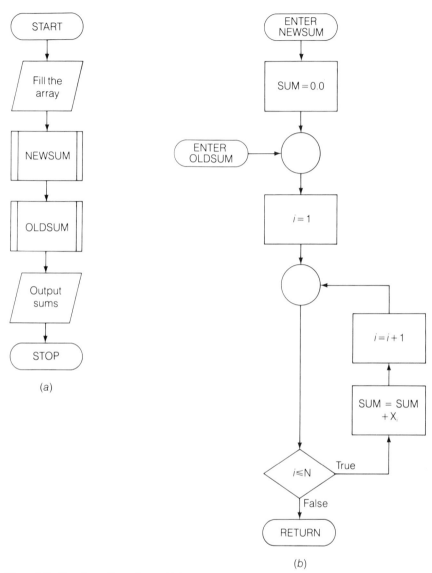

Figure 9.3 Flowcharts illustrating multiple entry points

9.7 SUBPROGRAMMING WITH CHARACTER DATA

Functions and subroutines can process all data types, including character data. In the following example, the function subprogram COUNT returns the integer count of the number of blanks found in the N byte character variable MYLINE.

```
      INTEGER FUNCTION COUNT(MYLINE,N)
      CHARACTER*N MYLINE
      COUNT=0
      IF(MYLINE(J:J).EQ.'b').COUNT=COUNT+1
   20 CONTINUE
      RETURN
      END
```

9.8 MULTIDIMENSIONAL ARRAYS AND SUBPROGRAMS

When one of the dummy arguments in a subprogram is the name of a multidimensional array and variable dimension declarators also appear as dummy arguments, the calling program must pass the dimensioned size of the array as actual arguments. For example, the subroutine statements

SUBROUTINE SUBS(Y,M,N)

DIMENSION Y(M,N)

declare Y as the dummy multidimensional array name and M,N as the dummy arguments for the variable dimension declarators. In the calling program, the actual arguments must be the dimensioned size of the array. For the specification statement

DIMENSION X(5,3)

the appropriate call would be

CALL SUBS(X,5,3)

In FORTRAN 77, the formula for calculating the location of a two-dimensional array element is

$$i + d(j - 1)$$

where i = row subscript, j = column subscript, and d is the dimension declarator for the row. For the previous example, if the subroutine call is CALL SUBS(X,1,1) or the subroutine dimension is Y(1,1), the referenced elements of the dummy Y array would not line up with the corresponding elements of the actual X array, as shown in Figure 9.4. Obviously, care must be exercised when working with multidimensional arrays as dummy arguments. For more information, see Section 5-6, American National Standard Programming Language FORTRAN, ANSI X3.9-1978.

Figure 9.4   Two-dimensional array access

Consider the following FORTRAN program.

```
     DIMENSION X(3,3)
     DATA X/1,2,3,4,5,6,7,8,9/
     DO 10 I=1,3
  10 WRITE(6,*)(X(I,J),J=1,3)
     CALL ZERO(X,2,2)
     DO 20 I=1,3
  20 WRITE(6,*)(X(I,J),J=1,3)
     END

     SUBROUTINE ZERO(Y,M,N)
     DIMENSION Y(M,N)
     DO 10 I=1,M
     DO 10 J=1,N
  10 Y(I,J)=0.0
     RETURN
     END
```

Output for this program is

```
1.00000     4.00000     7.00000
2.00000     5.00000     8.00000
3.00000     6.00000     9.00000
```

which is the original Y array, and

```
0.00000      0.00000      7.00000
0.00000      5.00000      8.00000
0.00000      6.00000      9.00000
```

which is the Y array after exiting the subroutine. Note the position of the zeros in the second output. This is correct, since the formula for calculating the array element location is $i + d(j - 1)$, with $d = 2$. Hence the array, within the subroutine, will be processed

```
i = 1    j = 1    Y(1,1) = X(1,1) = 0.0
i = 1    j = 2    Y(1.2) = X(3,1) = 0.0
i = 2    j = 1    Y(2,1) = X(2,1) = 0.0
i = 2    j = 2    Y(2,2) = X(1,2) = 0.0
```

If the calling statement were CALL ZERO(X,1,3), the first column of the X array is zeroed. If the calling statement were CALL ZERO(X,3,3), all nine elements of the X array are zeroed.

9.9 STEPWISE REFINEMENT

Subprogramming lends itself to the writing of structured programs using the technique known as *stepwise refinement*. This technique is based on the concept that the initial program consists of procedure calls that perform the major tasks. The procedures are then refined step by step until all necessary code is written. The following example illustrates the concept of stepwise refinement. In this example, a positive integer array of N elements is sorted into ascending order. The required steps are

- fill the integer array
- sort the array
- output the sorted array

In flowchart form, these steps are as shown in Figure 9.5.

The main program is written as a sequence programming structure consisting of these procedures.

```
C       MAIN PROGRAM
C
C       A       INTEGER ARRAY NAME
C       N       NUMBER OF ELEMENTS
C
```

```
      INTEGER A(20)
      CALL FILLA(N,A)
      CALL SORTA(N,A)
      CALL OUTPUT(N,A)
      STOP
      END
```

Each procedure or subprogram is further redefined.

```
      SUBROUTINE FILLA(NUM,ARR)
      INTEGER ARR(NUM)
      WRITE(6,*)'ENTER N '
      READ(5,*)NUM
      WRITE(6,*)'ENTER VALUES '
      READ(5,*)(ARR(I),I=1,NUM)
      RETURN
      END

      SUBROUTINE OUTPUT(NUM,ARR)
      INTEGER ARR(NUM)
      WRITE(6,100)(ARR(I),I=1,NUM)
 100  FORMAT(' OUTPUT IS'/(1X,5I5))
      RETURN
      END
```

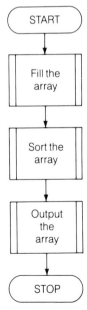

Figure 9.5 Flowchart for sorting an array

Procedure SORTA does the actual sorting of the array elements. The sort algorithm is based on the idea of moving the smallest array element to the bottom of the array by an exchange technique, which is the same as in the ranking procedure of Chapter 4. For example, let N = number of array elements, I = array element pointer, and J = location of the bottom array element. If the array contains the values

1   last element
9
5
2
3   first element

then N = 5 and N − 1 passes will be made through the array from J = 1 to J = N − 1. During each pass the array elements will be examined from I = J + 1 to I = N. Whenever the Ith element is less than the Jth element, these two elements will be exchanged. The sort proceeds as

Initially: array = 3 2 5 9 1
Pass 1:   I = 2   J = 1   exchange
                                    array = 2 3 5 9 1
             I = 3   J = 1   no exchange
             I = 4   J = 1   no exchange
             I = 5   J = 1   exchange
                                    array = 1 3 5 9 2
Pass 2:   I = 3   J = 2   no exchange
             I = 4   J = 2   no exchange
             I = 5   J = 2   exchange
                                    array = 1 2 5 9 3
Pass 3:   I = 4   J = 3   no exchange
             I = 5   J = 3   exchange
                                    array = 1 2 3 9 5
Pass 4:   I = 5   J = 4   exchange
                                    array = 1 2 3 5 9

Procedure SORTA can now be written as

```
      SUBROUTINE SORTA(NUM,ARR)
      INTEGER ARR(NUM)
      DO 10 J=1,NUM-1
      DO 10 I=J+1,NUM
      IF(ARR(I).LT.ARR(J))CALL XCHNG(ARR(I),ARR(J))
   10 CONTINUE
      RETURN
      END
```

Procedure XCHNG handles the exchange and requires the variable HOLD. The purpose of this variable is to hold the value of the Ith element while the exchange takes place, otherwise the two elements being exchanged would have the same value. Procedure XCHNG becomes

```
      SUBROUTINE XCHNG(IVAL,JVAL)
      INTEGER HOLD
      HOLD=IVAL
      IVAL=JVAL
      JVAL=HOLD
      RETURN
      END
```

The final FORTRAN programs for sorting the integer array are

```
C     MAIN PROGRAM
      INTEGER A(20)
      CALL FILLA(N,A)
      CALL SORTA(N,A)
      CALL OUTPUT(N,A)
      STOP
      END
C
C     PROCEDURES
C
      SUBROUTINE FILLA(NUM,ARR)
      INTEGER ARR(NUM)
      WRITE(6,*)'ENTER N '
      READ(5,*)NUM
      WRITE(6,*)'ENTER VALUES '
      READ(5,*)(ARR(I),I=1,NUM)
      RETURN
      END
C
      SUBROUTINE SORTA(NUM,ARR)
      INTEGER ARR(NUM)
      DO 10 J=1,NUM-1
      DO 10 I=J+1,NUM
      IF(ARR(I).LT.ARR(J))CALL XCHNG(ARR(I),ARR(J))
   10 CONTINUE
      RETURN
      END
C
      SUBROUTINE XCHNG(IVAL,JVAL)
      INTEGER HOLD
      HOLD=IVAL
      IVAL=JVAL
      JVAL=HOLD
```

```
       RETURN
       END
C
       SUBROUTINE OUTPUT(NUM,ARR)
       INTEGER ARR(NUM)
       WRITE(6,100)(ARR(I),I=1,NUM)
       RETURN
  100 FORMAT(' OUTPUT IS'/(1X,5I5))
       END
```

Input:

ENTER N 6

ENTER VALUES 3,7,5,1,-1,0

Output:

```
OUTPUT IS
      -1    0    1    3    5
       7
```

Figure 9.6 summarizes the technique of stepwise refinement as applied to sorting the integer array.

Fill the array	1. Enter the number of array elements. 2. Fill the array, element by element.	
Sort the array	1. Search the array, element by element. 2. Exchange elements so as to move the smallest element to the bottom of the list. 3. Check to ensure that all elements have been processed.	1. Do the actual exchange of two elements.
Output the array	1. Output heading. 2. Output the array, element by element.	
Level 1	Level 2	Level 3

Figure 9.6   Stepwise refinement and sorting

9.10 THE COMMON STATEMENT

COMMON is the name given to a data area of fixed size that can be common to the main program and all subprograms. The specification statement

COMMON array/variable list

establishes this common data area. COMMON is frequently used as a means of eliminating arguments in subprograms. For example, consider the subprogram NEWSUM and its calling program:

```
C       MAIN PROGRAM
        REAL A(10)
        READ(5,*)NUM
        READ(5,*)(A(I),I=1,NUM)
        CALL NEWSUM (NUM,A,SUM)
        WRITE(6,*)'SUM IS',SUM
        STOP
        END
C
C       SUBPROGRAM
C
        SUBROUTINE NEWSUM(N,X,SUM)
        DIMENSION X(N)
        SUM=0.0
        DO 20 I=1,N
     20 SUM=SUM+X(I)
        RETURN
        END
```

Using the COMMON specification statement, these programs become

```
C       MAIN PROGRAM
        COMMON NUM,SUM,A(10)
        READ(5,*)NUM
        READ(5,*)(A(I),I=1,NUM)
        CALL NEWSUM
        WRITE(6,*)'SUM IS',SUM
        STOP
        END
C
C       SUBPROGRAM
C
        SUBROUTINE NEWSUM
        COMMON N,SUM,X(10)
```

```
      SUM=0.0
      DO 20 I=1,N
   20 SUM=SUM+X(I)
      RETURN
      END
```

The COMMON statement in the MAIN PROGRAM and SUBPROGRAM establishes the common data area. Assuming one word per integer datum and two words per real datum, the common data area is 23 computer words. Reference to common is in the order in which the variables and/or arrays appear in the COMMON statement, as shown in Figure 9.7.

The main program references common as follows:

word 1	NUM
words 2–3	SUM
words 4–23	A(1) through A(10)

The subprogram references common in the following manner:

word 1	N
words 2–3	SUM
words 4–23	X(1) through X(10)

Several COMMON statements can be used to establish common, and they are used in their order of appearance. Thus

```
             COMMON NUM
             COMMON SUM
             COMMON A(10)
```

is equivalent to

```
          COMMON NUM,SUM,A(10)
```

whereas

```
             COMMON SUM
             COMMON NUM
             COMMON A(10)
```

is not equivalent even though the common data area is sized to 23 words.

In summary, the COMMON specification statement establishes a common data area available to the main program and all subprograms. Common variables and arrays reference memory in their order of appearance in the COMMON statement.

Figure 9.7 Common data area

COMMON is frequently referred to as a *global* data area since information stored in common is available to all program units through the COMMON specification statement.

COMMON is used to pass values between a main program and subprograms so that frequently used variable and array names need not be stated over and over again as actual or dummy arguments, thus reducing the size and complexity of subprogram statements.

The previous form of the COMMON statement is frequently referred to as *blank COMMON*, in which the entire COMMON area is treated as a unit. In addition to blank COMMON, there is the *named COMMON* form, where each COMMON block is assigned a name. In a FORTRAN subprogram, only those named COMMON blocks required by the subprogram need be specified. Consider the example where three arrays are to be processed by counting the number of negative elements in each array. A separate subroutine will be written for processing each array. In the main program, the code becomes:

```
C      MAIN PROGRAM
       COMMON /BLCK1/X(100),NRX,KX
       COMMON /BLCK2/Y(10,10),NRY,NCY,KY
       COMMON /BLCK3/Z(5,5,5),NRZ,NCZ,NZ,KZ
       READ(5,*)NRX
       READ(5,*)(X(I),I=1,NRX)
       CALL COUNTX
       WRITE(6,*)'X COUNT IS ',KX
       READ(5,*)NRY,NCY
       READ(5,*)((Y(I,J),J=1,NCY),I=1,NRY)
       CALL COUNTY
       WRITE(6,*)'Y COUNT IS ',KY
       READ(5,*)NRZ,NCZ,NZ
       READ(5,*)(((Z(I,J,K),K=1,NZ),J=1,NCZ),I=1,NRZ)
       CALL COUNTZ
       WRITE(6,*),'Z COUNT IS ',KZ
       END
```

The main program, through the first two read statements, accepts as input the number of elements, NRX, in the X array followed by filling the X array element by element. The next two read statements accept the number of rows, NRY, and columns, NCY, in the Y array and fills the Y array row by row. The final two read statements accept the number of rows, NRZ, columns, NCZ, and depth, NZ, of the Z array, followed by filling the Z array. Each call statement passes control to a subroutine that counts the number of negative values in the X, Y, and Z arrays. Each array and its size is passed through COMMON to its respective subroutine COUNTX, COUNTY and COUNTZ. The count of the number of negative values KX, KY and KZ are returned through COMMON. The three subroutines become:

```
C       SUBPROGRAM
        SUBROUTINE COUNTX
        COMMON /BLCK1/X(100),NRX,KX
        KX=0
        DO 10 I=1,NRX
        IF(X(I).LT.0.0)KX=KX+1
   10 CONTINUE
        RETURN
        END


C       SUBPROGRAM
        SUBROUTINE COUNTY
        COMMON /BLCK2/Y(10,10),NRY,NCY,KY
        KY=0
        DO 10 I=1,NRY
        DO 10 J=1,NCY
        IF(Y(I,J).LT.0.0)KY=KY+1
   10 CONTINUE
        RETURN
        END


C       SUBPROGRAM
        SUBROUTINE COUNTZ
        COMMON /BLCK3/Z(5,5,5),NRZ,NCZ,NZ,KZ
        KZ=0
        DO 10 I=1,NRZ
        DO 10 J=1,NCZ
        DO 10 K=1,NZ
        IF(Z(I,J,K).LT.0.0)KZ=KZ+1
   10 CONTINUE
        RETURN
        END
```

The same variable and array names were used for named COMMON in the main program and the three subprograms. This is an arbitrary choice, since there is no

Figure 9.8   Proper order of FORTRAN statements

FORTRAN requirement that these names be different. Within each COMMON block, the order of the arrays and variables must be the same in the main program and each subroutine. The block names, BLK1, BLK2, and BLK3 must be the same throughout.

9.11   ORDERING FORTRAN STATEMENTS

Chapter 9 completes the discussion of the essential FORTRAN statements. The ordering of these statements can now be shown. Figure 9.8 presents the required order, where vertical lines separate statements that can be intermixed. For example, ENTRY statements can be intermixed with PARAMETER and DATA statements, but PARAMETER statements must come before DATA statements.

9.12   SUMMARY

Intrinsic functions are built into the computer. In FORTRAN 77 the intrinsic function name is generic, and hence the function type is set by the type of the argument. The arithmetic-statement function is user-defined and may be any function that can be defined in one statement.

The function subprogram is used to return a single value, the calculated value of the function. The subroutine subprogram returns multiple values. The only link between the subprogram and the calling program is the subprogram name and its arguments. All other variables, arrays, and labels with the subprogram are undefined outside the subprogram, except for variables and arrays defined in COMMON. Stepwise refinement is a technique used in developing a FORTRAN program from the top down. This method of programming leads to a modular design, in which each module (main program or subprogram) is clear in intent and simple in purpose.

EXERCISES

1. Correct all errors in the following program.

```
      WRITE 6,100
     DO I=1,10
10   WRITE(6,200)I,SQR(I)
     STOP
100  FORMAT('TABLE OF SQUARE ROOTS'/)
200  FORMAT(1X,I5,3X,I12)
     END
```

2. Write arithmetic-statement functions to implement the following algebraic functions.

$$f(x) = \text{secant}(x)$$
$$f(x,y,z) = \sqrt{x^2 + y^2 + z^2}$$
$$f(w) = a + \log(w)$$

3. Write a FORTRAN program to calculate and output a table of tangents from 0 to 90 degrees in increments of 5 degrees. What happens at 90 degrees?

4. Repeat exercise 3 to calculate and output a table of double-precision tangents.

5. Write a main program that will fill, through a DATA statement, a one-dimensional array of up to 20 elements. The program should then CALL a subroutine that will count the number of positive and negative integers and

RETURN the two counts. The two counts are to be output from the main program. Use as test data the seven integers 1, 2, -3, 4, -3, 1, and 2.

6. Write a main program that will fill, through a DATA statement, a one-dimensional integer array of up to 20 elements. Write two function subprograms, one to RETURN the number of positive integers and the other to RETURN the number of negative integers. Output the two counts from the main program.

7. Write a FORTRAN program that will include a function subprogram to round off a real constant to any given number of decimal places. Input the number of decimal places desired and the real constant and output the real constant correct to the given number of decimal places. Label all output.

8. The position of a particle moving in a straight line with constant acceleration is given by the equation

$$x = x_0 + v_0 t + \frac{1}{2}at^2$$

where x_0 is the initial position, v_0 is the initial velocity, a is the constant acceleration, and t is the time. Write a function subprogram to RETURN the double-precision value of the displacement x. Incorporate this into a main program that inputs x_0, v_0, a, and t and outputs the double-precision value of x as well as the input values. Label all output.

9. It is desired to incorporate a ceiling function in a FORTRAN program. The ceiling function gives an integer value for a real argument such that

$$CEI(-11.3) = -11$$
$$CEI(11.3) = 12$$

Write a function subprogram that returns this integer value for any real dummy argument. Test your program using X $= -3.5, +3.5, -2.1$.

10. Given that an integer is either odd or even, write and test a subroutine subprogram that has as its arguments the integer variable N and the logical variable VALUE. If N is even, set VALUE to true; otherwise, set VALUE to false.

11. Write a function subprogram that calculates and returns the mean deviation of N elements of the real X array, where

$$\text{mean deviation} = \frac{\sum_{i=1}^{N} |(X_i - \overline{X})|}{N} \quad \text{and} \quad \overline{X} = \text{mean} = \frac{\sum_{i=1}^{N} X_i}{N}$$

12. It is desired to sort a real array into descending sequence. Write and test a subroutine subprogram to accomplish this sort. Use as test data the real values 0.1, -5.5, 0.0, -18.0, 9.3, 32.0, 0.1, 1E20.

13. Write a function subprogram that returns the dot product of two vectors A and B, where

$$\text{dot product} = A \cdot B = A_1B_1 + A_2B_2 + A_3B_3$$

Represent each vector as a real, one-dimensional array.

14. Write and test a subroutine subprogram that fills an N row by M column two-dimensional array with ones.

15. Modify the ROOTS subprogram whose flowchart is shown in Figure 9.2 to return the double-precision roots of the function $f(x) = ax^2 + bx + c = 0$.

16. It is desired to count the number of times the string 'THE' appears in a character variable. Write and test a function subprogram that returns this count. Use as test data the character constant

    'THE NUMBER OF TIMES THE APPEARS IN THE LINE IS 3'

17. Write a function subprogram that calculates the double-precision cube root of x. Use as your function name CUBR. Test your function for $x = -27.0$, 0.0, 27.0.

18. Write a FORTRAN program that will store a string array consisting of up to 100 lines with up to 75 characters each, then execute a subroutine subprogram to search the array and RETURN the line number in which any of the words *a*, *an*, or *the* appear. Output the line numbers in the main program. Use as test data the statement of this exercise.

19. Modify the program of the previous exercise to also return and output the number of times each of the three key words appear in a line.

20. Write a FORTRAN function subprogram that will RETURN the product of the major diagonal elements of an n × n real array.

21. Write a FORTRAN subprogram that will RETURN each element of an nxn array ($n = 6$) whenever the subscripts sum to 7.

22. Write a FORTRAN function subprogram that will RETURN the largest absolute value of a real m × n array.

23. Write a FORTRAN subroutine subprogram called EVEN that searches an integer two-dimensional array for even integers and, in turn, will CALL and RETURN a one-dimensional array of the even integers in ascending order.

24. Write a FORTRAN program to search a real, two-dimensional 5×4 array and output the count of the number of zeros in each row and each column. Your program should call a subroutine that returns a nine element one-dimensional array, each element being the number of zeros in each of the five rows and four columns of the two-dimensional array. Initialize the two-dimensional array through a DATA statement. Label and FORMAT the output.

25. Write a function subprogram that has as its dummy argument an integer variable value that is to be converted to a six-byte constant. This constant is to be assigned to the function name KONVRT. The function should process integers as follows:

Integer value	Value assigned to KONVRT
18	'ƀƀƀƀ18'
-32	'ƀƀƀ$-$32'
0	'ƀƀƀƀƀ0'
32767	'ƀ32767'
-32768	'$-$32768'
>32767	'ƀERROR'
<-32768	'ƀERROR'

Use this table to test your character function KONVRT.

26. A real, three-dimensional array is to be searched for the largest and the smallest elements. Write and test a subroutine subprogram to accomplish this search. Use as dummy arguments

ARRAY	array name
BIG	value of largest element
SMALL	value of smallest element
I,J,K	dimensions of the array

27. Write a subroutine subprogram that returns the components of the cross product of two vectors A and B, where

$$\text{cross product} = R = A \times B$$

Represent each vector as a real, one-dimensional array consisting of three elements.

$$A = A_1 + A_2 + A_3$$
$$B = B_1 + B_2 + B_3$$

$$R = R_1 + R_2 + R_3$$
$$R_1 = A_2B_3 - A_3B_2$$
$$R_2 = A_3B_1 - A_1B_3$$
$$R_3 = A_1B_2 - A_2B_1$$

28. Compile and execute the following FORTRAN statements and comment on the results.

```
    DIMENSION X(3,3)
    DATA X/1.0,2.0,3.0,4.0,5.0,6.0,7.0,8.0,9.0/
    DO 10 I=1,3
 10 WRITE(6,*)(X(I,J),J=1,3)
    CALL ZERO(X,3,1)
    DO 20 I=1,3
 20 WRITE(6,*)(X(I,J),J=1,3)
    END

    SUBROUTINE ZERO(Y,M,N)
    DIMENSION Y(M,N)
    DO 10 I=1,M
    DO 10 J=1,N
 10 Y(I,J)=0.0
    RETURN
    END
```

29. Repeat exercise 12 by placing the real array in COMMON. Use the statement

```
COMMON X(8)
```

in the main program and subprogram. Your CALL statement should now be

```
CALL SORTIT
```

where SORTIT is the name of the subroutine that sorts the real array into descending sequence.

chapter 10

Applications

The computer is a powerful tool when applied to numerical solutions of problems in engineering and science. This chapter will discuss a few of the more common numerical methods for the solution of such problems. The techniques selected for presentation were chosen for their ease of understanding. They work and are useful; however, they may not always be the most efficient. Moreover, this discussion is not intended to be exhaustive or rigorous but rather to give you an idea of some of the numerical applications of computer problem solving.

10.1 ROOT SEARCH

Root search will be considered first. A number of techniques can be applied to find the roots of equations of the form $f(x) = 0$. We will restrict our search to real roots only. Given an equation of the form $f(x) = 0$ and assuming that a real root exists, two values of x, x_1 and x_2, can be found such that $f(x_1) \cdot f(x_2) < 0$. The values x_1 and x_2 are said to bracket the solution value x_r—that is, where $f(x_r) = 0$. The idea now is to halve the interval (x_1, x_2) by finding a new value, x_3, such that $x_3 = (x_1 + x_2)/2$.

   If the sign of $f(x_3)$ is the same as the sign of $f(x_2)$, then one can assume that x_r lies between x_1 and x_3. Therefore, choose an $x_4 = (x_1 + x_3)/2$ and test $f(x_4)$. However, if the sign of $f(x_3)$ is opposite to the sign of $f(x_2)$, then assume x_r is between x_3 and x_2. Choose $x_4 = (x_3 + x_2)/2$ and test $f(x_4)$. Programmatically, this testing for the next half interval can be accomplished as follows:

If $\qquad\qquad f(x_1) \cdot f(x_3) < 0 \qquad x_4 = (x_1 + x_3)/2$

or if $\qquad\qquad f(x_1) \cdot f(x_3) > 0 \qquad x_4 = (x_3 + x_2)/2$

However, when $f(x_1) \cdot f(x_3) = 0$, then a root is found at x_3. The series of interval halving is shown in Figure 10.1.

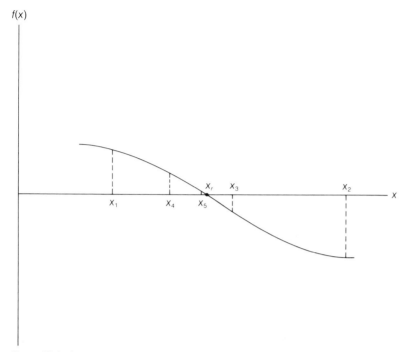

Figure 10.1   Interval-halving method

This halving method is repeated until $|f(x_m)| < \varepsilon$, where ε is the absolute allowable error and x_m is the approximate root.

As an example, find the root of $f(x) = 0$, given $f(x) = e^{-x} - \sin(\pi x/2) = 0$ and $\varepsilon = 0.01$.

Choose $x_1 = 0$, then $f(x_1) = 1$. Choose $x_2 = 1$, then $f(x_2) = -.6321$. We assume that a root x_r lies between x_1 and x_2 because $f(x_1)$ and $f(x_2)$ are of opposite signs. Let $x_3 = (x_1 + x_2)/2$, or $x_3 = 0.5$. Table 10.1 carries on the interval-halving method until $|f(x_m)| < .01$.

TABLE 10.1   Interval-Halving Root Search

Step	x_i	x_j	$x_m = (x_i + x_j)/2$	$f(x_m)$	$\dfrac{f(x_i)}{f(x_m)}$
1	0	1.0	0.5	-0.1006	$-$
2	0	0.5	0.25	0.3961	$+$
3	0.25	0.5	0.375	0.1317	$+$
4	0.375	0.5	0.4375	0.0112	$+$
5	0.4375	0.5	0.46875	-0.0458	$-$
6	0.4375	0.46875	0.453125	-0.0175	$-$
7	0.4375	0.453125	0.4453125	-0.0032	$-$

$f(x)$

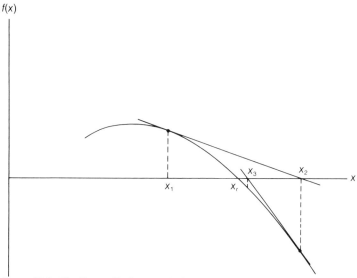

Figure 10.2 The Newton-Raphson method

Another technique for calculating the roots of a function is the Newton-Raphson method. Referring to Figure 10.2, assume a value, x_1, for the root and draw a tangent to the curve at x_1. Where this tangent intersects the x axis, pick a new value of x, x_2, and draw another tangent at x_2. It can be seen in the figure that x_i approaches x_r. The slope of the tangent to the curve at x_1 is given by

$$f'(x_1) = \frac{0 - f(x_1)}{x_2 - x_1} \qquad \text{or} \qquad x_2 = x_1 - \frac{f(x_1)}{f'(x_1)}$$

Similarly

$$f'(x_2) = \frac{f(x_2) - 0}{x_2 - x_3} \qquad \text{or} \qquad x_3 = x_2 - \frac{f(x_2)}{f'(x_2)}$$

This equation is applied successively until $|f(x_{i+1})| < \epsilon$, where ϵ is the absolute allowable error. As an example, find a root of $f(x)$, given $f(x) = e^{-x} - \sin(\pi x/2) = 0$ and $\epsilon = .01$. Table 10.2 shows the successive application of the Newton-Raphson equation where $f'(x) = -e^{-x} - (\pi/2)\cos(\pi x/2)$. The approximate root is $x = .44195$ for $\epsilon = .01$. Note should be taken of the fewer steps required than for the interval-halving method.

A FORTRAN program for the Newton-Raphson method is shown in Figure 10.3.

The Newton-Raphson method of root search can be used to find complex roots. In the case of a possible complex root, the initial guess must be a complex number and the absolute value of the function, $f(x_{i+1})$, is defined as the square root of the

TABLE 10.2   Successive Approximations for the Newton-Raphson Method

Step	x_i	x_{i+1}	$f(x_{i+1})$
1	0	.38898	.10381
2	.38898	.44195	.003

```
C     DEFINE PI

      PARAMETER (PI=3.14159)

C     DEFINE FUNCTIONS AND ERROR
      FCN(X)=EXP(-X)-SIN(PI*X/2.)
      DFCN(X)=-EXP(-X)-PI/2*COS(PI*X/2)
      ERROR=0.01
      WRITE(6,*)'STARTING VALUE'
      READ(5,*)XNEW
C     CALCULATE ROOT APPROXIMATION
   10 XOLD=XNEW
      XNEW=XOLD-FCN(XOLD)/DFCN(XOLD)
C     TEST ACCURACY OF ROOT
      IF(ABS(FCN(XNEW)).LT.ERROR)THEN
C     OUTPUT ROOT
      WRITE(6,*)XNEW,FCN(XNEW)
      ELSE
      GO TO 10
      ENDIF
      STOP
      END
```

Figure 10.3   Programming the Newton-Raphson method

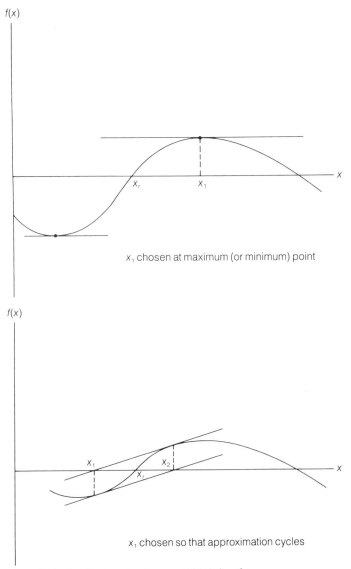

x_1 chosen at maximum (or minimum) point

x_1 chosen so that approximation cycles

Figure 10.4 Graphical results of a poor initial choice of x_1

sum of the squares of the real part and the imaginary part. In other words, $|f(x_{i+1})|$ $= [a^2 + b^2]^{1/2}$, where a is the real part of the complex function and b is the imaginary part.

There are two obvious problems with the application of the Newton-Raphson root search. These problems depend primarily on the initial guess, x_1. If the initial guess happens to be at a maximum or minimum point on the curve, then the derivative is zero, which would make the Newton-Raphson equation increase without bound. The initial guess can also result in a cycling effect with no convergence to the real root. Figure 10.4 illustrates these problems. To guard against these problems, the initial guess should be as close to the true root as practicable. One technique is to use interval-halving to get near the root, then transfer to Newton-Raphson to complete the search. This makes for a good programming exercise. Furthermore, if possible, when programming the Newton-Raphson root search, tests should be provided to respond to these problems when they are encountered.

10.2   NUMERICAL INTEGRATION

Many numerical problems involve the definite integration of complicated functions. If we consider the definite integral as the area under the curve representing the function, then there are several methods of approximating this area and hence integrating the function. Such methods are called *numerical integration.*

The first of the methods of numerical integration to be discussed is called the *midpoint* or *rectangular rule.*

In Figure 10.5 the exact area under the curve from a to b is given by

$$A = \int_a^b f(x)\ dx$$

which can be approximated by summing the areas of the n rectangles, of width h. The fundamental area under the curve, of width h, is called a *cell*. The area of a

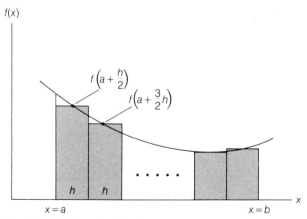

Figure 10.5   The rectangular rule

single rectangle is $hf(x_m)$ where x_m is the midpoint of interval h. Note that the two small triangular areas to the right and left of $f(x_m)$ nearly cancel each other. The smaller the interval h (the larger the n), the more closely the summation approximates the integral.

In programming the rectangular rule, start with an initial value of n (the number of cells). The area is calculated using a value of $h = |b - a|/n$. Then the value of n is increased and a new area is computed. If the absolute value of the difference between two successively calculated areas is less than ϵ, the absolute error, the last computed area is assumed to be a good approximation of the integral, where

$$|\text{area}_i - \text{area}_{i+1}| < \epsilon$$

A second method for determining the area under a curve (evaluating a definite integral) is called the *trapezoidal rule*.

The exact area under the curve from a to b can be approximated by the sum of the areas of n trapezoids of equal width. The area of a single trapezoid is given by

$$\text{area} \simeq \tfrac{1}{2}h[f(x) + f(x + h)]$$

The sum of the areas of the n trapezoids from a to b approximates the area under the curve. Hence,

$$\frac{h}{2}[f(a) + f(a + h)] + \frac{h}{2}[f(a + h) + f(a + 2h)] + \cdots + \frac{h}{2}\{f[a + (n - 1)h] + f(b)\}$$

where $n = $ number of trapezoids. Simplifying gives area A as

$$A = h\left[\tfrac{1}{2}f(a) + f(a + h) + f(a + 2h) + \cdots + \tfrac{1}{2}f(b)\right]$$

The smaller the value for h, the more closely the summation approximates the integral.

If, in Figure 10.6, $a = 1$, $b = 4$ when $n = 6$, the value for h is

$$h = \frac{4 - 1}{6} = 0.5$$

At the two end points

$$f(a) = f(1) \quad \text{and} \quad f(b) = f(4)$$

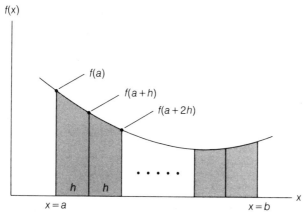

Figure 10.6   The trapezoidal rule

and the five intermediate points are

$$f(1.5) \quad f(2.0) \quad f(2.5) \quad f(3.0) \quad f(3.5)$$

Therefore the area approximating the integral is

$$A = 0.5\left[\tfrac{1}{2}f(1) + f(1.5) + f(2.0) + f(2.5) + f(3.0) + f(3.5) + \tfrac{1}{2}f(4)\right]$$

The trapezoidal rule for numerical integration can be programmed to evaluate the definite integral $\int_a^b x^2 \, dx$, as

```
      FNY(X)=X**2
      READ(5,100)A,B,N
      AREA=0.5*(FNY(A)+FNY(B))
      H=ABS(A-B)/REAL(N)
      DO 10 I=1,N-1
   10 AREA=AREA+FNY(A+REAL(I)*H)
      WRITE(6,200)AREA*H
      STOP
  100 FORMAT(2F5.0,I5)
  200 FORMAT(' AREA=',G14.6)
      END
```

In addition to the rectangular rule (area under a set of constant functions) and the trapezoidal rule (area under a set of linear functions) a formula exists for the area under a set of quadratic functions that leads to Simpson's rule for numerical integration. A more accurate integration formula, to approximate the integral, should be expected if a set of quadratic functions is defined for each interval. In Figure 10.6 a quadratic curve can be made to pass through points at $f(a)$, $f(a + h)$, $f(a + 2h)$. Each quadratic curve is of the form $f_i(x) = A_i x^2 + B_i x + C_i$. If A_i, B_i, C_i are determined so that $f_i(x)$ is exactly satisfied at $x = a$, $x = a + h$ and $x = a + 2h$, the area under the curve is given by the equation

$$\text{area}_1 = \frac{h}{3}[f(a) + 4f(a + h) + f(a + 2h)]$$

This is Simpson's rule! Note that the width of the fundamental area is $2h$, not h as in the previous two methods of numerical integration. This implies that the number of h's must be even. Now if the process is repeated for the next two areas in Figure 10.6 the result is

$$\text{area}_2 = \frac{h}{3}[f(a + 2h) + 4f(a + 3h) + f(a + 4h)]$$

Continuing the application of Simpson's rule for all $2h$ areas from a to b the general rule results.

$$\int_a^b f(x)dx = \sum \text{area}_i = \frac{h}{3}[f(a) + 4f(a + h) +$$
$$2f(a + 2h) + 4f(a + 3h) + 2f(a + 4h) + \cdots + f(b)]$$

A closer look at the above general rule reveals a repetition of terms, such as those with the coefficient of 4 and those with the coefficient 2. This repetitiveness is made to order for the looping capability of a computer. A similar looping was seen in the rectangular rule and trapezoidal rule. In order to see how the series can be summed by a DO-loop rewrite the series in the so-called closed form. The reader can verify that for the number of cells greater than two, where N is one-half the number of cells.

$$\int_a^b f(x)dx = \frac{h}{3}\left[f(a) + 4\sum_{n=1}^{N} f(a + (2n - 1)h) + 2\sum_{n=1}^{N-1} f(a + 2nh) + f(b)\right]$$

where $\sum$ means "sum of." Remember that for this form of Simpson's rule the number of cells must be even. Other forms of Simpson's rule can be found in any standard textbook on numerical methods.

Finally, one should consider the error involved in numerical integration. The computation of error bounds depending on the cell size, h, can be found in standard textbooks on numerical methods. Suffice it to say that error decreases with cell size. However, there may be a limit beyond which the error will increase due the roundoff errors of increased calculations. These roundoff errors arise from decimal to binary conversion.

10.3   LINEAR INTERPOLATION

Any set of experimental data is both discrete and finite. That is to say, the very nature of experiment leads to discrete data points as a result of that experiment and the number of data points that can be mathematically and graphically manipulated is clearly finite. As a matter of fact the engineer will often run an experiment only so far as to obtain a meaningful set of data points. As James Watt, the eighteenth century British inventor said, "(After the experiment) I laid down a curve *sufficient for my purposes.*"

Years ago before the age of hand calculators, sines and cosines (and other trigonometric functions) were obtained from calculated tables. These tables were themselves calculated with precision to the nearest degree and some to the nearest hundredth of a degree. They required hand calculation using a series expansion for sines and cosines. However, no matter how precise the tables, an application might require greater precision. This is what *interpolation* is all about. The problem can be stated as follows: given two points on a curve (or two sets of values in a table) find the location of a point intermediate to the given points. Graphically, *linear interpolation* is shown in Figure 10.7, where the point P' on the straight line is an approximation to P, the actual interpolated point desired. Two things should be clear from Figure 10.7. First, the actual function $f(x)$ from P_i to P_{i+1} is being approximated by a straight line; second, the greater the interval x_i to x_{i+1} or the greater the curvature of $f(x)$, the greater will be the error of a linear interpolation. For example, if one looks at the trigonometric sine function the curvature in the vicinity of 90° is seen to be much greater than in the vicinity of 180°. This means that the same interval x_i to x_{i+1} will produce greater errors for the linear interpolation technique around 90° than around 180°. The mathematics of linear interpolation is based on the equation for the slope of a straight line. The slope of P_iP_{i+1} as shown in Figure 10.7 is

$$\frac{y_{i+1} - y_i}{x_{i+1} - x_i}$$

The slope of P_iP' is

$$\frac{y' - y_i}{x - x_i}$$

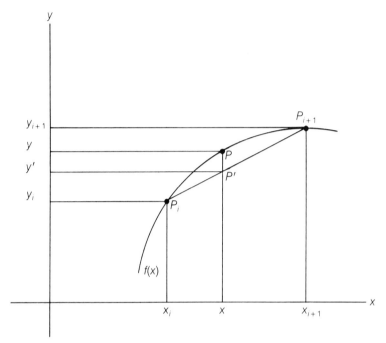

Figure 10.7 A linear interpolation

Because P_iP' is a segment of P_iP_{i+1} the slopes must be equal and solving the resulting equation for y' yields the approximation for the ordinate of P', the approximation to P,

$$y' = y_i + (x - x_i)\left[\frac{y_{i+1} - y_i}{x_{i+1} - x_i}\right]$$

Example: Given a partial table of sines find the sine of 36 degrees.

x_i (degrees)	20	30	40	50
$y_i = \sin(x_i)$	.3420	.5000	.6428	.7660

To solve the interpolation, let $x = 36$, $x_i = 30$, $x_{i+1} = 40$, $y_i = .5000$, and $y_{i+1} = .6428$. Substituting gives

$$y_{36} = \frac{.5000(36 - 40) - .6428(36 - 30)}{30 - 40} = .5857$$

Comparing this result with that obtained using a hand calculator for sin 36° shows a difference of about 0.35%.

There are other, more sophisticated interpolation techniques such as Lagrange's Method or Newton's Difference Method, both of which can be found in any standard work on numerical methods.

10.4 CURVE FITTING

In approximating a set of experimental data with a function, there are two basic strategies that can be applied. One requires the plot of the function to pass through every point. This clearly means that the approximating curve will be, in actuality, a set of straight lines from point to point, as shown in Figure 10.8. The equations used in Section 10.3 are just such point-to-point equations and we can use linear interpolation methods to find what is called a "piecewise" function.

The other strategy for approximating graphical data with functions is called "least squares." As the name implies, the attempt in this strategy is to find a curve for which the sum of the squares of distances between the observed value of the dependent variable and its calculated value is a minimum. The usual assumption is that the experimental, or observed, values are without error. The idea is to minimize the error of the calculated value of the dependent variable. The reason the *square* of the error is used is that data points could be quite a distance from the approximating curve but some would be above (+) the curve and some would be below

Figure 10.8 Piecewise curve-fitting

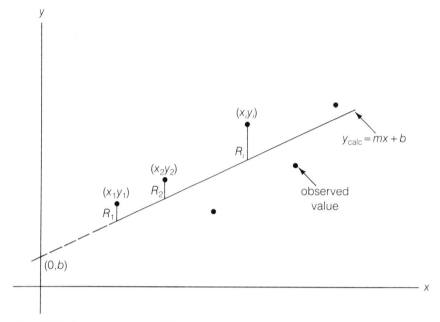

Figure 10.9 Least squares curve-fitting

$(-)$ and the algebraic sum could be very small indicating a possible minimum, but the approximation would be useless for the data points involved. A *linear* least squares is shown in Figure 10.9. Consider the linear equation

$$y = mx + b$$

where m is the slope of the straight line and b is the y-intercept. The goal is to determine values for m and b such that the sum of the squares of the distances between the observed value of y and the calculated value of y is minimized. The distances will be called *residuals* and represented by R_i. Mathematically, one wants to minimize $\sum R_i^2$ where $\sum$ means "sum of." In this development only linear least squares will be considered, although the least squares method can apply to higher order equations.

For linear least squares, then,

$$R_i = y_{observed} - y_{calculated}$$
$$y_{calculated} = mx_i + b$$
$$R_i^2 = [y_i - (mx_i + b)]^2$$

where y_i is the observed value.

Expanding the right side and summing over N sets of data $(x_i y_i)$ yields

$$\sum R_i^2 = \sum_{i=1}^{N} [y_i^2 - 2my_i x_i - 2by_i + m^2 x_i^2 + 2mbx_i + b^2]$$

where the summation proceeds as $i = 1$ to N, and N is the number of data points.

The idea now is to vary m and b so that the $\sum R_i^2$ is a minimum. The differential calculus provides a method whereby minimizing an expression is made easy. Without the calculus, while the arithmetic is somewhat cumbersome, the minimizing of the square of the residuals is based on the idea that for a minimum when m is varied a little bit (say Δm) and with b held constant the difference between $\sum R_i^2$ with m replaced by $m + \Delta m$ and $\sum R_i^2$ with m alone must be equal to zero. Thus for m

$$\sum R_i^2 = \sum [y_i^2 - 2mx_i y_i - 2by_i + m^2 x_i^2 + 2mbx_i + b^2]$$

and for $m + \Delta m$

$$\sum R_i^2 = \sum [y_i^2 - 2(m + \Delta m)x_i y_i - 2by_i + (m + \Delta m)^2 x_i^2 + 2(m + \Delta m)bx_i + b^2]$$

the difference between these two functions is

$$\sum [2\Delta m\, x_i y_i + m^2 x_i^2 - (m + \Delta m)^2 x_i^2 - 2\Delta mbx_i]$$

When $(m + \Delta m)^2$ is expanded the $(\Delta m)^2$ can be neglected as it is the square of a very small quantity. Finally, we want this difference to be as small as possible (i.e., equal to zero). Hence,

$$\sum [2\Delta m\, x_i y_i - 2m\Delta mx_i^2 - 2\Delta mbx_i] = 0$$

or

$$\sum_{i=1}^{N} x_i y_i - m \sum_{i=1}^{N} x_i^2 - b \sum_{i=1}^{N} x_i = 0$$

If b is varied by an amount Δb while m is held constant the same procedure yields the second equation in m and b as

$$\sum_{i=1}^{N} y_i - m \sum_{i=1}^{N} x_i - Nb = 0$$

These two equations are the so-called *normal equations* for the least squares straight line. One must remember that throughout this development it was assumed that the independent variable x_i was without error. If such is not the case the problem of least squares approximation is compounded beyond the scope of our consideration here.

Least squares approximations can be made with any assumed polynomial equation (quadratic, cubic, etc.) but the mathematics becomes more involved as the order of the equation increases. For example, if we wanted to fit a quadratic equation to data points it would take three normal equations rather than two. However, an exponential approximation can be linearized. Given $y = ke^{cx}$ the linearized equation is $ln(y) = ln(k) + cx$. This is a linear equation where the dependent variable is $ln\ y$, the slope is c, and the y-intercept is $ln\ k$.

Example: In a tensile experiment of metal bars that have identical composition and cross-sectional area, but different lengths, the data is given by the table

length (*in.*)	5	10	15	20	25	30	35
elongation (*in.*)	.01	.019	.032	.042	.049	.058	.070

Fit a least squares straight line to the given data. Let x = length in inches and y = elongation in inches. There are seven sets of data; hence, $N = 7$.

The *normal equations* are

$$\sum_{i=1}^{N} x_i y_i - m \sum_{i=1}^{N} x_i^2 - b \sum_{i=1}^{N} x_i = 0$$
$$\sum_{i=1}^{N} y_i - m \sum_{i=1}^{N} x_i - Nb = 0$$

The summations are obtained from

$$\sum_{i=1}^{7} x_i y_i = 5(.01) + 10(.019) + 15(.032) + 20(.042)$$
$$+ 25(.049) + 30(.058) + 35(.070) = 6.975$$
$$\sum_{i=1}^{7} x_i^2 = 5^2 + 10^2 + 15^2 + 20^2 + 25^2 + 30^2 + 35^2 = 3500$$
$$\sum_{i=1}^{7} x_i = 140 \qquad \sum_{i=1}^{7} y_i = 0.28$$

Substituting in the normal equations

$$6.975 - 3500m - 140b = 0$$
$$.280 - 140m - 7b = 0$$

Solving simultaneously,

$$1.375 - 700m = 0, m = .00196$$
$$.040 - 20(.00196) - b = 0, b = -.00071$$

Thus the least squares straight line approximation is

$$y = .00196x - .00071$$

10.5 MATRIX OPERATIONS

A matrix is an array of elements arranged in rows and columns. For example:

$$[A] = \begin{bmatrix} a_{11} & a_{12} & a_{13} \\ a_{21} & a_{22} & a_{23} \\ a_{31} & a_{32} & a_{33} \end{bmatrix}$$

is called an A matrix. It is a matrix of three rows and three columns. Each element of the matrix has two subscripts; the first subscript refers to the row and the second subscript refers to the column. Hence a_{23} is the element found in row 2, column 3. When the number of rows equals the number of columns, [A] is termed a *square* matrix. Matrices consisting of one column are called *column vectors*; matrices with only one row are called *row vectors*. (Note the similarity between matrices and two-dimensional arrays, discussed in Chapter 6.)

Matrices are added (or subtracted) by adding (or subtracting) the corresponding elements of each matrix to form a new matrix. That is,

$$[C] = [A] + [B]$$

where each element can be obtained from

$$c_{ij} = a_{ij} + b_{ij}$$

In order to add (or subtract) matrices, the number of rows in [A] must equal the number of rows in [B], and the number of columns in [A] must equal the number of columns in [B]. The resultant [C] also has the same number of rows and columns as [A] and [B]. As an example, if

$$[A] = \begin{bmatrix} 1 & -1 & 2 \\ 2 & 3 & -2 \\ 1 & 0 & 1 \end{bmatrix} \quad \text{and} \quad [B] = \begin{bmatrix} 1 & 2 & 1 \\ -1 & 2 & 3 \\ 1 & -2 & 1 \end{bmatrix}$$

then

$$[C] = [A] + [B] = \begin{bmatrix} 2 & 1 & 3 \\ 1 & 5 & 1 \\ 2 & -2 & 2 \end{bmatrix}$$

A matrix may be multiplied by a scalar, by multiplying each element of the matrix by that scalar. Thus

$$[C] = a[B], \text{ where } c_{ij} = ab_{ij}$$

$$\text{Let } [B] = \begin{bmatrix} 1 & 1 & 3 \\ -2 & 0 & 8 \end{bmatrix} \text{ and } a = 2$$

$$\text{then } [C] = a[B] = \begin{bmatrix} 2 & 2 & 6 \\ -4 & 0 & 16 \end{bmatrix}$$

Two matrices may be multiplied to form a new matrix

$$[C] = [A][B]$$

The two matrices can be multiplied provided that the number of columns of the first array is equal to the number of rows in the second. The product is an array with the number of rows equal to the number of rows of the first array and the number of columns equal to the number of columns of the second array. The multiplication proceeds as the sum of the products of the elements of a row from $[A]$, where $[A]$ is n rows by m columns, and the elements of a column from $[B]$, which is m rows by l columns—that is,

$$c_{ij} = \sum_{k=1}^{m} a_{ik}b_{kj}$$

$$\text{Given } [A] = \begin{bmatrix} 1 & 4 & -1 \\ 3 & 2 & 2 \end{bmatrix} \text{ and } [B] = \begin{bmatrix} 2 & 1 & 0 \\ 3 & 6 & 1 \\ 4 & 5 & 2 \end{bmatrix}$$

Since the number of columns for $[A]$ is three and number of rows for $[B]$ is three, the matrices can be multiplied to form $[C]$, a matrix two rows by three columns. The upper limits for k in the above summation equals three (columns for $[A]$ or rows for $[B]$).

$$[C] = [A][B]$$

$$C_{11} = \sum_{k=1}^{3} a_{1k}b_{k1} = 1\cdot 2 + 4\cdot 3 + (-1)\cdot 4 = 10$$

$$C_{12} = \sum_{k=1}^{3} a_{1k}b_{k2} = 1\cdot 1 + 4\cdot 6 + (-1)\cdot 5 = 20$$

$$C_{13} = \sum_{k=1}^{3} a_{1k}b_{k3} = 1\cdot 0 + 4\cdot 1 + (-1)\cdot 2 = 2$$

$$C_{21} = \sum_{k=1}^{3} a_{2k}b_{k1} = 3\cdot 2 + 2\cdot 3 + 2\cdot 4 = 20$$

$$C_{22} = \sum_{k=1}^{3} a_{2k}b_{k2} = 3\cdot 1 + 2\cdot 6 + 2\cdot 5 = 25$$

$$C_{23} = \sum_{k=1}^{3} a_{2k}b_{k3} = 3\cdot 0 + 2\cdot 1 + 2\cdot 2 = 6$$

Thus

$$[C] = \begin{bmatrix} 10 & 20 & 2 \\ 20 & 25 & 6 \end{bmatrix}$$

Matrix multiplication is not commutative. That is, $[A][B] \neq [B][A]$. Obviously, in the example given above $[B][A]$ cannot be performed as the number of columns in $[B]$ is not equal to the number of rows in $[A]$.

The transpose of a matrix is found by interchanging rows and columns. The transpose of $[A]$ is written as

$$[a_{ij}]^{T} = a_{ji}$$

$$\text{Given } [A] = \begin{bmatrix} 1 & 3 & 3 \\ 4 & 5 & 6 \\ 7 & 8 & 0 \end{bmatrix}$$

$$\text{then } [A]^{T} = \begin{bmatrix} 1 & 4 & 7 \\ 3 & 5 & 8 \\ 3 & 6 & 0 \end{bmatrix}$$

The identity matrix is a square matrix that contains ones along the diagonal and zeros elsewhere—that is, $I_{ij} = 1$ if $i = j$ and zero if $i \neq j$. The identity matrix is represented by [I]. The identity matrix also has the property that $[I][A] = [A]$. For example,

$$\begin{bmatrix} 1 & 0 \\ 0 & 1 \end{bmatrix} \begin{bmatrix} 1 & 3 \\ 8 & 2 \end{bmatrix} = \begin{bmatrix} 1 \cdot 1 + 0 \cdot 8 & 1 \cdot 3 + 0 \cdot 2 \\ 0 \cdot 1 + 1 \cdot 8 & 0 \cdot 3 + 1 \cdot 2 \end{bmatrix} = \begin{bmatrix} 1 & 3 \\ 8 & 2 \end{bmatrix}$$

The inverse of a matrix is particularly useful in solving simultaneous linear equations of the form

$$a_{11}x_1 + a_{12}x_2 + a_{13}x_3 = c_1$$
$$a_{21}x_1 + a_{22}x_2 + a_{23}x_3 = c_2$$
$$a_{31}x_1 + a_{32}x_2 + a_{33}x_3 = c_3$$

We can write the system of equations in matrix form as

$$[A][X] = [C]$$

where

$$[A] = \begin{bmatrix} a_{11} & a_{12} & a_{13} \\ a_{21} & a_{22} & a_{23} \\ a_{31} & a_{32} & a_{33} \end{bmatrix}$$

$$[X] = \begin{bmatrix} x_1 \\ x_2 \\ x_3 \end{bmatrix} \quad \text{and} \quad [C] = \begin{bmatrix} c_1 \\ c_2 \\ c_3 \end{bmatrix}$$

[A] is called the *coefficient* matrix, [X] is the matrix of the *unknowns*, and [C] is the *constant* matrix. If both sides of the matrix equation are multiplied by the inverse of matrix [A], $[A]^{-1}$, we obtain

$$[A]^{-1}[A][X] = [A]^{-1}[C]$$
$$[I][X] = [A]^{-1}[C]$$
$$[X] = [A]^{-1}[C]$$

where [X], the matrix of unknowns, is now equal to the product of $[A]^{-1}$ and [C]. If the inverse of [A] can be determined, the [X] matrix is easily found.

The Gauss-Jordan elimination method is a technique that can be used to invert a matrix. It is a popular computer method for matrix inversion. The technique itself develops as follows:

1. Append a unit matrix to A so as to form a double square matrix, called the *augmented* matrix.

$$\begin{bmatrix} a_{11} & a_{12} & a_{13} & 1 & 0 & 0 \\ a_{21} & a_{22} & a_{23} & 0 & 1 & 0 \\ a_{31} & a_{32} & a_{33} & 0 & 0 & 1 \end{bmatrix}$$

2. Normalize row 1 by dividing each element in the row by a_{11} and then eliminate a_{21} and a_{31}. Repeat this procedure for row 2 and row 3. The result will be

$$\begin{bmatrix} 1 & 0 & 0 & b_{11} & b_{12} & b_{13} \\ 0 & 1 & 0 & b_{21} & b_{22} & b_{23} \\ 0 & 0 & 1 & b_{31} & b_{32} & b_{33} \end{bmatrix}$$

The last three columns of the matrix include the elements of the inverse of A, where

$$[A]^{-1} = \begin{bmatrix} b_{11} & b_{12} & b_{13} \\ b_{21} & b_{22} & b_{23} \\ b_{31} & b_{32} & b_{33} \end{bmatrix}$$

As an example, consider inverting

$$[A] = \begin{bmatrix} 3 & -6 & 7 \\ 9 & 0 & -5 \\ 5 & -8 & 6 \end{bmatrix}$$

Append a unit matrix to obtain

$$\begin{bmatrix} 3 & -6 & 7 & 1 & 0 & 0 \\ 9 & 0 & -5 & 0 & 1 & 0 \\ 5 & -8 & 6 & 0 & 0 & 1 \end{bmatrix}$$

Pass 1 (pivot row is row 1)

New row 1 = row 1/3; 3 is the normalizing factor

$$\begin{bmatrix} 1 & -2 & 2.33 & .33 & 0 & 0 \\ 9 & 0 & -5 & 0 & 1 & 0 \\ 5 & -8 & 6 & 0 & 0 & 1 \end{bmatrix}$$

New row 2 = row 2 − (9 · row 1)

$$\begin{bmatrix} 1 & -2 & 2.33 & .33 & 0 & 0 \\ 0 & 18 & -26 & -3 & 1 & 0 \\ 5 & -8 & 6 & 0 & 0 & 1 \end{bmatrix}$$

New row 3 = row 3 − (5 · row 1)

$$\begin{bmatrix} 1 & -2 & 2.33 & .33 & 0 & 0 \\ 0 & 18 & -26 & -3 & 1 & 0 \\ 0 & 2 & -5.65 & -1.65 & 0 & 1 \end{bmatrix}$$

Pass 2 (pivot row is row 2)

New row 2 = row 2/18; 18 is the normalizing factor

$$\begin{bmatrix} 1 & -2 & 2.33 & .33 & 0 & 0 \\ 0 & 1 & -1.44 & -.17 & .06 & 0 \\ 0 & 2 & -5.65 & -1.65 & 0 & 1 \end{bmatrix}$$

New row 1 = row 1 − (− 2 · row 2)

$$\begin{bmatrix} 1 & 0 & -.55 & -.01 & .12 & 0 \\ 0 & 1 & -1.44 & -.17 & .06 & 0 \\ 0 & 2 & -5.65 & -1.65 & 0 & 1 \end{bmatrix}$$

New row 3 = row 3 − (2 · row 2)

$$\begin{bmatrix} 1 & 0 & -.55 & -.01 & .12 & 0 \\ 0 & 1 & -1.44 & -.17 & .06 & 0 \\ 0 & 0 & -2.77 & -1.31 & -.12 & 1 \end{bmatrix}$$

Pass 3 (pivot row is row 3)

New row 3 = row 3/(− 2.77); − 2.77 is the normalizing factor

$$\begin{bmatrix} 1 & 0 & -.55 & -.01 & .12 & 0 \\ 0 & 1 & -1.44 & -.17 & .06 & 0 \\ 0 & 0 & 1 & .48 & .04 & -.36 \end{bmatrix}$$

New row 2 = row 2 − (−1.44 · row 3)

$$\begin{bmatrix} 1 & 0 & -.55 & -.01 & .12 & 0 \\ 0 & 1 & 0 & .52 & .12 & -.52 \\ 0 & 0 & 1 & .48 & .04 & -.36 \end{bmatrix}$$

New row 1 = row 1 − (−.55 · row 3)

$$\begin{bmatrix} 1 & 0 & 0 & .26 & .14 & -.20 \\ 0 & 1 & 0 & .52 & .12 & -.52 \\ 0 & 0 & 1 & .48 & .04 & -.36 \end{bmatrix}$$

The inverse of [A] is

$$[A]^{-1} = \begin{bmatrix} .26 & .14 & -.20 \\ .52 & .12 & -.52 \\ .48 & .04 & -.36 \end{bmatrix}$$

This result can be checked by $[A]^{-1}[A] = [I]$. There is a round-off error due to intermediate calculations to the nearest hundredth. The determinant of [A] is represented by $|A|$ and is simply the product of the normalizing factors. For the example shown,

$$|A| = (3)\ (18)\ (-2.77) = -149.58$$

The FORTRAN program to invert the 3 × 3 matrix is given in Figure 10.10. The algorithm is shown in Figure 10.11.

```
 1      C234567
 2      C
 3      C        THE INVERSION OF A 3X3 MATRIX USING GAUSS METHOD
 4      C
 5               DIMENSION AMAT(3,6),Al(3,6)
 6               DATA ((AMAT(I,J),J=1,6),I=1,3)/3,-6,7,1,0,0,9,0,-5
 7             *0,1,0,5,-8,6,0,0,1/
 8      10       FORMAT (X,6F7.2)
 9               DO 40 K=1,3
10               XN=AMAT(K,K)
11      C
12      C        NORMALIZE PIVOT ROW K
13      C
14               DO 20 J=1,6
15      20       AMAT(K,J)=AMAT(K,J)/XN
16               DO 40 I=1,3
17               IF(I.EQ.K)GOTO 40
18               Al(I,K)=AMAT(I,K)
19      C
20      C        USE NORMALIZING FACTOR XN TO GET NEW ROWS
21      C
22               DO 30 J=1,6
23      30       AMAT(I,J)=AMAT(I,J)-Al(I,K)*AMAT(K,J)
24      40       CONTINUE
25      C
26      C        OUTPUT INVERTED AUGMENTED MATRIX
27      C
28               DO 50 I=1.3
29      50       WRITE(6,10) (AMAT(I,J),J=1,6)
30               STOP
31               END
```

Figure 10.10   FORTRAN 77 Program for Inverting a 3 × 3 Matrix

1. Input augmented matrix.
2. DOWHILE k ≤ 3
   (a) Let normalizing factor xn = a_{kk}
   (b) DOWHILE j ≤ 6
       (i) $a_{kj} = a_{kj}/xn$
       (ii) increment j = j + 1
   (c) DOWHILE i ≤ 3
       (i) is i = k?
       (ii) IF true THEN proceed
            ELSE
              $al_{ik} = a_{ik}$
              DOWHILE j ≤ 6
                $a_{ij} = a_{ij} - al_{ik}*a_{kj}$
                increment j = j + 1
       (iii) increment i = i + 1
   (d) increment k = k + 1
3. Output inverted, augmented matrix.
4. STOP

Figure 10.11   Algorithm for Inverting a 3 × 3 Matrix

In a programming language such as FORTRAN, matrices are represented as arrays. For example,

$$\text{DIMENSION} \quad A(3,3), C(3), X(3)$$

represents the square matrix A and the two column matrices C and X. In FORTRAN, matrix operations are commonly performed by subroutines. A subroutine to multiply two matrices, [C] = [A][B], would be

```
      SUBROUTINE MATMUL(A,B,C,N,M,L)
      DIMENSION A(N,M),B(M,L),C(N,L)
      DO 10 I=1,N
      DO 10 J=1,L
      C(I,J)=0.0
      DO 10 K=1,M
      C(I,J)=C(I,J)+A(I,K)*B(K,J)
   10 CONTINUE
      RETURN
      END
```

To transpose a matrix, a suitable subroutine would be

```
      SUBROUTINE MATTRN(A,B,N)
      DIMENSION A(N,N),B(N,N)
      DO 10 I=1,N
      DO 10 J=1,N
      B(I,J)=A(J,I)
   10 CONTINUE
      RETURN
      END
```

where $[B] = [A]^T$.

Matrix input and output can be processed in FORTRAN through the use of implied loops. If we desire to fill an N row by M column A array, the code would be as follows (where input is row by row):

$$DO\ 10\ I=1,N$$
$$10\quad READ(5,100)(A(I,J),J=1,M)$$

or as an alternative use

$$READ(5,100)((A(I,J),J=1,M),I=1,N)$$

Output would be similar with READ replaced by WRITE and unit 5 replaced by unit 6.

$$DO\ 10\ I=1,N$$
$$10\quad WRITE(6,100)(A(I,J),J=1,M)$$
$$\text{or}\qquad WRITE(6,100)((A(I,J),J=1,M),I=1,N)$$

The student is cautioned that care must be taken when dealing with two-dimensional arrays that use variable dimensioning in subprograms. The problem was discussed at length in Chapter 9, but will be briefly reconsidered here. FORTRAN arrays are stored internally in column-major (column-by-column) form and strange results may occur when the dimension in the main program differs from that in the subprogram. For example, consider

$$[A] \quad = \quad \begin{bmatrix} 11 & 12 & 13 \\ 21 & 22 & 23 \\ 31 & 32 & 33 \end{bmatrix}$$

A subroutine is to be written to copy [A] into [B]. The partial program is as follows:

```
DIMENSION A(3,3),B(3,3)
.
.
.
CALL MATCOP(A,B,N)
.
.
.
```

If the subroutine is written using variable dimensioning,

```
     SUBROUTINE MATCOP(A,B,N)
     DIMENSION A(N,N),B(N,N)
     DO 10 I=1,N
     DO 10 J=1,N
     B(I,J)=A(I,J)
  10 CONTINUE
     RETURN
     END
```

when N = 3 the value returned for [B] will be

$$\begin{bmatrix} 11 & 12 & 13 \\ 21 & 22 & 23 \\ 31 & 32 & 33 \end{bmatrix}$$

but when N = 2, [B] will be

$$\begin{bmatrix} 11 & 12 & ? \\ 21 & ? & ? \\ 31 & ? & ? \end{bmatrix}$$

Remember the array is stored in computer memory in column-major form

11	When N = 2 the first four elements are
21	processed with variable dimensioning
31	
12	
22	
32	
13	
23	
33	

However, if the subroutine is written without the use of the variable dimension

```
      SUBROUTINE MATCOP(A,B,N)
      DIMENSION A(3,3),B(3,3)
      DO 10 I=1,N
      DO 10 J=1,N
   10 B(I,J)=A(I,J)
      RETURN
      END
```

When N = 3 the value returned for [B] will be

$$
\begin{bmatrix}
11 & 12 & 13 \\
21 & 22 & 23 \\
31 & 32 & 33
\end{bmatrix}
$$

and when N = 2, [B] will be

$$
\begin{bmatrix}
11 & 12 & ? \\
21 & 22 & ? \\
? & ? & ?
\end{bmatrix}
$$

10.6 SUMMARY

A number of numerical methods in engineering and science lend themselves to computer solution. This is particularly true of those methods that can take advantage of the looping capability of the computer. Root search, numerical integration, linear interpolation, curve fitting, and matrix manipulation are examples of such methods discussed in this chapter.

Two types of root search are considered: interval halving and Newton-Raphson. The convergence of the interval-halving method to the approximate root depends on bracketing the true value of the root by calculating the region where the function changes sign. The convergence of the Newton-Raphson method depends on the successive calculation of

$$
x_{i+1} = x_i - \frac{f(x_i)}{f'(x_i)}
$$

FORTRAN code for the Newton-Raphson method is presented.

Three examples of numerical integration (area under a curve) are presented. The trapezoidal integration consists of dividing the area into small trapezoids of equal width and summing these areas. The midpoint integration consists of dividing the area into small rectangles of equal width and using the midpoint of the width to calculate the height of the rectangle. The areas of the individual rectangles are then summed. FORTRAN code for the trapezoidal rule is supplied. Simpson's rule approximates the curve with quadratic functions, and then sums the areas under these functions. The number of cells for Simpson's rule must be even, because the summing is done two cells at a time.

Linear interpolation provides a method for obtaining intermediate points in a table. It generally consists of writing the straight line equation between two known points and using this equation to solve for the dependent variable at any intermediate value of the independent variable.

Least squares curve fitting is a method whereby an equation can be generated that best fits a set of data. The goal is to calculate the constants of a polynomial equation such that the square of the residuals (difference between the calculated and observed values) is minimized. The minimizing process leads to a set of simultaneous equations called *normal* equations that are solved for the equation constants.

A matrix is an array of numbers in rows and columns. Matrix algebra is the mathematical manipulation of those arrays. Addition, subtraction, and multiplication—*but not division*—are defined for matrices. Transposition and inversion of a matrix are discussed. FORTRAN coding is supplied for matrix multiplication, transposition, and inversion.

EXERCISES

1. Complete Table 10.1 for calculating the root of

$$f(x) = e^{-x} - \sin\left(\frac{\pi x}{2}\right) = 0$$

   by the interval-halving method for $\varepsilon = 0.001$.

2. Write a FORTRAN program to find the root of

$$f(x) = e^{-x} - \sin\left(\frac{\pi x}{2}\right) = 0$$

   by the interval-halving method for $\varepsilon = 0.0001$.

3. Evaluate, by hand, using the midpoint rule, the integral

$$\int_0^2 x^3 \, dx$$

   Output a table of n, the number of intervals, the area under the curve, and the calculated error, starting at $n = 8$. Terminate the table when $\epsilon = 0.001$. Also, write a FORTRAN program to evaluate the integral.

4. The shape of a cable hanging freely between two supports (such as a trans-
    mission line) is a curve called a *catenary*. The equation for maximum tension
    in the cable is given by $T_{max} = T_0 \cosh \dfrac{wL}{2T_0}$ where T_0 is the tension at the
    center, w is the weight per foot of the cable, and L is the distance between
    supports (span). The equation that relates the total weight of the cable, W, to
    the tension at the midpoint of the cable, is $W = 2T_0 \sinh \dfrac{wL}{2T_0}$. To find T_{max}
    we must first find T_0, which requires knowledge of the root of the equation

    $$\sinh \frac{wL}{2T_0} - \frac{W}{2T_0} = 0$$

    Given that $w = 5$ lb/ft, $L = 800$ ft, and the length of the cable $s = 1000$ ft,
    write a FORTRAN program to estimate T_0. Note that the hyperbolic functions
    are intrinsics in FORTRAN 77.

5. Write a FORTRAN program to estimate the roots of any polynomial equation
    given constant coefficients and the order of the equation. The root searching
    should be done in a subroutine subprogram with the set of coefficients passed
    over from the main program as a one-dimensional array along with the order
    of the polynomial. Each time a root is found, it should be passed back to the
    main program for printing. Use as a test equation, $x^4 - 10x^3 + 35x^2 - 50x
    + 24 = 0$.

6. Write a FORTRAN function subprogram to calculate and RETURN the
    double precision value of the root of the equation $x^3 = n$, where n is a REAL
    constant. Use the Newton-Raphson root search in your subprogram. Incor-
    porate this subprogram into a main program that will read in the value of n
    and the starting value of x and output the root correct to 10 decimal places.

7. Write a FORTRAN program to estimate the first positive root of

    $$f(x) = 1 + e^x \sin(\pi x/2) = 0$$

    correct to 5 significant figures. Use interval-halving root search and output
    the estimated root, the number of trials and the final value of the function.
    FORMAT and label your output.

8. Write a FORTRAN program to estimate the cube root of N to 10 significant
    figures using the Newton-Raphson root search. FORMAT and label your
    output.

9. By the least squares method, fit a straight line, $y = mx + b$, to the data

x	1.0	1.9	2.6	3.2	4.0
y	0.9	3.0	4.0	5.5	6.9

10. Write a FORTRAN program to fit a straight line, $y = mx + b$, to the data of exercise 9.

11. Linearize the following equations:

$$y = 10^{ax + k}$$

$$y = \frac{1}{ax + k}$$

$$y = kx^a$$

12. Repeat exercise 3 but use the trapezoidal rule and a relative error of 0.01 with a starting value of $n = 4$.

13. Write a FORTRAN program that will accept a starting value of $n = 4$ and an error of 0.01. This program should call the subroutine TRAP, which will evaluate the integral

$$\int_{-\pi/2}^{+\pi/2} e^x \sin x \, dx$$

by the trapezoidal rule and return the integral value and the number of intervals required. The output should be the value of the integral correct to four decimal places.

14. A stream of gas in a petroleum refinery is contaminated with hydrogen sulphide (H_2S), a very toxic substance. Before venting this gas to the atmosphere the H_2S must be removed by scrubbing the gas with water. For this scrubbing process a "gas absorption column" is used. The height of the column depends on the concentration of H_2S in the gas as well as the flow rates of the gas and of the water. The following design equation can be used

$$\text{Height} = k \int_{y_{out}}^{y_{in}} \frac{dy}{Y(y)}$$

where $Y(y)$ is a measure of the difference between the H_2S concentration in the gas and in the water, and y measures the concentration in the gas. For simplicity we will assume k to be unity. Given is a table of concentrations and differences.

Concentration y	Difference $1/Y$
.00001	100,000
.00002	80,000
.00004	57,140
.00006	44,440
.00008	36,360
.00010	30,770
.00020	17,390
.00030	12,120
.00040	9,300
.00050	7,550
.00060	6,350
.00070	5,480
.00080	4,820
.00090	4,300
.00100	3,880

Let the initial concentration of H_2S in the gas be .00100 and the concentration when it is safe to vent the gas be .00001.

(a) Plot the graph of $1/Y$ versus y.

(b) Apply the rectangular rule for estimating the integral from the graph in (a). Choosing your own cell size write a FORTRAN program to numerically integrate the function $1/Y$.

15. In electrical circuit theory the so-called "root mean square" voltage is a measure of the voltage to deliver power to a resistive load. For example, in the normal house circuit, the effective sinusoidal voltage at 60 cycles per second is the familiar 110 volts. If the root mean square (rms) voltage (effective voltage) is defined by an integral as

$$V_{eff} = \left[\frac{1}{\pi} \int_0^\pi (\cos 2t + \sin 2t)^2 dt \right]^{1/2}$$

when the alternating voltage is given by $\cos 2t + \sin 2t$. Write a FORTRAN program that will evaluate the integral using Simpson's rule with 20 cells.

16. The table shown here is for life expectancies in Europe. Write a FORTRAN program to input a year and output the corresponding life expectancy. Test for years out of range of the table. Use linear interpolation for intermediate years.

Year (A.D.)	Life expectancy (yrs.)
1000	30
1200	32
1380	34
1600	37
1760	39
1850	42
1900	45
1920	52
1940	59
1960	66
1980	73

17. Given a table of population growth of the United States, write a FORTRAN program that will input the table, input a given year, and output the population for that year, using linear interpolation. Test your program using the table and the year 1970.

year	1924	1944	1964	1984
population (millions)	100	150	190	210

18. When a gas is heated at constant volume from $0°$ to $t°C$ the pressure increases linearly from P_0 to P_t. An experiment is run that yields the following results:

$t(C)$	10	15	20	25	30	35	40
$P_t(Pa)$	10.55	10.7	10.9	11.1	11.3	11.45	11.75

Write a FORTRAN program that will input the data through a DATA statement, store the data in two one-dimensional arrays, and output the least squares equation.

19. Write a FORTRAN program that will fit a linear least squares line to the following data points:

$$P_1(0, -.1), P_2(2, 1.3) P_3(4, 1.9), P_4(6, 2.8), P_5(8, 4.3), P_6(10, 5.1)$$

Plot the least squares line and the data points.

20. By the least squares method, fit a straight line, $y = mx + b$, to the data

x	-40	-20	0	20	40	60
y	-10	-1	11	20	32	44

21. Write and test a FORTRAN subroutine to add two matrices. Your subroutine should be a general program that handles matrices of N rows by M columns.

22. Write a FORTRAN program to incorporate SUBROUTINE MATMUL. The program should accept [A] and [B] and output [C]. Use as test data

$$[A] = \begin{bmatrix} 1 & 8 & 6 & 4 \\ 2 & 1 & 9 & 3 \end{bmatrix}$$

$$[B] = \begin{bmatrix} 1 & 3 & 4 \\ 2 & 7 & 9 \\ 1 & 6 & 8 \\ 4 & 5 & 1 \end{bmatrix}$$

23. Given the two matrices [A] and [B], prove that $[A][B] \neq [B][A]$.

24. Write and test a FORTRAN subroutine that will transpose an N row by M column matrix. As test data use

$$[A] = \begin{bmatrix} 1 & 2 \\ 4 & 6 \\ 5 & 8 \end{bmatrix}$$

The transpose is

$$[A]^T = \begin{bmatrix} 1 & 4 & 5 \\ 2 & 6 & 8 \end{bmatrix}$$

25 Write a FORTRAN subroutine that will transpose a square matrix into itself—that is, the subprogram will use but one matrix to form the transpose.

```
SUBROUTINE MATTRN(A,N)
DIMENSION A(N,N)
    .        .
    .        .
    .        .
```

26. Check the library of programs available at your computer center for subprograms that deal with matrices. Obtain a listing of those subprograms and study how they are called and what matrix operations they perform.

27. Calculate the inverse of matrix A

$$[A] = \begin{bmatrix} 0 & -6 & 9 \\ 7 & 0 & -5 \\ 5 & -8 & 6 \end{bmatrix}$$

using the Gauss-Jordan elimination method.

28. Show that matrix B is the inverse of matrix A, given

$$[A] = \begin{bmatrix} 2 & 1 \\ 1 & 1 \end{bmatrix} \qquad [B] = \begin{bmatrix} 1 & -1 \\ -1 & 2 \end{bmatrix}$$

29. A matrix is symmetric if $a_{i,j} = a_{j,i}$ for all i,j. Write a FORTRAN subroutine subprogram that prints out the messages MATRIX A IS SYMMETRIC or MATRIX A IS NOT SYMMETRIC depending on whether the symmetry condition is met.

30. A contracting company is working on three jobs and keeps a record of the hours spent on each job by each of four crafts; plumbers, electricians, carpenters, and plasterers. The company wants to determine its labor costs per job.

    The hours spent can be written in matrix form as:

$$(\text{Hours}) = \begin{bmatrix} 50 & 40 & 30 & 60 \\ 90 & 20 & 80 & 70 \\ 10 & 50 & 50 & 100 \end{bmatrix}$$

where the row is the job number and the column is the craft (plumbers, electricians, carpenters, and plasterers, specifically). Assume the wage rate for each of the crafts is \$14.50 for plumbers, \$13.50 for electricians, \$10.50 for carpenters, and \$9.00 for plasterers. This rate structure can be written as a column matrix

$$(\text{RATE}) = \begin{vmatrix} 14.50 \\ 13.50 \\ 10.50 \\ 9.00 \end{vmatrix}$$

The product of the two matrices (HOURS)(RATE) will yield a three-element column matrix.

    Using matrix multiplication, write a FORTRAN program that will determine the cost of each of the three jobs as well as the total cost of all three jobs.

31. The table at the left gives the production per day for each of four manufacturing departments at each of four plant locations. The table at the right gives the percentage of production shipped by each department.

Dept.

	1	2	3	4
A	1200	1200	2000	900
B	1300	1400	2200	900
C	1100	1500	1700	1000
D	1050	1400	1900	1100

Plant (row labels A–D)

Plant

	A	B	C	D
1	20	21	23	19
2	32	30	30	33
3	25	25	26	22
4	27	25	25	26

Write a FORTRAN program that will output the total of the shipments for each plant.

32. The probability of defective parts that are produced by five machines at each of three plant locations is given by the following table:

Machine

	1	2	3	4	5
A	.02	.04	.01	.05	.10
Plant B	.11	.06	.07	.02	.03
C	.06	.09	.02	.02	.03

The output of the five machines on each of four production runs is given by the following table:

Run

	1	2	3	4
1	100	200	350	250
2	100	450	300	150
Machine 3	100	400	300	400
4	200	300	100	600
5	500	100	600	100

Using matrix multiplication, determine the number of defective parts turned out by each plant at the end of each production run.

chapter 11

File Processing

All input to a FORTRAN program and output from a FORTRAN program is processed as a file, where a file is a collection of one or more records. Since a file is composed of records it is a data structure. Keyboard input from a terminal consists of a sequence of records. Each record is entered, starting with the first record and proceeding sequentially, record by record, until the last record is entered. This method of file processing is termed *sequential*. In general, sequential file processing consists of the input or output of file records, starting with the first record and proceeding sequentially, record by record, until either all records are processed (the end of the file is reached) or the desired record is found. Input from a terminal keyboard or card reader and output to a terminal display or line printer are examples of sequential file processing.

In FORTRAN, a file can be either a text file or a binary file. A *text file* consists of records whose individual fields are made up of characters. When a text file is processed by a FORTRAN input or output statement, each field is converted from an external display form to its internal binary form or from its internal binary form to an external display form. This is accomplished through the FORTRAN formatter, which uses each field descriptor during this conversion. The required format can be explicitly stated in a FORMAT specification statement or implied through list-directed input/output. Thus the statement READ(5, *)A,B,I causes a record of input to be read from logical unit 5. There are five fields processed: a real field for A, a separator field, a real field for B, a separator field, and an integer field for I. The characters that make up the two real field and one integer field are converted to internal binary form by the FORTRAN formatter. This formatter, part of the system software, is built into the FORTRAN language. It is the machine implementation of the rules governing how FORMAT specifications are stated. Thus all input/output of text files undergoes a conversion, where the internal binary form is the way in which each field is stored in main memory and the external display form is a text file consisting of one or more records. A text file record consists of one or more fields, which in turn consist of one or more characters. The commonly used character representation is either ASCII or EBCDIC.

A *binary file* is one in which the individual fields that make up each file record have not undergone conversion by the formatter. Each field is transferred to or from main memory without change and the individual fields that comprise each record are binary. For example, WRITE(8)A,B,I results in a record of output sent to logical unit 8 consisting of three fields, the first two of which are binary real and the third is a binary integer. The contents of a binary file cannot meaningfully be displayed on a printer or terminal, nor can it be input from a card reader or terminal keyboard. These devices accept only text files. A binary file can be stored on a magnetic storage device such as disk or tape. Binary files are frequently used to save the results of intermediate processing for later use by the same or another FORTRAN program. The binary form of the READ and WRITE statements omit any reference to formatting, since a binary file bypasses the formatter. For input/output of binary files, only the logical unit number is stated.

11.1   FILE READ AND WRITE

In discussing file input/output, the following assumptions are made: (1) logical unit 5 defaults to the principal input device, a terminal keyboard or card reader, (2) logical unit 6 defaults to the principal output device, a terminal display or line printer, (3) any other logical unit number defaults to a magnetic storage device, specifically a magnetic disk, and (4) the range of logical unit number is from 1 to 99, inclusive. Each input file and each output file must be assigned a unique logical unit number.

As an example, to create a data file consisting of hourly temperature and barometric pressure readings over any one day, the FORTRAN program becomes

```
C     CREATE A SEQUENTIAL FILE
      DO 10 IHOUR=1,24
      READ(5,*)TEMP,PRES
      WRITE(13,100)IHOUR,TEMP,PRES
   10 CONTINUE
  100 FORMAT(I2,F5.1,F5.2)
      END
```

Each file record consists of three fields. Each file record is 12 characters in length. The sequential text file created by this program contains 24 records, and it is written to logical unit 13. Since this unit is not a display device, such as a printer or terminal, no carriage control character is needed in the FORMAT statement. Data entry, through either a terminal keyboard or card reader, is sequential. If the WRITE statement is changed to WRITE(13)IHOUR,TEMP,PRES the output is a sequential binary file that is 24 records long, with each file record containing three fields. Assuming a 32-bit format for real and a 16-bit format for integer, a binary file record is 10 bytes in length. In either case, the sequential file is available for processing by another FORTRAN program or by expanding the program used to create the file. For example, a separate program that processes the sequential file and outputs a table of temperatures, pressures, and the average temperature becomes

```
C      PROCESS THE FILE
       SUM=0.0
       DO 10 KOUNT=1,24
       READ(13,100)IHOUR,TEMP,PRES
       WRITE(6,*)IHOUR,TEMP,PRES
   10  SUM=SUM+TEMP
       WRITE(6,*)TEMP/24.0
  100  FORMAT(I2,F5.1,F5.2)
       END
```

The sequential file must be read using the same format in which it was written. If the format is different, the individual fields may be read incorrectly.

This program should raise the questions: why is a counter needed? is there some method by which a READ statement can recognize the end of file? can the file be processed sequentially, and when the data runs out (there are no more records), can the end of file be detected? A more general form of the READ statement answers these questions. The statement

```
READ(logical unit number,s,END=statement label)list
```

detects the end of file. That is, when FORTRAN tries to read beyond the last file record, control is transferred to the statement whose label appears in END = statement label. The file processing program can now be written as

```
C      PROCESS THE FILE
       SUM=0.0
   10  READ(13,100,END=20)IHOUR,TEMP,PRES
       WRITE(6,*)IHOUR,TEMP,PRES
       SUM=SUM+TEMP
       GO TO 10
   20  WRITE(6,*)TEMP/24.0
  100  FORMAT(I2,F5.1,F5.2)
       END
```

Being able to detect the end of file eliminates the counter and its associated DO loop. There is no need to know in advance how many records are in the file. If necessary, the number of file records can be counted as they are processed, and it is no longer necessary to input a count of the number of records in the file.

11.2   OPEN STATEMENT

A file must be opened before it can be processed using FORTRAN input/output statements. Opening a file grants access to that file. IN FORTRAN, the statement

```
OPEN(logical unit number,FILE=file name,STATUS=status)
```

grants file access. The file name is a character expression that contains the name of the file or a device name and status is a character expression whose value is OLD, NEW, SCRATCH, or UNKNOWN. If OLD is specified, the file must exist, while if NEW is specified, the file must not exist. SCRATCH opens a temporary file that disappears when the program terminates execution. UNKNOWN opens a file whose status is machine dependent. If an OPEN statement does not precede the first file read or write, FORTRAN implicitly issues an OPEN when the first READ or WRITE statement is executed. Since the OPEN statement equates a FORTRAN logical unit number to a file name or device; failure to explicitly issue an OPEN statement results in the logical unit number being assigned to some file or device by default. This default assignment is machine dependent and may result in the creation of a temporary file that disappears when the program terminates execution.

In order to illustrate the OPEN statement, the FORTRAN program to create a new sequential data file becomes

```
C     CREATE A SEQUENTIAL FILE
      OPEN(13,FILE='MYDATA',STATUS='NEW')
      DO 10 IHOUR=1,24
      READ(5,*)TEMP,PRES
      WRITE(13,100)IHOUR,TEMP,PRES
   10 CONTINUE
  100 FORMAT(I2,F5.1,F5.2)
      END
```

The sequential file, written to logical unit 13, becomes a permanent file whose name is MYDATA. This file normally is stored, by default, on magnetic disk. MYDATA is available to other FORTRAN programs by issuing an OPEN statement. Any logical unit number can be used when processing this file as long as the logical unit number is equated to the file name MYDATA in an OPEN statement. The logical unit number is required in the OPEN statement. The file name or the device name should be specified, but it is optional for standard input/output devices. Status is also optional; however, its use is strongly recommended for disk files. If unformatted input/output is used with a sequential file, then the OPEN statement requires the additional parameter ACCESS = 'UNFORMATTED'.

The rules for formulating a file name or a device name is machine dependent, and the programmer should consult system manuals for this information. FORTRAN input/output can be redirected through the OPEN statement. For example, logical unit number 5 can read from a (disk) file when the statement

OPEN(5,FILE = file name,STATUS = status) is used. Logical unit number 13 can be terminal output when the statement OPEN(6,FILE = device name) is used, where device name is the system name for the terminal. This capability to redirect input/output requires a knowledge of the system software and the peripherals associated with the computer.

11.3 ADDITIONAL FILE STATEMENTS

In some applications, the file needs to be read sequentially several times. When this is the case, a FORTRAN statement is needed that resets the file so that processing begins with the first file record. The statement

```
REWIND logical unit number
```

resets a file. If a file is processed sequentially—either by reading the end of file or by locating the desired record—and there is a need to process the file again within the same program, then a REWIND statement should be used.

When a sequential file is processed and that file is not to be used again within the program, then the FORTRAN statement

```
CLOSE(logical unit number,STATUS=status)
```

can be used. This statement closes the file and ensures that no further file access can be made. Status is a character expression whose value is KEEP (save the file) or DELETE (remove the file). The CLOSE statement guarantees that a file is secure from later access within a program. Once a file is closed, an OPEN statement makes the file available for processing, starting with the first file record. The logical unit number is required in the CLOSE statement. Status is optional and its use is strongly recommended for disk files. FORTRAN implicitly closes all open files when the program terminates execution on a STOP or END statement.

11.4 A COMPLETE EXAMPLE

The following programs illustrate the FORTRAN file statements. In this example, a text file that contains student names and campus phone numbers is created and accessed. Each file record consists of three fields:

student last name	20 characters in length
student first name	10 characters in length
phone number	4 digit extension

The record length is 34 characters. Three FORTRAN programs are needed. The first program creates the text file. The second program lists the text file. The third program searches the text file sequentially for a match on a student last name. Multiple searches are permitted. Data entry is from a terminal keyboard.

```
C      CREATE THE FILE
       CHARACTER*20 LNAME
       CHARACTER*10 FNAME
       INTEGER EXT
       OPEN(8,FILE='STUDATA',STATUS='NEW')
       WRITE(6,*)'ENTER DATA, RECORD BY RECORD'
       WRITE(6,*)'HIT ENTER KEY TO TERMINATE'
   20  READ(5,100)LNAME,FNAME,EXT
       IF(LNAME(1:1).EQ.' ')THEN
          CLOSE(8,STATUS='KEEP')
          STOP
       ELSE
          WRITE(8,100)LNAME,FNAME,EXT
          GO TO 20
       ENDIF
  100  FORMAT(A20,A10,I4)
       END
```

Data is entered, record by record in formatted form, until a single space is detected as the first character of an input record. This space terminates data entry, the file is closed, and the program terminates execution. The file, assumed to reside on disk, is saved as a permanent file under the name STUDATA.

```
C      DISPLAY THE FILE
       CHARACTER*20 LNAME
       CHARACTER*10 FNAME
       INTEGER EXT
       OPEN(8,FILE='STUDATA',STATUS='OLD')
   20  READ(8,100,END=40)LNAME,FNAME,EXT
       WRITE(6,200)LNAME,FNAME,EXT
       GO TO 20
   40  CLOSE(8,STATUS='KEEP')
       STOP
  100  FORMAT(A20,A10,I4)
  200  FORMAT(1X,A20,2X,A10,2X,I4)
       END
```

The file is displayed in tabular form. Output requires a carriage control character, since it is sent to a display device.

```
C     SEARCH THE FILE
      CHARACTER*20 LNAME
      CHARACTER*10 FNAME
      CHARACTER*20 TARGET
      INTEGER EXT
      OPEN(8,FILE='STUDATA',STATUS='OLD')
   25 WRITE(6,*)
      WRITE(6,*)'ENTER LAST NAME OF STUDENT WHOSE EXTENSION'
      WRITE(6,*)'IS DESIRED OR HIT ENTER KEY TO TERMINATE'
      READ(5,100)TARGET
      IF(TARGET(1:1).EQ.' ')THEN
        CLOSE(8,STATUS='KEEP)
        STOP
      ENDIF
   50 READ(8,200,END=75)LNAME,FNAME,EXT
      IF(TARGET.EQ.LNAME)THEN
        WRITE(6,*)'DESIRED EXTENSION IS ',EXT
        REWIND 8
        GO TO 25
      ELSE
        GO TO 50
      ENDIF
   75 WRITE(6,*)'NO SUCH LAST NAME'
      REWIND 8
      GO TO 25
  100 FORMAT(A20)
  200 FORMAT(A20,A10,I4)
      END
```

This program searches the text file STUDATA sequentially. If a match is found, based on the student last name, the corresponding extension is displayed; otherwise, at the end of file the message NO SUCH LAST NAME is displayed. This program does not provide for the case when there are duplicate last names in the file. The logical unit number does not have to be the same in all three programs. Only the file name, used in the OPEN statement to which the logical unit number is equated, must be the same throughout.

If the input to the program CREATE A FILE is

```
col. 1              col. 21      col. 31
↓                   ↓            ↓
SMITH               JOHN         2345
CRANSTON            LAMONT       9999
WILEY               JOHN         1115
QUINCY              ROXANNE      9009
```

null record generated by striking the enter key

Output from this program is the permanent file STUDATA consisting of four file records, each record is 34 bytes long. The contents of the file are

col. 1	col. 21	col. 31
↓	↓	↓
SMITH	JOHN	2345
CRANSTON	LAMONT	9999
WILEY	JOHN	1115
QUINCY	ROXANNE	9009

Output from the program DISPLAY THE FILE is

col. 1	col. 23	col. 35
↓	↓	↓
SMITH	JOHN	2345
CRANSTON	LAMONT	9999
WILEY	JOHN	1115
QUINCY	ROXANNE	9009

Execution of the program SEARCH THE FILE yields, for the input shown

```
ENTER LAST NAME OF STUDENT WHOSE EXTENSION
IS DESIRED OR HIT ENTER KEY TO TERMINATE
```

col. 1   input
↓
```
WILEY
DESIRED EXTENSION IS 1115
```

```
ENTER LAST NAME OF STUDENT WHOSE EXTENSION
IS DESIRED OR HIT ENTER KEY TO TERMINATE
```

col. 1   input
↓
```
SMITHE
NO SUCH LAST NAME
```

```
ENTER LAST NAME OF STUDENT WHOSE EXTENSION
IS DESIRED OR HIT ENTER KEY TO TERMINATE
```

col. 1   input
↓
null record generated by pressing the ENTER key

11.5 RANDOM ACCESS FILES

A *random access file* allows the FORTRAN programmer to directly read from or write to a specific file record. For random access files, the READ statement is

```
READ(logical unit number,s,REC=number,END=statement label)list
```

and the WRITE statement is

```
WRITE(logical unit number,s,REC=number)list
```

where REC=number points directly to the desired record. If the number is one, then the first file record is processed. If the number is ten, then the tenth file record is processed. This number can be an integer constant, variable, or expression.

The OPEN statement requires additional parameters when random file access is specified. This statement now becomes

```
OPEN(logical unit number,FILE=file name,STATUS=status,
FORM=form,ACCESS=access,RECL=record length)
```

where form is either the character expression FORMATTED or UNFOR-MATTED; FORMATTED input/output is assumed for sequential files and UNFORMATTED input/output is assumed for random access files, access is the character string DIRECT (the default is SEQUENTIAL) and record length is the number of characters in each file record. The record length must be specified for random access files; otherwise, it is omitted.

As an example of random file access, consider the program to create a data file consisting of hourly temperature and barometric pressure readings over any one day, as discussed in sections 11.1 and 11.2.

```
C     CREATE THE FILE
      OPEN(13,FILE='MYDATA',STATUS='NEW')
      DO 10 IHOUR=1,24
      READ(5,*)TEMP,PRES
      WRITE(13,100)IHOUR,TEMP,PRES
   10 CONTINUE
      CLOSE(13,STATUS='KEEP')
  100 FORMAT(I2,F5.1,F5.2)
      END
```

Assume that the program should directly access a specific file record based on the hour of the day. The FORTRAN program to randomly access the file becomes

```
C     ACCESS THE FILE
      OPEN(13,FILE='MYDATA',STATUS='OLD',FORM='FORMATTED',
     1        ACCESS='DIRECT',RECL=12)
      WRITE(6,*)'ENTER HOUR '
      READ(5,*)IHOUR
      READ(13,300,REC=IHOUR,END=100)IHOUR,TEMP,PRES
      WRITE(6,*)'TEMPERATURE IS ',TEMP
      WRITE(6,*)'PRESSURE IS ',PRES
      GO TO 200
  100 WRITE(6,*)'INVALID RECORD NUMBER'
  200 CLOSE(13,STATUS='KEEP')
  300 FORMAT(I2,F5.1,F5.2)
      END
```

When the desired hour is entered as data input, then the READ statement goes directly to the file record specified by IHOUR and output consists of the temperature and pressure for that hour.

A file can be created sequentially in one part of a program and accessed randomly in another part of the same program, provided that OPEN and CLOSE statements are properly placed.

```
C     CREATE THE FILE SEQUENTIALLY
      OPEN(logical unit number,FILE=file name,STATUS=status)
      .                    .
      .                    .
      (create and write file records sequentially)
      .                    .
      .                    .
      CLOSE(logical unit number,STATUS=status)
      .                    .
      .                    .
C     ACCESS THE FILE RANDOMLY
      OPEN(logical unit number,FILE=file name,STATUS=status,
          FORM=form,ACCESS=access,RECL=record length)
      .                    .
      .                    .
      (directly access the desired file records)
      .                    .
      .                    .
      CLOSE(logical unit number,STATUS=status)
      .                    .
      .                    .
      END
```

Binary files can also be accessed randomly.

11.6 SUMMARY

Sequential file processing is supported by FORTRAN. A sequential file can be a text file or a binary file. The records of a text file consist of characters that must be processed by the FORTRAN formatter. Text files can be read from a terminal keyboard, card reader, and magnetic storage media such as disk or tape. Text files can be written to a terminal display, line printer, and magnetic storage media such as disk or tape. Binary files contain records whose fields are in internal binary form. These file records, when input or output, bypass the FORTRAN formatter and are read from or written to magnetic storage media. Text files can, in general, be transported from machine to machine. Binary files can only be transferred between machines whose internal storage format is identical. Text files are more commonly used; however, binary files can be preferable if the resulting data is to be processed internally within the FORTRAN program. Sequential files can be created through a FORTRAN program. Sequential text files can also be created through a text editor. Many additional options and statements exist for file processing. For more information about these statements, see section 12 of the American National Standard Programming Language FORTRAN, ANSI X3.9–1978. FORTRAN also supports random access files, where a specific file record can be accessed directly when its location within the file is known.

EXERCISES

1. Write a FORTRAN program to create a sequential text file consisting of eight records. Each file record contains a single integer field. Run your program, using as test data

$$1, 3, -8, 16, 0, 9, 30, -2$$

   Write a separate FORTRAN program to output the file in order to verify its contents.

2. Redo exercise 1 by creating a sequential binary file instead of a sequential text file. What are the relative advantages and disadvantages of creating a binary file as compared to a text file?

3. Modify the program SEARCH THE FILE from section 11.4 so that output occurs for multiple occurrences of the student last name within the file STUDATA.

4. What changes must be made to the program SEARCH THE FILE from section 11.4 if both the first and last name are to be used when searching the file STUDATA?

5. Modify the following FORTRAN program so that the output is written to a new text file named DOUT.

```
C     TABLE OF NATURAL LOGS
C
      DO 10 A=0.1,10.0,0.1
   10 WRITE(6,*)A,ALOG(A)
      STOP
      END
```

6. Examination grades for a computer programming course are to be processed by a FORTRAN program. The grades are stored in a text file whose structure consists of file records, where each record contains four examination grades per student. The file is to be processed sequentially to compute and output the average grade for each student record. Write a FORTRAN program to accomplish this processing and use as test data the text file:

100	80	80	65
90	90	95	90
60	65	65	55
85	50	95	60
100	95	93	98
70	80	85	60
55	55	40	95
100	90	90	90
90	90	80	95
95	70	80	65

7. Write a FORTRAN program to search a text file consisting of 80-byte records for the occurrence of a keyword. Test the program by creating a text file consisting of the first paragraph of this chapter; use TERMINAL as the keyword. Output should be a count of the number of times the keyword appears in the file.

8. For your computing system:

    (a) What is the logical unit number of the principal input device?

    (b) What is the logical unit number of the principal output device?

    (c) Does your computer have a text editor? If so, briefly outline the steps for creating a sequential file.

9. Given the following FORTRAN program:

```
CHARACTER*80 LINE
N=8
```

```
      DO 10 I=1,N
      READ(5,*)LINE
10    WRITE(20,20)LINE
20    FORMAT(A80)
      END
```

(a)   How many output file records are created?

(b)   Is the output file a text file or a binary file?

(c)   How many bytes are there in each file record?

(d)   How many bytes are there in the output file?

(e)   How can the output file be saved as a permanent file?

10.   Under what conditions would a binary file be selected for output? Under what conditions would a text file be selected for output?

11.   How does random file access differ from sequential file access? Under what conditions would random access be selected instead of sequential access?

chapter 12

Microcomputer FORTRAN

Microcomputers have brought to the individual user many of the applications available on larger, time-shared machines. The microcomputer, in many cases, is a single-user system consisting of a microprocessor, support hardware, and peripherals for input/output (see Figures 12.1 and 12.2). The microprocessor, which is analogous to the CPU in larger machines, may be an 8-, 16-, or 32-bit unit. Typical peripherals are a keyboard for input, a CRT display for output, and one or more disk drives for magnetic storage. Optional printers and plotters are also available to the microcomputer user. Main memory runs from 128 kilobytes to over 1 megabyte. Disk storage ranges from over 300 kilobytes for a removable diskette to over 100 megabytes for nonremovable, built-in multiplatter fixed disks. Microcomputers can be connected into networks and can communicate with larger computer systems. FORTRAN, BASIC, COBOL, Pascal, and other programming languages are supported on microcomputers. Application such as line editors, word processors, spreadsheets, and interactive graphics packages are also available.

12.1 FORTRAN FOR MICROCOMPUTERS

FORTRAN is implemented as a compiler on most microcomputers. In general, microcomputer FORTRAN meets all of the features discussed in this text. The user should consult the FORTRAN reference manual, supplied with the language software, for details regarding the statements that are available. Using a text editor, the user creates a text file consisting of the FORTRAN source statements. This source program file serves as input to the compiler. Output from the compiler is an object file that contains the binary code. This object file is the input to a system program called the *linker*. The linker takes the object file and links it with the FORTRAN

243

Figure 12.1   A Microcomputer System (*Photo courtesy of American Telephone and Telegraph Information Systems, Morristown, NJ.*)

system library to create, as output, an execute file. The execute file is the machine language file and it is relocatable, which means that when this file is run, the loader relocates the machine code into allocated memory space. After loading, execution of the program proceeds, and data is entered; then the results are displayed.

Figure 12.2   An IBM PC Computer (*Photo Jack Polin. Courtesy International Business Machines.*)

12.2   LANGUAGE SPECIFICATIONS

Microcomputer FORTRAN meets most of the ANSI standards. The following discussion on language specifications is based on MS-FORTRAN, a popular microcomputer implementation of FORTRAN, developed by Microsoft Corporation. Numeric data consists of integer, real or floating-point, double-precision, logical, and complex. The range of integer data is 32767 to -32768. The magnitude of real data is approximately $1E \pm 38$ and seven significant digits are used for computation. Double-precision data has a magnitude of $1E \pm 308$ and 15 significant digits are used for computation. Logical data is either true or false, and complex data are represented as an ordered pair of floating-point numbers. The first number specifies the real part and the second number specifies the imaginary part. Nonnumeric or character data uses the ASCII code. Upper- and lowercase alphabetic characters are acceptable, and lowercase is treated as if it were uppercase when it appears in a FORTRAN statement. Thus AREA = PI*RAD*RAD is equivalent to area = pi*rad*rad but 'THIS IS A CONSTANT' is not the same as 'this is a constant'. Single and multidimensional arrays, records, text files, and binary files are supported. An asterisk in place of the logical unit number denotes the principal input

Table 12.1 Device Names

Name	Assignment
CON	the keyboard for input or the CRT display for output
AUX	an auxiliary device such as an RS232 serial communications port
LST	output is sent to a listing device, usually a printer
PRN	output is sent to a printer
NUL	input/output sent to a null or dummy file; used to test programs; nothing is input or output

or output device, which is the keyboard or CRT display. Certain device names are standard in MS-FORTRAN; they are shown in Table 12.1. These features are typical of microcomputer FORTRAN.

Consider, for example, the FORTRAN program to calculate and output the arithmetic average of n real numbers.

```
c      average program
       sum=0.0
       read(*,*)n
       do 10 i=1,n
       read(*,*)x
10 sum=sum+x
       write(*,*)'ave ',sum/real(n)
       end
```

The use of upper- or lowercase alphabetic characters is a matter of convenience. Only the character constant 'ave' is affected by the choice of upper- or lowercase. The first asterisk in the READ and WRITE statements denotes the keyboard for input and the CRT display for output. The second asterisk specifies list-directed input/output. If the program is to be written using logical unit 5 for input and logical unit 6 for output, two OPEN statements are needed to specify that unit 5 is input from the keyboard and that unit 6 is output to the CRT display. The program for this option becomes

```
c      average program
       open(5,file='CON')
       open(6,file='CON')
       sum=0.0
       read(5,*)n
       do 10 i=1,n
       read(5,*)x
10 sum=sum+x
       write(6,*)'ave ',sum/real(n)
       close(5)
```

```
      close(6)
      end
```

Two CLOSE statements are included in the program, but they are optional, since all files are closed when the END statement is executed.

12.3   APPLICATIONS AND SAMPLE PROGRAMS

Several applications, numeric and nonnumeric, are examined in this chapter. Specifically, sorting a character array, double-precision Newton-Raphson iteration, and a simple plotting routine are discussed; the FORTRAN program for each application is listed.

Sorting a character array into ascending sequence requires the following steps:

1. Fill the character array: subroutine FILL
2. Sort the character array: subroutine SORT
3. Output the sorted array: subroutine OUTPUT

The logic required for sorting an array is discussed in Chapter 9. The main program is written to call three subroutines. It is assumed that each array element consists of 20 characters.

```
C     MAIN PROGRAM TO SORT A CHARACTER ARRAY

C     NAMES         CHARACTER ARRAY
C     NUM           NUMBER OF ELEMENTS

      CHARACTER*20 NAMES(16)
      COMMON NAMES,NUM
      CALL FILL
      CALL SORT
      CALL OUTPUT
      END
```

The character array and the number of elements are placed in COMMON. This is one option, the other being the use of arguments. The subroutines for sorting the array become:

```
C     SORT THE CHARACTER ARRAY

      SUBROUTINE FILL
      CHARACTER*20 NAMES(16)
      COMMON NAMES,NUM
```

```
      WRITE(*,*)'ENTER NUMBER OF ELEMENTS'
      READ(*,*)NUM
      IF(NUM.LT.1.OR.NUM.GT.16)THEN
        WRITE(*,*)'NUMBER OUT OF RANGE'
        STOP
      ENDIF
      WRITE(*.*)'ENTER ARRAY ELEMENTS'
      DO 10 I=1,NUM
   10 READ(*,20)NAMES(I)
      RETURN
   20 FORMAT(A20)
      END

C     SORT THE CHARACTER ARRAY

      SUBROUTINE SORT
      CHARACTER*20 NAMES(16),HOLD
      COMMON NAMES,NUM
      DO 10 J=1,NUM-1
      DO 10 I=J+1,NUM
      IF(NAMES(I).LT.NAMES(J))THEN
        HOLD=NAMES(I)
        NAMES(I)=NAMES(J)
        NAMES(J)=HOLD
      ENDIF
   10 CONTINUE
      RETURN
      END

C     OUTPUT THE SORTED ARRAY

      SUBROUTINE OUTPUT
      CHARACTER*20 NAMES(16)
      COMMON NAMES,NUM
      WRITE(*,*)
      WRITE(*,*)'THE SORTED ARRAY IS'
      DO 10 I=1,NUM
   10 WRITE(*,20)NAMES(I)
      RETURN
   20 FORMAT(1X,A20)
      END
```

Input:

```
ENTER NUMBER OF ELEMENTS
5
ENTER ARRAY ELEMENTS
```

```
JOHN
SALLY
PAUL
ZELDA
ALBERT
```

Output:

```
THE SORTED ARRAY IS
ALBERT
JOHN
PAUL
SALLY
ZELDA
```

Input is on a new line when a READ statement follows a WRITE statement. Sample programs in previous chapters showed input on the same line as the character string that prompts for data entry. This format, the new line for data entry, may vary from computer system to computer system.

The Newton-Raphson formula for estimating the root of a function is given by

$$x_{new} = x_{old} - fcn(x_{old})/\text{derivative of } fcn(x_{old})$$

If the function, whose root is to be estimated, is given by

$$fcn(x) = x^{1.7} - 13.0 = 0$$

then the

$$\text{derivative of } fcn(x) = 1.7x^{0.7}$$

and

$$x_{new} = x_{old} - (x_{old}^{1.7} - 13.0)/1.7x_{old}^{0.7}$$

The FORTRAN program to estimate the double-precision root becomes

```
C     NEWTON-RAPHSON ITERATION

      IMPLICIT DOUBLE PRECISION (A-H,O-Z)
      FCN(X)=X**1.7-13.0
      DFCN(X)=1.7*X**0.7
      WRITE(*,*)'ENTER ALLOWABLE ERROR'
      READ(*,*)ERROR
      XNEW=1.0
```

```
   10 XOLD=XNEW
      XNEW=XOLD-FCN(XOLD)/DFCN(XOLD)
      IF(ABS(FCN(XOLD)).LT.ERROR)THEN
         WRITE(*,*)XNEW,FCN(XNEW)
      ELSE
         GO TO 10
      ENDIF
      END
```

Input:

```
ENTER ALLOWABLE ERROR
ID-10
```

Output:

```
4.52127347926740  0.0000000000000E+000
```

Plotting the elements of a real, one-dimensional X array versus the corresponding elements of a real, one-dimensional Y array, requires the following steps: (1) fill the X and Y arrays, and (2) scale and plot the arrays. To illustrate a simple plotting routine, consider the function $y = sin(x)$. A plot is to be generated for $x = 0$ to $x = 6.4$ in steps of 0.2, for a total of 33 X-Y values. The arrays must first be declared

```
   REAL X(33),Y(33)
```

and a plot line specified.

```
   CHARACTER*61 LINE
```

The next step is to fill the arrays.

```
      DO 10 I=1,33
   10 X(I)=(I-1)/5.0
      DO 20 I=1,33
   20 Y(I)=SIN(X(I))
```

The X array is generated using the formula $(I - 1)/5.0$, thus for $I = 1$, $X(1) = 0.0$; $I = 2$, $X(2) = 0.2$; $I = 3$, $X(3) = 0.4$ . . . $I = 33$, $X(33) = 6.4$. The corresponding elements of the Y array contain the sine of X. The range of the Y array is determined by finding the maximum Y and minimum Y.

```
      YMAX=Y(1)
      DO 30 I=2,33
      IF(Y(I).GT.YMAX)YMAX=Y(I)
   30 CONTINUE
      YMIN=Y(1)
      DO 40 I=2,33
      IF(Y(I).LT.YMIN)YMIN=Y(I)
   40 CONTINUE
```

Given the range, a position IPOS is calculated such that a Y value is located within the character variable LINE. This location is relative, that is

```
IPOS=(Y(I)-YMIN)/(YMAX-YMIN)*60+1
```

Hence the smallest Y value has IPOS = 1 and the largest Y value has IPOS = 61. If a symbol is assigned to the IPOS position and the character variable LINE is initialized to blanks, that symbol, an asterisk, can be placed in its relative position within LINE.

```
      LINE=' '
      IPOS=(Y(I)-YMIN)/(YMAX-YMIN)*60+1
      LINE(IPOS:IPOS)='*'
```

This is to be repeated for the entire array and a WRITE statement added to output LINE for each X–Y value.

```
      DO 60 I=1,33
      LINE=' '
      IPOS=(Y(I)-YMIN)/(YMAX-YMIN)*60+1
      LINE(IPOS:IPOS)='*'
      WRITE(*,200)LINE
   60 CONTINUE
```

Statements are added to output an ordinate, abscissa, and zero-based lines. The final program becomes

```
C     PLOTTING ROUTINE
      REAL X(33),Y(33)
      CHARACTER*61 LINE
C     FILL THE X AND Y ARRAYS
      DO 10 I=1,33
   10 X(I)=(I-1)5.0
      DO 20 I=1,33
```

```
   20 Y(I)=SIN(X(I))
C     FIND THE RANGE
      YMAX=Y(1)
      DO 30 I=2,33
      IF(Y(I).CT.YMAX)YMAX=Y(I)
   30 CONTINUE
      YMIN=Y(1)
      DO 40 I=2,33
      IF(Y(1).LT.YMIN)YMIN=Y(I)
   40 CONTINUE
C     PLOT
      WRITE(*,100)YMIN,YMAX
      DO 50 I=1,61
      LINE(I:I)='+'
   50 CONTINUE
      IZERO=(0.0-YMIN)/(YMAX-YMIN)*60+1
      LINE(IZERO:IZERO)='0'
      WRITE(*,150)LINE
      DO 60 I=1,33
      LINE=''
      LINE(IZERO:IZERO)='0'
      IPOS=(Y(I)-YMIN)/(YMAX-YMIN)*60+1
      LINE(IPOS:IPOS)='*'
      WRITE(*,200)X(I),LINE
   60 CONTINUE
      STOP
  100 FORMAT('1',7X,F5.3,51X,F5.3)
  150 FORMAT(8X,A61)
  200 FORMAT(1X,F5.3,2X,A61)
      END
```

Output is shown in Figure 12.3. This output appears with X values located down the display and Y values located across the display. The X values should be equally spaced, since each line of output is an X value. The plotting program can be coded without the use of CHARACTER variable substrings. A CHARACTER array can be declared, and this array becomes the plot line. The following program shows this change.

```
C     PLOTTING ROUTINE
      REAL X(33),Y(33)
      CHARACTER LINE(61)
C     FILL THE X AND Y ARRAYS
      DO 10 I=1,33
   10 X(I)=(I-1)/5.0
      DO 20 I=1,33
   20 Y(I)=SIN(X(I))
```

```
           -.996                                                              1.000
           +++++++++++++++++++++++++++++++++0+++++++++++++++++++++++++++++++++++++
    .000                                     *
    .200                                     0         *
    .400                                     0              *
    .600                                     0                   *
    .800                                     0                       *
   1.000                                     0                         *
   1.200                                     0                          *
   1.400                                     0                           *
   1.600                                     0                            *
   1.800                                     0                           *
   2.000                                     0                          *
   2.200                                     0                       *
   2.400                                     0                    *
   2.600                                     0                 *
   2.800                                     0            *
   3.000                                     0       *
   3.200                                    *0
   3.400                          *          0
   3.600                      *              0
   3.800                 *                   0
   4.000             *                       0
   4.200          *                          0
   4.400       *                             0
   4.600       *                             0
   4.800       *                             0
   5.000        *                            0
   5.200          *                          0
   5.400           *                         0
   5.600             *                       0
   5.800                 *                   0
   6.000                    *                0
   6.200                        *  0
   6.400                                     0    *
```

Figure 12.3 Plotting routine output

```fortran
C       FIND THE RANGE
        YMAX=Y(1)
        DO 30 I=2,33
        IF(Y(I).GT.YMAX)YMAX=Y(I)
   30 CONTINUE
        YMIN=Y(1)
        DO 40 I=2,33
        IF(Y(I).LT.YMIN)YMIN=Y(I)
   40 CONTINUE
```

```
C     PLOT
      WRITE(*,100)YMIN,YMAX
      DO 50 I=1,61
      LINE(I)='+'
   50 CONTINUE
      IZERO=(0.0-YMIN)/(YMAX-YMIN)*60+1
      LINE(IZERO)='0'
      WRITE(*,150)LINE
      DO 60 I=1,33
      DO 55 J=1,61
   55 LINE(J)=' '
      LINE(IZERO)='0'
      IPOS=(Y(I)-YMIN)/(YMAX-YMIN)*60+1
      LINE(IPOS)='*'
      WRITE(*,200)X(I),LINE
   60 CONTINUE
      STOP
  100 FORMAT('1',7X,F5.3,51X,F5.3)
  150 FORMAT(8X,61A1)
  200 FORMAT(1X,F5.3,2X,61A1)
      END
```

12.4 SUMMARY

In general, microcomputers are single user systems. They consist of support hardware and peripherals. Main memory runs from 128 kilobytes to well over 1 megabyte. Disk storage can range from over 300 kilobytes for diskettes to over 100 megabytes for hard disks. FORTRAN, BASIC, COBOL and Pascal are supported on micros in addition to applications software for design graphics and word processing.

FORTRAN is implemented as a compiler on most micros. On a micro the user creates a text file using an editor. The text file is sent to the compiler where an object file is prepared which is then linked to the FORTRAN system library to create an execute file.

Microcomputers meet most of the ANSI standards. Language specification in this chapter is based on MS-FORTRAN.

The several applications discussed here include sorting a character array, double-precision Newton-Raphson iteration, and a simple plotting routine.

The ability of micros to communicate with larger computers offers a great range of possibilities for application.

The student who has access to a micro can program any of the exercises in this text.

EXERCISES

1. For your microcomputer, what is the range of integers? What is the magnitude and precision of real data? What is the magnitude and precision of double-precision data?

2. Compile and execute the following FORTRAN program.

```
C       TABLE OF FACTORIALS
        FAC=1.0
        DO 10 I=1,16
        FAC=FAC*I
   10 WRITE(*,20)I,FAC
   20 FORMAT(1X,I2,2X,G13.6)
        END
```

3. Does your microcomputer support communications with a larger, central system? If so, briefly outline how this can be accomplished.

4. Outline the FORTRAN language specifications for your microcomputer. In what ways does it meet or exceed the ANSI specifications?

5. Write a FORTRAN program that calculates and outputs the root of the function

$$f(x) = x**m - n = 0$$

where m and n are nonzero, positive integers. Use as test data, $m = 3$ and $n = 8$.

6. Outline the compilation process for your implementation of microcomputer FORTRAN.

7. Is it possible to link subprograms written in other languages, such as Pascal, with a microcomputer FORTRAN main program? If so, how can this be done?

8. Compile and execute a plotting program for the function $y = \exp(x)$, for $x = 0$ to $x = 10$ in steps of 0.1.

9. Modify the plotting program so that it outputs a two-function plot. Test your program for $y = \sin(x)$ and $z = \cos(x)$.

Decimal Values of ASCII/EBCDIC Character Codes

Character	ASCII value	EBCDIC value
blank	32	64
currency symbol	36	91
apostrophe	39	125
left parenthesis	40	77
right parenthesis	41	93
asterisk	42	92
plus sign	43	78
comma	44	107
minus sign	45	96
decimal point	46	75
slash	47	97
colon	58	122
equal sign	61	126
0	48	240
1	49	241
2	50	242
3	51	243
4	52	244
5	53	245
6	54	246
7	55	247
8	56	248
9	57	249
A	65	193
B	66	194
C	67	195
D	68	196
E	69	197
F	70	198
F	71	199
H	72	200
I	73	201

(continued)

Character	ASCII value	EBCDIC value
J	74	209
K	75	210
L	76	211
M	77	212
N	78	213
O	79	214
P	80	215
Q	81	216
R	82	217
S	83	226
T	84	227
U	85	228
V	86	229
W	87	230
X	88	231
Y	89	232
Z	90	233

appendix B

Commonly Used Intrinsic Functions

Intrinsic function	Definition	Generic name	Argument type[a]	Function type
exponential	$e**a$	EXP	R,D,C	R,D,C
natural log	$\log (a)$	LOG	R,D,C	R,D,C
common log	$\log_{10} (a)$	LOG10	R,D,C	R,D,C
square root	$\sqrt{x}$	SQRT	R,D,C	R,D,C
sine	$\sin (a)$	SIN	R,D,C	R,D,C
cosine	$\cos (a)$	COS	R,D,C	R,D,C
tangent	$\tan (a)$	TAN	R,D,C	R,D,C
arc sine	$\arcsin (a)$	ASIN	R,D	R,D
arc cosine	$\arccos (a)$	ACOS	R,D	R,D
arc tangent	$\arctan (a)$	ATAN	R,D	R,D
hyperbolic sine	$\sinh (a)$	SINH	R,D	R,D
hyperbolic cosine	$\cosh (a)$	COSH	R,D	R,D
hyperbolic tangent	$\tanh (a)$	TANH	R,D	R,D
type conversion	to integer	INT	I,R,D,C	I
	to real	REAL	I,R,D,C	R
	to double precision	DBLE	I,R,D,C	D
	to complex	CMPLX	I,R,D,C,	C
absolute value	$\|a\|$	ABS	I,R,D,C	I,R,D
remaindering	$\mod (a_1,a_2)$ $= a_1 - int(a_1/a_2)a_2$	MOD	I,R,D	I,R,D
largest of a set	$\max(a_1,a_2, \ldots)$	MAX	I,R,D	I,R,D
smallest of a set	$\min(a_1,a_2, \ldots)$	MIN	I,R,D	I,R,D

[a] I INTEGER
R REAL
D DOUBLE PRECISION
C COMPLEX

appendix C

Statement Summary

Statement	Form	Example
arithmetic IF	IF(arithmetic expression)s_1,s_2,s_3	IF(A−B)20,10,15
arithmetic-statement function	function name (dummy arguments) = function definition	F(X,Y)=SQRT(X*X+Y*Y)
assignment	arithmetic variable = arithmetic expression[a]	Y=A*X**2+B*X+C
	character variable = character expression	TEST='THE'//'END'
	logical variable = logical expression	VALUE =A.NE.B

block IF	IF(logical expression)THEN
	    block 1
	ELSE
	    block 2
	ENDIF
		IF(X.LT.0.0)THEN
		    S=S+ABS(X)
		ELSE
		    S=S+X
		ENDIF

call	CALL name(actual arguments)	CALL QUAD (A,B,C,X1,X2)
character	CHARACTER v_1*len$_1,v_2*$len$_2, . . .$ or CHARACTER*len $v_1,v_2, . . .$	CHARACTER TEST*10 CHARACTER 10 * TEST
close	CLOSE(logical unit number, STATUS = status)	CLOSE(13,STATUS = 'KEEP')
common	COMMON array/variable list	COMMON X,Y,Z(5,5)
complex	COMPLEX $v_1,v_2,v_3, . . .$	COMPLEX A,B,C
computed GO TO	GO TO($s_1,s_2,s_3, . . .$),i	GO TO(10,20,40,15), KODE

[a]An arithmetic expression may be real, integer, double precision, or complex.   *(Continued)*

259

Statement	Form	Example
continue	s CONTINUE	50 CONTINUE
data	DATA nlist/clist	DATA X,I/3.0,10/
dimension	DIMENSION array name $(d[,d, \ldots])$	DIMENSION K(5,5),A(50)
do	DO S i = exp$_1$,exp$_2$,exp$_3$	DO 10 K = L1,L2,L3
double precision	DOUBLE PRECISION $v_1,v_2,v_3, \ldots$	DOUBLE PRECISION A8

else if	IF(logical expression)THEN
	  block 1
	ELSEIF(logical expression)THEN
	    block 2 . . .
	ENDIF
		IF(A.EQ.1)THEN
		  AMT = 100.0
		ELSEIF(A.EQ.2)THEN
		    AMT = 200.0
		ENDIF

end	END	END
entry	ENTRY name(dummy arguments)	ENTRY SUBS(X,Y,Z)
format	s FORMAT(field descriptors)	100 FORMAT(1X,3G12.4)
function	FUNCTION name(dummy arguments)	FUNCTION PHY(ARG1)
implicit	IMPLICIT TYPE$(a_1 - a_2), \ldots$	IMPLICIT REAL(I − N), INTEGER(A − H,O − Z)
integer	INTEGER $v_1,v_2,v_3, \ldots$	INTEGER COUNT,TIMES
logical	LOGICAL $v_1,v_2,v_3, \ldots$	LOGICAL TESTIT(100)
logical IF	IF(logical expression)statement	IF(A.GT.B)Y = SQRT(A − B)

open	OPEN(logical unit number,FILE =
	  file name,STATUS = status)
		OPEN(13,FILE = 'DATAIN',
		    STATUS = OLD)

parameter	PARAMETER $(p_1 = e_1, p_2 = e_2, \ldots)$	PARAMETER (PI = 3.14159)
read	READ(logical unit number, s)list READ(logical unit number,s, END = statement label)list	READ(5,*)A,B,C READ(5,100)X,Y,Z READ(13,*,END = 100)A,B,C
real	REAL $v_1,v_2,v_3, \ldots$	REAL IRAY,W(100)
return	RETURN	RETURN
rewind	REWIND(logical unit number)	REWIND 13
stop	STOP	STOP
subroutine	SUBROUTINE name(dummy arguments)	SUBROUTINE XD(X,N)
unconditional GO TO	GO TO s	GO TO 60
write	WRITE(logical unit number, s)list	WRITE(6,*)'ANSWER', Q8 WRITE(6,200)A,A + B,A − B

appendix D

Debugging the Program

Some thoughts regarding debugging a FORTRAN program that compiles but does not execute correctly due to one or more logic errors. Most FORTRAN compilers incorporate a debugging or trace feature that allows selected variables/arrays/statements to be displayed during program execution. Thus intermediate results can be output and analyzed so that logic errors can be isolated and corrected. These built-in trace features are not ANSI standard. They are dependent on the particular compiler being used. A more general debugging technique is to insert list-directed write statements at strategic locations within the source code. By incorporating labels and selecting appropriate variables and arrays, intermediate results can be displayed that will aid in quickly locating logic errors.

Consider, for example, the source program for calculating the real roots of

$$f(x) = ax^2 + bx + c = 0$$

```
C     ENTER DATA
      WRITE(6,*)'ENTER A,B,C '
      READ(5,*)A,B,C
C     CALCULATE DISCRIMINANT
      D=B*B-4.0*A*C
C     CHECK FOR REAL ROOTS
      IF(D.LT.0.0)THEN
        WRITE(6,*)'NO REAL ROOTS'
      ELSE
        R1=(-B+SQRT(D))/2.0*A
        R2=(-B-SQRT(D))/2.0*A
        WRITE(6,*)'REAL ROOTS',R1,R2
      ENDIF
      END
```

When the program is run using test data such as

A=1.0, B=5.0, C=4.0

which yields as real roots

R=-1.0, R2=-4.0

the program outputs

```
REAL ROOTS -1.00000      -4.00000
```

but when the test data

A=2.0, B=5.0, C=2.0

is used, the calculated roots are

R1=-0.5, R2=-2.0

but the program outputs

```
REAL ROOTS -200000      -8.00000
```

Placing write statements as follows will output intermediate results that should aid in debugging the program.

```
C       ENTER DATA
        WRITE(6,*)'ENTER A,B,C '
        READ(5,*)A,B,C
C       CALCULATE DISCRIMINANT
        D=B*B-4.0*A*C
          WRITE(6,*)'D=',D
C       CHECK FOR REAL ROOTS
        IF(D.LT.0.0)THEN
          WRITE(6,*)'NO REAL ROOTS'
        ELSE
          WRITE(6,*)'NUMERATOR=',
     1          -B+SQRT(D),-B-SQRT(D)
          WRITE(6,*)'DENOMINATOR=',2.0*A
          R1=(-B+SQRT(D))/2.0*A
```

```
      R2=(-B-SQRT(D))/2.0*A
        WRITE(6,*)'REAL ROOTS',R1,R2
      ENDIF
      END
```

The three write statements trace program execution and output the intermediate results and should quickly isolate the logic error at the assignment statements for R1 and R2. Inspection of these two statements shows that parentheses are needed and as corrected

```
R1=(-B+SQRT(D))/(2.0*A)
R2=(-BA-SQRT(D))/(2.0*A)
```

As a second example, consider the source program for calculating the arithmetic average of the real, ten element, A array.

```
      DIMENSION A(10)
      WRITE(6,*)'ENTER DATA '
      READ(5,*)A
      DO 10 J=1,10
      SUM=SUM+A(J)
  10  CONTINUE
      WRITE(6,*)'AVERAGE IS',SUM/10.0
      END
```

Upon execution and using the test data

```
1.0,2.0,3.0,4.0,5.0,6.0,7.0,8.0,9.0,10.0
```

The expected output is

```
AVERAGE IS 5.50000
```

The output actually displayed is some ridiculous value. Inserting the write statement

```
WRITE(6,*)'SUM=',SUM
```

before and after $SUM = SUM + A(J)$ should, upon execution, trace intermediate values assigned to SUM. Inspection of the output quickly shows that SUM was never initialized and the statement

```
SUM=0.0
```

must be inserted before the DO loop.

appendix E

Solutions to Odd-Numbered Exercises

CHAPTER 1

1. A computer word is usually 16 or 32 bits. Depending on machine architecture, however, a computer word may range from 8 to 60 bits.

3. Answer is site dependent, but the size of computer memory should be some power of 2.

5. The number and combined storage capacity of the disk units is site dependent. Storage capacity is usually given in bytes (characters). The typical range is from several million to hundreds of millions of bytes per unit.

7. Most computing systems support one or more of the following languages:

   FORTRAN (FORmula TRANslation)—engineering and science
   COBOL (COmmon Business Oriented Language)—business
   BASIC (Beginners All-purpose Symbolic Instruction Code)—general
   APL (A Programming Language)—mathematics
   PL/1 (Programming Language One)—general
   Pascal (after Blaise Pascal)—systems and applications

9.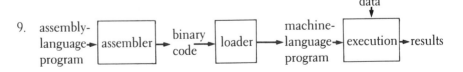

The assembler (or translator) and loader are system programs. Execution takes place under control of the system software.

11.   An IOP is a highly sophisticated interface that handles computer I/O and frees the CPU for processing data.

13.   Priorities are useful in a time-shared environment because some programs must run before other programs. Critical system programs must, at times, interrupt noncritical user programs. The critical programs need to have a higher priority than noncritical programs.

CHAPTER 2

1.   372.65625 = 101110100.10101
             1032 = 10000001000
         1777.75 = 11011110001.11
           10020 = 10011100100100
           0.375 = 0.011
             100 = 1100100

3.   32767 = 0111111111111111
             0 = 0000000000000000
         −64 = 1111111111000000
         100 = 0000000001100100
     −32768 = 1000000000000000
         1600 = 0000011001000000

5.   115 = 0000000001110011
       53 = 0000000000110101
           0000000010101000 = 168

       48 = 0000000000110000
     −92 = 1111111110100100
           1111111111010100 = −44

     128 = 0000000010000000
   −123 = 1111111110000101
           0000000000000101 = 5

7.   There is no exact conversion (representation). The approximate answer is given by

       0   01111011   10011001100110011001100
       ↑   ↑   ↑
     bit 31   bit 23   bit 0

This answer is based on the internal representation of real data using IEEE format.

9. real part: 00111111100000000000000000000000
   imag. part: 00000000000000000000000000000000
   This answer is based on the internal representation of real data using IEEE format.

11. A(−3) ◄— 1st element
    A(−2)
    A(−1)
    A(0)   ◄— 4th element
    A(1)
    A(2)
    A(3)
    A(4)
    A(5)
    A(6)
    A(7)
    A(8)
    A(9)
    A(10)
    A(11)
    A(12) ◄—last element

    The 16-element, real A array requires 16 (32-bit) memory words. A(0) references the fourth memory word.

13.

L	unused	word 3
T	A	word 2
T	O	word 1

16-bit memory word

L	unused	unused	unused
T	O	T	A

32-bit memory word

T = 227   O = 214   A = 193   L = 211

Answer is site dependent. Some computers pack character data so as to eliminate unused bytes. These answers assume that data begins at a word boundary.

15. Specification statements deal exclusively with data.

17. $\sin x = x - \dfrac{x^3}{3!} + \dfrac{x^5}{5!} - \dfrac{x^7}{7!} + \cdots$

$x = \pi/4 = 0.785498$

The first four terms are needed.

$\text{error} = \dfrac{x^7/7!}{x - (x^3/3!) + (x^5/5!) - (x^7/7!)} = \dfrac{0.0000366}{0.7071065}$

$\text{error} = 0.000052$

19. The magnitude would be increased by a power of 2.

21. There are six letters available for the first character of an integer variable name, followed by 5 alphabetic or numeric characters. Thus, the number of default 6 character integer variable names = $6 \cdot 36 \cdot 36 \cdot 36 \cdot 36 \cdot 36$. Repeat this for 5, 4, 3, 2 and 1 character variable name to obtain

$$6 \cdot 36^5 + 6 \cdot 36^4 + 6 \cdot 36^3 + 6 \cdot 36^2 + 6 \cdot 36 + 6 = 373162686.$$

TIMES is typed as integer by the specification statement INTEGER TIMES.

CHAPTER 3

1. The valid FORTRAN real variable names are:
   A3   BOOT   APPLE   ABCD   ANS2

3.
`Y=3.0+A÷B`	replace ÷ by/
`K=K-I/J`	OK
`10END`	
`3.14159=PI`	backward assignment
`D=(A*A+B*B+C*C)**0.5`	OK
`WRITE(IUNIT,*)A,B,JOBNO`	OK
`RADIUS=DIAMETER/2.0`	DIAMETER too long
`READ(5,*)A,B,I,J`	OK
`10 D=(SIDEA-5.0)(SIDEB-2.0)`	operator missing

5.
line 4:		`DISTANCE=SQRT((X2-X1)**2`	need parenthesis
		`+(Y2-Y1)**2+(Z2-Z1)**2)`	
line 5:	C	`INPUT DATA`	need C for comment
line 6:		`READ(5,*)X1,Y1,Z1,X2,Y2,Z2`	need READ
line 7:	C	`OUTPUT RESULTS`	need C for comment
line 8:		`WRITE(6,*)'DISTANCE IS ',DISTANCE`	need Write
line 9:		`STOP`	
line 10:		`END`	STOP comes before END

7. ØØØØØ1ØØ.333333ØØØØØ.666667ØØØØ
   Ø.150000ØØØØ
   Ø10.0000ØØØØ
   Ø15.0000ØØØØ
   Ø.666667ØØØØØØ.444444ØØØØØØ909091.ØØØØ

   The exact form of the printed output will be site dependent.

9.

Z	600.0
J	5
I	14
Y	−500.0
X	100.0

11. The answer is site dependent. Typically, real data have a range of $10^{\pm 38}$ and a precision of seven significant figures.

13. Line 3: C   ALT=ALTITUDE
    Line 5:   AREA=3.14159*DIAM**2/4.0
    Line 6:   VOLUME=(1./3.)*AREA*ALT

15. NO. When $b^2 - 4ac < 0$, the roots will be complex, and the square root of a negative (real) value does not exist. The FORTRAN program will terminate in an error state when $b^2 - 4ac < 0$.

17.
```
C234567
      WRITE(6,*)'ENTER VALUES '
      READ(5,*)R1,R2,R3
      R=R1*R2/(R1+R2)+R3
      WRITE(6,*)'RESISTANCE IS',R
      STOP
      END
```

19.
```
C     JET ENGINE EFFICIENCY
C
      READ(5,*)R,U,V
      E=1.0/(1.0+(0.5*(1.0+R)(U/V-1.0)**2)/
     1     ((1.0+R)*(U/V)-1.0))
      WRITE(6,*)'EFFICIENCY=',E
      STOP
      END
```

21. ```
C234567
        A=3.0
        B=4.0
        WRITE(6,*)'FOR A =',A,'AND B=',B
        HYP=SQRT(A*A+B*B)
        WRITE(6,*)'THE HYPOTENUSE IS',HYP
        STOP
        END
```

23. ```
C234567
        WRITE(6,*)'ENTER T '
        READ(5,*)T
        CP=2.706+0.29*T-90.6E-7*T**2
        WRITE(6,*)'HEAT CAPACITY IS',CP
        END
```

25. ```
C   PERIOD OF A PENDULUM
        G=9.8
        WRITE(6,*)'ENTER LENGTH '
        READ(5,*)RL
        T=2.0*3.14159*(RL/G)**0.5
        WRITE(6,*)'PERIOD IS/',T
        STOP
        END
```

## CHAPTER 4

The solutions to the exercises in Chapter 4 are presented in algorithm form.

1. (1) Input sales
   (2) Are sales > 12000?
       IF true THEN commission = 175 + 0.05 (sales − 12000)
       ELSE commission = 175
   (3) Output sales, commission
   (4) STOP

3. (1) Initialize
         sum = 0
           N = 0
   (2) DOWHILE N < = 24
       (a) sum = sum + $1/2^N$
       (b) N = N + 1
   (3) Output sum
   (4) STOP
```

5. (1) Input amount, years, percent interest
   (2) Months = 12 * years
   (3) Rate = percent interest/100
   (4) Counter = 1
   (5) DOUNTIL counter > months
       (a) amount = amount (1 + rate)
       (b) counter = counter + 1
   (6) Output months, rate, amount
   (7) STOP

7. (1) Initialize
           counter = 1
   (2) DOWHILE counter < = 500
       (a) input gross pay, pension, tax, hospital
       (b) deductions = pension + tax + hospital
       (c) net pay = gross pay − deductions
       (d) output gross pay, deductions, net pay
       (e) counter = counter + 1
   (3) STOP

9. (1) Initialize
           counter = 1
   (2) DOWHILE counter < = 50
       (a) input a, b, c
       (b) is $c^2 = a^2 + b^2$?
           IF true THEN output 'RIGHT TRIANGLE'
           ELSE output 'NO RIGHT TRIANGLE'
       (c) counter = counter + 1
   (3) STOP

11. (1) Input N
    (2) Fill the N element X array
    (3) Initialize
            sum = 0
              i = 1
    (4) DOWHILE i < = N
        (a) sum = sum + x_i
        (b) i = i + 1
    (5) Average = sum/N
    (6) Output average
    (7) STOP

13. (1) input x
    (2) initialize
              series sum = 0.0
                     i = 0
    (3) DOWHILE i < = 9
              series term = $x^i/i!$
              series sum = series sum + series term
                     i = i + 1
    (4) output x, series sum
    (5) STOP

15. (1) Input N, R
    (2) Calculate
              N!
              (N − R)!
    (3) P = N!/(N − R)!
    (4) Output P
    (5) STOP

CHAPTER 5

1. 2.00000   0.00000
   2.00000   4.00000
   3.00000   9.00000

3. 1   1   2
   1   2   3
   1   3   4
   1   4   4
   3   1   4
   3   2   5
   3   3   6
   3   4   6
   5   1   6
   5   2   7
   5   3   8
   5   4   8
   7   4   8

```
5.  (a)     IF(X-0.0)10,20,30
        10  Y=ABS(X)
            GO TO 40
        20  WRITE(6,*)X
            GO TO 40
        30  Z=X*X
        40  CONTINUE
```

```
    (b) IF(B*B-4.0*A*C.LT.0.0)THEN
          WRITE(6,*)'ROOTS COMPLEX'
        ELSE
          WRITE(6,*)'ROOTS REAL'
        ENDIF
```

```
    (c) IF(X.EQ.TERM)THEN
          X=X+1.0
        ELSE
          WRITE(6,*)X
        ENDIF
```

```
    (d) 10 IF(Z*Z.LE.100.0)GO TO 20
           WRITE(6,*)Z
           GO TO 30
        20 IF(Z.GE.0.0)THEN
           Z=Z+1.0
           ELSE
           Z=Z-1.0
           ENDIF
           GO TO 10
        30 CONTINUE
```

```
7.    N=12
      DO 20 I=1,N-1
   20 WRITE(6,*)I*I
      END
```
Output will be I squared for I = 1 to I = 11 in steps of 1.

9.
```
C       ARITHMETIC AVERAGE
C
        WRITE(6,*)'ENTER N '
        READ(5,*)N
        KOUNT=1
        SUM=0.0
     10 IF(KOUNT.LE.N)THEN
           WRITE(5,*)'ENTER A VALUE '
           READ(5,*)VALUE
           SUM=SUM+VALUE
           KOUNT=KOUNT+1
           GO TO 10
        ENDIF
        WRITE(6,*)'AVERAGE OS',SUM/N
        STOP
        END
```

11.
```
C       RIGHT TRIANGLE PROBLEM
C
        WRITE(6,*)'ENTER A,B,C '
        READ(5,*)A,B,C
        IF(A*A+B*B.EQ.C*C)THEN
           WRITE(6,*)'RIGHT TRIANGLE '
        ELSE
           WRITE(6,*)'NO RIGHT TRIANGLE '
        ENDIF
        STOP
        END
```

13. Answer is site dependent.

15.
```
C       SIMPLY SUPPORTED BEAM
C
        WRITE(6,*)'FEET   MOMENT'
        DO 10  X=0.0,10.0,1.0
        IF(X.LT.7.0)THEN
           BEND=300.0*X
        ELSE
           BEND=7000.0-700.0*X
        ENDIF
     10 WRITE(6,*)X,BEND
        STOP
        END
```

```
17.  C      N-TH ROOT
     C      DOWHILE N<>0 AND Y>0
     C
            WRITE(6,*)'ENTER N,Y '
            READ(5,*)N,Y
     C  20  IF(N.NE.0.AND.Y.GT.0.0)THEN
            WRITE(6,*)'ANSWER IS',Y**(1.0/N)
            WRITE(6,*)'ENTER N,Y '
            READ(5,*)N,Y
            GO TO 20
            ENDIF
            END

19.  C      COMBINATIONS
     C
            WRITE(6,*)'ENTER N,R '
            READ(5,*)N,IR
     C      CALCULATE FACTORIALS
            FACN=1.0
            DO 10 I=1,N
        10  FACN=FACN*I
            FACR=1.0
            DO 20 I=1,IR
        20  FACR=FACR*I
            FACNR=1.0
            DO 30 I=1,N-IR
        30  FACNR=FACNR*I
     C      CALCULATE RESULTS
            COMB=FACN/FACR*FACNR
     C      OUTPUT RESULTS
            WRITE(6,*)'COMBINATIONS ARE',COMB
            STOP
            END

21.  C      ODD OR EVEN
     C
            WRITE(6,*)'ENTER A NUMBER '
            READ(5,*)NUM
       100  IF(NUM.LE.0)STOP
            IF(2*(NUM/2).EQ.NUM)THEN
              WRITE(6,*)'EVEN'
            ELSE
              WRITE(6,*)'ODD'
            ENDIF
            WRITE(6,*)'ENTER A NUMBER '
            READ(5,*)NUM
            GO TO 100
            END
```

23.
```
    C       COSINE SERIES
            WRITE(6,*)'ENTER ANGLE IN RADIANS '
            READ(5,*)T
            N=2
        10  SERIES=1.0
            DO 30 K=1,N-1
            FAC=1.0
            DO 20 I=1,2*K
        20  FAC=FAC*I
        30  SERIES=SERIES+(-1)**K*T**(2*K)/FAC
            WRITE(6,*)'NUMBER OF TERMS=',N
            WRITE(6,*)'ESTIMATED COSINE=',SERIES
            WRITE(6,*)'ACTUAL COSINE=',COS(T)
            WRITE(6,*)
            N=N*2
            IF(N.LE.8)GO TO 10
            STOP
            END
```

25.
```
    C       VALUE OF THE LIMIT
    C
            WRITE(6,*)'VALUE OF X    VALUE OF LIMIT'
            WRITE(6,*)
            DO 100 X=0.9,1.0,0.001
       100  WRITE(6,*)X,(X*X-1.0)/(X-1.0)
            STOP
            END
```

27. The solution is a trial-and-error procedure where the root of the function

$$(P + \frac{n^2 a}{v^2})(V - nb) - RT = 0$$

must be estimated. Use the code from sample problem 2 where V replaces X and DELV replaces DELX. For ϕ use

$$PHI = (P + RN*RN*A/(V*V))*(V - RN*B) - R*T$$

29. C   TABLE OF OUTPUT
     C
            WRITE(6,*)'   X   10**X   LOG X'
            DO 100 X=0,10,0.25
        100 WRITE(6,*)X,10**X,ALOG(X)
            STOP
            END

Execution fails since there is no natural log of zero. Reversing the parameters to DO 100 X = 10,0, − 0.25 will output all but the natural log of zero.

31. C   SERIES SUMMATION
     C
            WRITE(6,*)'INPUT X '
            READ(5,*)X
            SUM=0,0
            FAC=1.0
            DO 10 I=0,9
            IF(I.GT.0)FAC=FAC*I
            TERM=X**I/FAC
         10 SERIES=SERIES+TERM
            RERROR=TERM/SERIES
            WRITE(6,*)X,SERIES,RERROR
            STOP
            END

CHAPTER 6

1. The valid array elements are:

X(300)	K(I)	A(K(J))
D3(K/J)	WOO(69)	X(I + J)

3. (a) Y(10)   element 61
    (b) Y(1)   element 52
    (c) Y(− 5)   element 46
    (d) Y(5)   element 56
    (e) Y(− 40)   element 11
    (f) Y(100)   outside dimensioned bounds

5.   JOB(3, 2)   0
      JOB(1, 2)   −3
      JOB(2, 2)   6
      JOB(4, 8)   outside dimensioned bounds

7.
```
      DIMENSION XRAY(20)
      DO 10 K=1,19,2
   10 XRAY(K)=K*K
      STOP
      END
      XRAY(15)=225.0
      XRAY(9)=81.0
      XRAY(12) is undefined
```

9.
```
      DIMENSION ABLE(13,15)
      DO 50 I=1,13,3
      DO 50 J=1,15,2
   50 ABLE(I,J)=I*J
      END
      ABLE(4,3)=12.0
      ABLE(10,11)=110.0
      ABLE(4,6) is undefined
```

11.
```
C     SEARCH INTEGER ARRAY
C
C     IRRY  ARRAY NAME
C     IBIG  LARGEST VALUE
C     ISML  SMALLEST VALUE
C     N     NUMBER OF ELEMENTS
C
      DIMENSION IRRY(100)
      WRITE(6,*)'ENTER N '
      READ(5,*)N
      IF(N.LT.2.OR.N.GT.100)STOP
C     FILL THE ARRAY
      WRITE(6,*)'ENTER INTEGERS '
      READ(5,*)(IRRY(J),J=1,N)
C     SEARCH THE ARRAY
      IBIG=IRRY(1)
      ISML=IRRY(1)
      DO 100 I=2,N
      IF(IRRY(I).GT.IBIG)THEN
        IBIG=IRRY(J)
```

```
          ELSE
            IF(IRRY(I).LT.ISML)ISML=IRRY(I)
          ENDIF
       100 CONTINUE
     C      OUTPUT RESULTS
          WRITE(6,*)'BIG=',IBIG,'SMALL=',ISML
          END
```

13.
```
     C      SORT AN N ELEMENT ARRAY
     C
     C      X    ARRAY NAME
     C      N    NUMBER OF ELEMENTS
     C
          DIMENSION X(20)
          WRITE(6,*)'ENTER N '
          READ(5,*)N
          WRITE(6,*)'ENTER VALUES '
          READ(5,*)(X(K),K=1,N)
     C      OUTPUT ORIGINAL ARRAY
          WRITE(6,*)
          WRITE(6,*)'BEFORE SORTING:'
          WRITE(6,*)(X(K),K=1,N)
     C      SORT THE ARRAY
          DO 10 K=1,N-1
          DO 10 L=K+1,N
          IF(X(L).GT.X(K))THEN
            XHOLD=X(L)
             X(L)=X(K)
             X(K)=XHOLD
          ENDIF
        10 CONTINUE
     C      OUTPUT SORTED ARRAY
          WRITE(6,*)
          WRITE(6,*)'AFTER SORTING:'
          WRITE(6,)(X(K),K=1,N)
          STOP
          END
```

15.
```
     C      GRADES PROGRAM
     C
     C      G   GRADE ARRAY
     C      SUM RUNNING SUM
     C      IR  ROW POINTER (STUDENTS)
     C      IC  COL POINTER (TESTS)
     C
          DIMENSION G(10,4)
```

```
C       FILL THE G ARRAY
        DO 10 IR=1,10
   10 READ(5,*)(G(IR,IC),IC=1,4)
C       CALCULATE STUDENT AVERAGES
        DO 30 IR=1,10
        SUM=0.0
        DO 20 IC=1,4
   20 SUM=SUM+G(IR,IC)
   30 WRITE(6,*)'FOR STUDENT',IR,' AVE IS',SUM/4.0
C       CALCULATE TEST AVERAGES
        DO 50 IC=1,4
        SUM=0.0
        DO 40 IR=1,10
   40 SUM=SUM+G(IR,IC)
   50 WRITE(6,*)'FOR TEST', IC,' AVE IS',SUM/10.0
        STOP
        END
```

17.
```
C       ADD MATRICES
C
        DIMENSION A(3,2),B(3,2),C(3,2)
        DO 10 IR=1,3
   10 READ(5,*)(A(IR,IC),IC=1,2)
        DO 20 IR=1,3
   20 READ(5,*)(B(IR,IC),IC=1,2)
        DO 30 IR=1,3
        DO 30 IC=1,2
   30 C(IR,IC)=A(IR,IC)+B(IR,IC)
        DO 40 IR=1,3
   40 WRITE(6,*)(C(IR,IC),IC=1,2)
        END
```

19.
```
JUNK(1,1,1,1)=1      1st element
JUNK(2,1,1,1)=3
JUNK(1,2,1,1)=7
JUNK(2,2,1,1)=19
JUNK(1,1,2,1)=11
JUNK(2,1,2,1)=0
JUNK(1,2,2,1)=32
JUNK(2,2,2,1)=8
JUNK(1,1,1,2)=9
JUNK(2,1,1,2)=14
JUNK(1,2,1,2)=2
JUNK(2,2,1,2)=50
JUNK(1,1,2,2)=33
JUNK(2,1,2,2)=15
JUNK(1,2,2,2)=6
JUNK(2,2,2,2)=16     last element
```

21.
```
      C        ARRAY DIFFERENCES
      C
               DIMENSION A(25,25)
               WRITE(6,*)'ENTER M '
               READ(5,*)M
               WRITE(6,*)'ENTER DATA, ROW BY ROW'
               WRITE(6,*)
               DO 10 IR=1,M
        10 READ(5,*)(A(IR,IC),IC=1,M)
               DO 100 IC=1,M-1
               DO 100 IR=1,M
               IF(A(IR,IC)-A(IR,IC+1))20,40,60
        20 WRITE(6,*)'DIFFERENCE IS NEGATIVE',IR,IC
               GO TO 100
        40 WRITE(6,*)'DIFFERENCE IS ZERO     ',IR,IC
               GO TO 100
        60 WRITE(6,*)'DIFFERENCE IS POSITIVE',IR,IC
       100 CONTINUE
               STOP
               END
```

23.
```
      C        POSITIVE/NEGATIVE ELEMENTS
      C
               DIMENSION INUM(25),IPOS(25),INEG(25)
               WRITE(6,*)'ENTER NUMBER OF ELEMENTS '
               READ(5,*)N
               WRITE(6,*)'ENTER DATA '
               READ(5,*)(INUM(I),I=1,N)
               NPOS=0
               NNEG=0
               DO 10 I=1,N
               IF(INUM(I).GT.0)THEN
                 NPOS=NPOS+1
                 IPOS(NPOS)=INUM(I)
               ELSE IF(INUM(I).LT.0)THEN
                       NNEG=NNEG+1
                       INEG(NNEG)=INUM(I)
               ENDIF
        10 CONTINUE
               WRITE(6,*)NPOS,' POSITIVE ELEMENTS'
               WRITE(6,*)(IPOS(I),I=1,NPOS)
               WRITE(6,*)NNEG,' NEGATIVE ELEMENTS'
               WRITE(6,*)(INEG(I),I=1,NNEG)
               STOP
               END
```

```
25. C      LARGEST/SMALLEST VALUE
    C
           DIMENSION A(25,25)
           WRITE(6,*)'ENTER M '
           READ(5,*)M
           WRITE(6,*)'ENTER DATA, ROW BY ROW'
           WRITE(6,*)
           LARGE=1E-38
           SMALL=1E+38
           DO 10 IR=1,M
        10 READ(5,*)(A(IR,IC),IC=1,M)
           DO 100 IR=1,M
           DO 100 IC=1,M
           IF(A(IR,IC).GT.LARGE)THEN
              LARGE=A(IR,IC)
              IRLRG=IR
              ICLRG=IC
           ELSE IF(A(IR,IC).LT.SMALL)THEN
                  SMALL=A(IR,IC)
                  IRSML=IR
                  ICSML=IC
           ENDIF
       100 CONTINUE
           WRITE(6,*)'LARGEST VALUE IS',LARGE
           WRITE(6,*)'OCCURS AT ROW',IRLRG,'  COLUMN',ICLRG
           WRITE(6,*)'SMALLEST VALUE IS',SMALL
           WRITE(6,*)'OCCURS AT ROW',IRSML,'  COLUMN',ICSML
           STOP
           END

27. C      SET DIAGONALS TO ONES
    C
           DIMENSION MN(25,25)
           WRITE(6,*)'ENTER M '
           READ(5,*)M
    C      ZERO THE ARRAY
           DO 100 IR=1,M
           DO 100 IC=1,M
           MN(IR,IC)=0
       100 CONTINUE
    C      SET DIAGONALS
           DO 20 IRC=1,M
        20 MN(IRC,IRC)=1
           DO 30 IRC=1,M
        30 MN(IRC,M-IRC+1)=1
    C      OUTPUT THE ARRAY
           DO 40 IR=1,M
        40 WRITE(6,*)(MN(IR,IC),IC=1,M)
           STOP
           END
```

```
29.  C       POSITIVE/NEGATIVE NUMBERS
     C
             DIMENSION IX(200)
     C       FILL THE ARRAY
             KOUNT=1
             WRITE(6,*)'ENTER VALUES '
       10 READ(5,*)IX(KOUNT)
             IF(IX(KOUNT).EQ.0)THEN
               CONTINUE
             ELSE
               KOUNT=KOUNT+1
               GO TO 10
             ENDIF
             N=KOUNT-1
     C       OUTPUT NUMBERS
             WRITE(6,*)
             WRITE(6,*)'POSITIVE   NEGATIVE'
             DO 20 KOUNT=1,N
             IF(IX(KOUNT).GT.0)THEN
               WRITE(6,*)IX(KOUNT)
             ELSE
               WRITE(6,*)'           ',IX(KOUNT)
             ENDIF
       20 CONTINUE
             STOP
             END




31.  C       2-D ARRAY PROCESSING
     C
             DIMENSION IX(25,25)
             WRITE(6,*)'ENTER M LIMIT '
             READ(5,*)MLIM
             WRITE(6,*)'ENTER N LIMIT '
             READ(5,*)NLIM
     C       FILL THE ARRAY
             DO 10 M=1,MLIM
             DO 10 N=1,NLIM
       10 IX(M,N)=M*M+N*N
     C       OUTPUT THE ARRAY
             WRITE(6,*)
             WRITE(6,*)'THE ARRAY CONTAINS:'
             DO 30 M=1,MLIM
       30 WRITE(6,*)(IX(M,N),N=1,NLIM)
             STOP
             END
```

33.
```
    C       CALCULATE AND STORE F(X)
    C
            DIMENSION FX(-10:10)
    C       FILL THE FX ARRAY
            DO 10 X=-5.0,5.0,0.5
            INDEX=2.0*X
            FX(INDEX)=(X-2.0)**2
        10 CONTINUE
    C       OUTPUT RESULTS
            WRITE(6,*)'INDEX        X              F(X)'
            DO 20 INDEX=-10,10
        20 WRITE(6,*)INDEX,INDEX/2.0,F(INDEX)
            STOP
            END
```

CHAPTER 7

1. 1095.00000ƀƀ25.38000-100.00000ƀƀ100
   1095.00000ƀƀ25.38000-100.00000
   ƀƀ100
   ƀƀ1095.000ƀƀƀƀ25.380ƀƀ-100.000ƀƀ100
   blank line
   ƀANSWERS
   1095.00000ƀƀ25.38000-100.00000
   ƀ100
   (G field output may be machine dependent.)

3. ƀ2ƀ0.15E-03ƀƀ10ƀƀƀ27.7

5. (a)   WRITE(6,50)I,BBET,ABET
        50 FORMAT(1X,I3,F9.4,F10.3)

   (b)   WRITE(6,60)J,BBET,I,ABET
        60 FORMAT(1X,I3,F9.4/1X,I3,F9.4)

   (c)   WRITE(6,70)J,I,BBET,ABET
        70 FORMAT(1X,I3,5X,I3/1X,F8.2,F10.2)

   (d)   WRITE(6,80)I,J,ABET,BBET
        80 FORMAT('ƀTHEƀINTEGERSƀARE',2I4/'ƀTHEƀREALƀNOSƀAREƀ,',2F5.1)

   (e)   WRITE(6,90)J,ABET,I,BBET
        90 FORMAT('ƀINTEGERSƀƀƀREALS'/1X,I5,5X,F6.1/1X,I5,5X,F6.1)

7. (a) 363.0ƀƀƀƀƀ11.95ƀƀƀƀƀƀ-200

    (b) 363.0
         ƀ-200
         11.95

    (c) 363.011.95ƀƀƀƀƀƀƀƀƀƀ-200

    (d) ƀ-200
         363.0ƀƀƀƀƀƀƀ11.95

A decimal in the input overrides the FORMAT specification.
The slash in input FORMAT specifications requires data on separate lines.

9.
```
       DO 20 J=1,10
       WRITE(6,100)(IRRYV(J,K),K=1,10)
    20 CONTINUE
       FORMAT(1X,10I8)
```

11.
```
C234567
       DO 10 I=1,3
       DO 10 J-1,3
       WRITE(6,100)I,J
    10 CONTINUE
       STOP
   100 FORMAT(1X,I1,2X,'+',I1)
       END
```
Comment line identifies column 7

Normal nested DO loops

CONTINUE statement optional. Could label the WRITE as 10 and delete CONTINUE.

13.
```
C234567
       READ(5,*)X
       N=0
       TERM=1.0
       EX=1.0
       FAC=1.0
    10 IF(TERM/EX.GE.1.0E-6)THEN
       N=N+1
       FAC=FAC*N
       TERM=X**N/FAC
       EX=EX+TERM
       GO TO 10
       ENDIF
       WRITE(6,20)X,EX
       STOP
    20 FORMAT('ƀEXP(',F4.1,')ƀ=',G13.6)
       END
```
Comment line identifies col. 7

Initialize variables

Block IF with a null ELSE

G-format adjusts to large values better than the F-format.

15.  ```
     C234567
           WRITE(6,100)
           DO 10 D=1.0,20.0,1.0
        10 WRITE(6,150)D,3.141593*D*D/4.0
           STOP
       100 FORMAT('bDIAM',2X,'AREA'/)
       150 FORMAT(1X,F4.0,2X,F7.3)
           END
     ```

17.  ```
           FAC=1.0
           DO 10 I=1,10
           FAC=FAC*I
        10 WRITE(6,20)I,FAC
        20 FORMAT(1X,I2,2X,F13.6)
           END
     ```

If the G13.6 is changed to F13.6, then the output for 10! exceeds the FOR-MAT specification of F13.6. If the G13.6 is changed to F15.6, then the output for 10! may exceed the allowable precision for real numbers.

19. All output for EXP(RI) exceeds the FORMAT specification of F6.0 for RI>11. All output for 1.0/RI is in error due to rounding caused by the FORMAT specification of F4.1 except for RI = 1, 2, 5, 10.

CHAPTER 8

1.  ```
     REAL I,J
     INTEGER FORM,DUMB
     DOUBLE PRECISION J
     ```

3.  ```
     REAL ION(10)
     DATA ION/0,1,0,1,0,1,0,1,0,1/
     ```

5.  ```
     C234567
           IMPLICIT DOUBLE PRECISION(A-H,O-Z)
           WRITE(6,*)'ENTER X'
           READ(5,*)X
           N=1
           SERIES=1.0
           FAC=1.0
           ERR=1.0D=10
           TERM=1.0
           RERR=TERM/SERIES
     ```
     Comment line identifies col. 7.
     ```

```
10 IF(RERR.GE.ERR)THEN                              Block IF with null ELSE
     FAC=FAC*N
     TERM=X**N/FAC
     SERIES=SERIES+TERM
     RERR=TERM/SERIES
     N=N+1
     GO TO 10
   ENDIF
   WRITE(6,*)'FOR X=',X
   WRITE(6,*)'EXPONENTIAL IS',SERIES
   WRITE(6,*)'AFTER',N,' TERMS'
   STOP
   END
```

YES, if x is typed complex the series will converge to the complex value of e^x.

7.
```
C234567                                             Comment line identifies col. 7.
     LOGICAL A,B
     WRITE(6,*)'ENTER A,B'
     READ(5,*)A,B
     WRITE(6,6)A.AND.B,A.OR.B,.NOT.A
     STOP
   6 FORMAT('0A.AND.B IS',L5/        Zero in carriage control column
   1         ' A.OR.B  IS',L5/       skips a line.
   2         ' .NOT.A  IS',L5)       1 and 2 in col. 6 for continuation
     END                            lines
```

9.
```
     COMPLEX DISCR,CX1,CX2
     WRITE(6,*)'ENTER A,B,C '
     READ(5,*)A,B,C
     DISCR=B*B-4.0*A*C
     CX1=(-B+SQRT(DISCR))/(2.0*A)
     CX2=(-B-SQRT(DISCR))/(2.0*A)
     IF(DISCR.LT.0.0)THEN                            Block IF
       WRITE(6,*)'COMPLEX ROOTS = ',CX1,CX2
     ELSE
       X1=CX1
       X2=CX2                       If DISCR is positive
       WRITE(6,*)'REAL ROOTS = ',X1,X2   roots are real and the
     ENDIF                          imaginary parts of
     STOP                           CX1, CX2 are zero.
     END
```

11.
```
      C       STUDENT INFORMATION TABLE
      C
              CHARACTER*24 NAME(10)
              CHARACTER*12 SSNO(10)
              CHARACTER*24 ADDR(10)
              KOUNT=1
              READ(5,*)NAME(KOUNT),SSNO(KOUNT),ADDR(KOUNT)
      25  IF(NAME(KOUNT).NE.'END OF DATA')THEN
                 KOUNT=KOUNT+1
                 READ(5,*)NAME(KOUNT),SSNO(KOUNT),ADDR(KOUNT)
                 GO TO 25
              ENDIF
              N=KOUNT-1
              WRITE(6,100)
              DO 50 KOUNT=1,N
      50  WRITE(6,200)NAME(KOUNT),SSNO(KOUNT),ADDR(KOUNT)
              STOP
     100  FORMAT('0NAME',20X,'SOC SEC #',3X,'ADDRESS'/)
     200  FORMAT(1X,3A)
              END
```

List-directed input requires each datum be delimited by apostrophes.

13.
```
      C       MAILING LABELS
      C
              CHARACTER*24 NAME
              CHARACTER*2 CLASS
              CHARACTER*24 ADDR
              WRITE(6,*)'ENTER NUMBER OF STUDENTS '
              READ(5,*)N
              DO 100 I=1,N
              READ(5,200)NAME,CLASS,ADDR
              WRITE(6,300)NAME,CLASS,ADDR
     100  CONTINUE
              STOP
     200  FORMAT(A24,2X,A2,A24)
     300  FORMAT('0',A24,4X,A2/1X,A24)
              END
```

Formatted input does not require apostrophes to delimit each datum.

15.
```
      C       MATRIX PROGRAM FOR +/-
      C
              CHARACTER MAT(10,10)
              INTEGER ROW,COL
      C       FILL THE MATRIX
              DO 10 ROW=1,10
```

```
           DO 10 COL=1,10
           IVAL=MOD(ROW+COL,2)
           IF(IVAL.EQ.0)THEN
             MAT(ROW,COL)='+'
           ELSE
             MAT(ROW,COL)='-'
           ENDIF
        10 CONTINUE
           WRITE(6,*)'MATRIX CONTAINS:'
           DO 20 ROW=1,10
        20 WRITE(6,30)(MAT(ROW,COL),COL=1,10)
           STOP
        30 FORMAT(10(1X,A))
           END
```

17.
```
     C     SORTING NAMES
     C
           CHARACTER*5 NAME(10),HOLD
           DATA NAME/'JOE','SALLY','FRED','JOHN','PAUL',
          1          'COSMO','JUDY','ALICE','ZELDA','PETE'/
     C     OUTPUT UNSORTED ARRAY
           WRITE(6,*)'UNSORTED ARRAY:'
           WRITE(6,20)NAME
     C     SORT THE ARRAY
           DO 10 I=1,9
           DO 10 J=I+1,10
           IF(NAME(J).LT.NAME(I))THEN
             HOLD=NAME(J)
             NAME(J)=NAME(I)
             NAME(I)=HOLD
           ENDIF
        10 CONTINUE
     C     OUTPUT SORTED ARRAY
           WRITE(6,*)
           WRITE(6,*)'SORTED ARRAY:'
           WRITE(6,20)NAME
           STOP
        20 FORMAT(10(1X,A))
           END
```

CHAPTER 9

1.
```
           DO 20 I=1,10
        10 WRITE(6,200)I,SQRT(I)
       200 FORMAT(1X,I5,3X,F12.5)
```

3.   C234567   Comment line identifies col. 7

```
            RAD(X)=3.141593*X/180.0
            DO 10 DEG=0.0,90.0,5.0
         10 WRITE(6,*)DEG,TAN(RAD(DEG))
            STOP
            END
```
TAN at 90 degrees approaches infinity.

5.   C
```
            MAIN PROGRAM
            INTEGER ARR(20),POS,NEG
            DATA(ARR(I),I=1,7)/1,2,-3,4-3,1,2/
            CALL COUNT(ARR,7,POS,NEG)
            WRITE(6,*)POS,NEG
            END
    C       SUBPROGRAM
            SUBROUTINE COUNT(IRR,N,IP,IN)
            INTEGER IRR(20)
            IP=0
            IN=0
            DO 10 I=1,N
            IF(IRR(I).GE.0)THEN
              IP=IP+1
            ELSE
              IN=IN+1
            ENDIF
         10 CONTINUE
            RETURN
            END
```

7.   C
```
            MAIN PROGRAM
            WRITE(6,*)'ENTER REAL VALUE '
            READ(5,*)VALU
            WRITE(6,*)'OUTPUT IS',ROUND(VALUE,2)
            END
    C       SUBPROGRAM
            FUNCTION ROUND(V,N)
    C       V IS THE VALUE TO BE ROUNDED
    C       N IS THE ROUNDING FACTOR
    C       N=2 ROUND TO HUNDREDTH
            IF(N.EQ.0)THEN
              V=INT(V+0.5)
            ELSE
              V=INT(10**N+0.5)
              V=V/(10**N)
            ENDIF
            RETURN
            END
```
May have to adjust rounding depending on floating point arithmetic.

9.
```
        INTEGER FUNCTION CEI(X)
        IF(X.LT.0.0.OR.X.EQ.INT(X))THEN          Block IF
          CEI=INT(X)
        ELSE
          CEI=INT(X)+1
        ENDIF
        RETURN
        END
```

11.
```
        REAL FUNCTION MEAN(N,X)            Type REAL
        DIMENSION X(N)                     Variable DIMENSION
        SUM=0.0                            in subprogram
        DO 10 I=1,N
     10 SUM=SUM+X(I)
        AVE=SUM/REAL(N)                    Intrinsic REAL
        SUM=0.0
        DO 20 I=1,N
     20 SUM=SUM+ABS(X(I)-AVE))
        MEAN=SUM/REAL(N)
        RETURN
        END
```

13.
```
        FUNCTION DOT(A,B)
        DIMENSION A(3),B(3)
        DOT=0.0
        DO 50 I=1,3                        CONTINUE optional in
     50 DOT=DOT+A(I)*B(I)                  FORTRAN 77
        RETURN
        END
```

15.
```
        SUBROUTINE DROOTS(A,B,C,R1,R2)
        DOUBLE PRECISION R1,R2                 Type double
        DISCR=B*B-.0*A*C                       precision
        IF(DISCR.LT.0.0)THEN                   for R1, R2
          R1=0.0
          R2=0.0
          WRITE(6,*)'ROOTS COMPLEX'            Block IF
        ELSE
          R1=(-B+SQRT(DBLE(DISCR)))/(2.0*A)
          R2=(-B-SQRT(DBLE(DISCR)))/(2.0*A)
        ENDIF
        RETURN
        END
```

17.
```
        DOUBLE PRECISION FUNCTION CUBR(X)
        DOUBLE PRECISION X
        CUBR=X**(1.0D+0/3.0D+0)
        RETURN
        END
```

19. Refer to sample problem 2, Chapter 8. Modify the DO loop parameters and replace the single test by the following three tests:

```
IF(TEXT(I)(J:J+4).EQ.THE)K1=K1+1
IF(TEXT(I)(J:J+3).EQ.AN)K2=K2+1
IF(TEXT(I)(J:J+2).EQ.A)K3=K3+1
```

21.
```
        SUBROUTINE SEVEN(A,N,R,K)
        DIMENSION A(N,N),R(N)
        K=0
        DO 10 I=1,N
        DO 10 J=1,N
        IF(I+J.EQ.7)THEN
          K=KH
          R(K)=A(I,J)
        ENDIF
        RETURN
     10 CONTINUE
        END
```

23.
```
        SUBROUTINE EVEN(IA,N,R)
        DIMENSION IA(N,N),R(N)
        K=0
        DO 10 I=1,N
        DO 10 J=1,N
        IF(IA(I,J)/2*2.EQ.IA(I,J))THEN
          K=K+1
          R(K)=IA(I,J)
        ELSE
     10 CONTINUE
        ENDIF
        CALL RANK(R,RI,K)
        RETURN
        END
        SUBROUTINE RANK(R,RI,K)
        DIMENSION R(K)
        DO 20 I-1,K-1
        N=I+1
        IF(R(I).LE.R(N))GO TO 20
        IHOLD=R(I)
        R(I)=R(N)
        R(N)=IHOLD
     20 CONTINUE
        RETURN
        END
```

25.
```
          CHARACTER*6 FUNCTION KONVRT(IV)
          CHARACTER*10 VALUE
          CHARACTER*6 HOLD
          LOGICAL FLAG
          INTEGER N(5),TEN(5)
C         INITIALIZE HOLD TO BLANKS AND SAVE IV
          HOLD=''
          IVSAVE=IV
C         FILL TENS ARRAY WITH POWERS OF TEN
          TENS(1)=1.0
          DO 10 I=2,5
       10 TENS(I)=TENS(I-1)*10.0
C         CHECK FOR ALLOWABLE INTEGERS
          IF(IV.GT.32767.OR.IV.LT.-32768)THEN
            KONVRT=' ERROR'
            RETURN
          ENDIF
C         CHECK SIGN OF IV
          IF(IV.LT.0.0)THEN
            FLAG=.TRUE.
          ELSE
            FLAG=.FALSE.
          ENDIF
          IV=ABS(IV)
C         FILL N ARRAY WITH IV DIGITS
          DO 20 I=5,1,-1
          N(I)=IV/TENS(I)
       20 IV=IV-N(I)*TENS(I)
C         CONVERT DIGITS IN N ARRAY TO
C         CHARACTERS AND ASSIGN TO HOLD
C         PROGRAM CONTINUED
          VALUE='0123456789'
          DO 30 I=1,5
       30 HOLD(7-I:7-I)=VALUE(N(I)+1:N(I)+1)
C         REPLACE LEADING ZEROS BY BLANKS
          DO 40 I=2,5
          IF(HOLD(I:I).NE.'0')GO TO 50
       40 HOLD(I:I)='b'
C         CHECK SIGN - IF FLAG TRUE NEED MINUS
       50 IF(FLAG)HOLD(I-1:I-1)='-'
C         ASSIGN HOLD TO KONVRT AND RESTORE IV
          KONVRT=HOLD
          IV=IVSAVE
          RETURN
          END
```

Compound block IF with null ELSE

Block IF

Comment: When the dummy argument IV $= -32768$, this character function must be modified if your computer uses 16 bit integers since ABS(-32768)

will result in an integer overflow. The final contents of important variables/arrays for a typical value of IV, e.g. -567, are:

```
TENS  array =  1      10     100    1000    100000
N     array =  7      6      5      0       0
FLAG        = .TRUE.
HOLD  array = ƀ00567(after DO 30) = ƀƀ-567(after stno.50)
```

27.
```
      SUBROUTINE CROSS(R,A,B)
      REAL R(3),A(3),B(3)
      R(1)=A(2)*B(3)-A(3)*B(2)
      R(2)=A(3)*B(1)-A(1)*B(3)
      R(3)=A(1)*B(2)-A(2)*B(1)
      RETURN
      END
```

29.
```
      SUBROUTINE SORTIT
      COMMON N
      COMMON X(8)
      DO 10 J=1,N-1
      DO 10 I=J+1,N
      IF(X(I).GT.X(J)THEN
         HOLD=X(I)
         X(I)=X(J)
         X(J)=HOLD
      ENDIF
   10 CONTINUE
      RETURN
      END
```

CHAPTER 10

1.

Step	x_i	x_j	x_m	$f(x_m)$	$f(x_i) \cdot f(x_m)$
1	0.00000	1.00000	0.50000	-0.100576	$-$
2	0.00000	0.50000	0.25000	0.396118	$+$
3	0.25000	0.50000	0.37500	0.131720	$+$
4	0.37500	0.50000	0.43750	0.0112557	$+$
5	0.43750	0.50000	0.46875	-0.0457744	$-$
6	0.43750	0.46875	0.43512	-0.0175336	$-$
7	0.43750	0.43512	0.44531	-0.0032072	$-$
8	0.43750	0.44531	0.44141	$.0040000$	$+$
9	0.44141	0.44531	0.44336	$.0003458$	

3.
```
C234567
      F(X)=X**3
      WRITE(6,*)'ENTER X1,X2,ERROR '
      READ(5,*)A,B,ERR
      N=8
      AOLD=0.0
   10 H=ABS(B-A)/REAL(N)
      AREA=0.0
      X=A+H/2.0
      DO 20 I=1,N
      AREA=AREA+F(X)*H
   20 X=X+H
      WRITE(6,*)N,AREA,ABS(AREA-AOLD)
      IF(ABS(AREA-AOLD).LT.ERR)THEN
        CONTINUE
      ELSE
        AOLD=AREA
        N=N*2
        GO TO 10
      ENDIF
      END
```

Input:
ENTER X1,X2,ERROR 0.0,2.0,0.001
Output:
```
  8 3.96875   3.96875
 16 3.99219   0.0234375
 32 3.99805   5.85691E-03
 64 3.99951   1.46508E-03
128 3.99988   3.65973E-04
```

5.
```
C      ROOT SEARCH,INTERVAL HALVING
C
       FCN(X)=X**4-10*X**3+5*X*X-50*X+24
       WRITE(6,*)'ENTER DATA'
       READ(5,*)X1,X2,ERROR
C
C      TEST WHEN ROOT IS BRACKETED
C
   10  IF(FCN(X1)*FCN(X2).GT.0)THEN
         X2=X2+.15
         GO TO 10
       ENDIF
  100  XR=(X1+X2)/2
       IF(ABS(FCN(XR)).LE.ERROR)GO TO 200
C
```

```
      C       TEST FOR WHICH HALF ROOT IS IN
      C
              IF(FCN(X1)*FCN(XR).LT.0)THEN
                X2=XR
              ELSE
                X1=XR
              ENDIF
      C
      C       OUTPUT
      C
        200 WRITE(6,*)XR,FCN(XR)
              STOP
              END
```

7.
```
      C       ROOT SEARCH BY INTERVAL HALVING
      C
              PARAMETER PI=3.14159
              FCN(X)=1+EXP(X)*SIN(PI*X/2)
              WRITE(6,*)'ENTER DATA'
              READ(5,*)X1,X2,ERROR
      C
      C       PRINT TABLE HEADINGS
      C
              WRITE(6,25)
         25 FORMAT(X,' XR ',7X,' FCN(XR) ',' N ')
         50 IF(FCN(X1)*FCN(X2).GT.0)THEN
                X2=X2+.15
                GO TO 50
              ENDIF
              N=0
      C
      C       HALVING THE INTERVAL
      C
        100 XR=(X1+X2)/2
              IF(ABS(FCN(XR)).LE.ERROR)GO TO 200
              IF(FCN(X1)*FCN(XR).LT.0)THEN
                X2=XR
              ELSE
                X1=XR
              ENDIF
              N=N+1
              WRITE(6,150) XR,FCN(XR),N
        150 FORMAT(X,F7.5,3X,F8.5,I5)
              GO TO 100
        200 WRITE(6,150) XR,FCN(XR),N+1
              STOP
              END
```

9. slope $= 1.98767$ intercept $= -0.988678$

11. $y = 10^{ax} + k$ $\qquad \log_{10}y = ax + \log_{10}k$

$y = \dfrac{1}{ax + k}$ $\qquad \dfrac{1}{y} = ax + k$

$y = kx^a$ $\qquad \ln y = a \ln x + \ln k$

13.
```
C234567
      SUBROUTINE TRAP(A,B,N,ERROR,AREA)
      AOLD=0.0
   20 H=ABS(B-A)/REAL(N)
      AREA=0.5*(F(A)+F(B))
      DO 40 I=1,N-1
   40 AREA=AREA+F(A+REAL(I)*H)
      AREA=AREA*H
      IF(ABS(AREA-AOLD).LT.ERROR)THEN
        RETURN
      ELSE
        AOLD=AREA
        N=N*2
        GO TO 20
      ENDIF
      END
C
      FUNCTION F(X)
      F=EXP(X)*SIN(X)
      RETURN
      END
C     MAIN PROGRAM
      N=4
      CALL TRAP(-3.14159/2.0,3.14159/2.0,N,0.01,AREA)
      WRITE(6,*)'AREA= ',AREA
      WRITE(6,*)'NUMBER OF INTERVALS = ',N
      STOP
      END
```

15.
```
C     RMS VOLTAGE BY NUMERICAL INTEGRATION
C
      FCN(T)=(COS(2*T)+SIN(2*T))**2
      WRITE)6,*) 'ENTER LIMITS'
C
C     INPUT LIMITS AND NO. OF CALLS
C
      READ(5,*) A,B,N
```

```
        AREA=FCN(A)+FCN(B)
        H=ABS(A-B)/REAL(N)
        N=N/2
C
C       SIMPSON'S RULE
C
        DO 10 I=1,N
        AREA=AREA+4*FCN(A+(2*I-1)*H)+2*FCN(A+2*I*H)
     10 CONTINUE
        XINT=AREA*H/3
C
C       OUTPUT
C
        WRITE(6,*) 'INTEGRAL IS ',XINT
        WRITE(6,*) 'EFFECTIVE VOLTAGE IS ',SQRT(XINT)/3.1416
        STOP
        END
```

17.
```
C       INTERPOLATION IN A POPULATION TABLE
C
        INTEGER YEAR(25),POP(25)
        WRITE(6,*) 'ENTER NO. OF YEARS IN TABLE'
        READ(5,*) N
        WRITE(6,*)'ENTER TABLE'
        WRITE(6,*)
        READ(5,*)(YEAR(I),I=1,N)
        READ(5,*)(POP(I),I=1,N)
        WRITE(6,*)'ENTER GIVEN YEAR'
        READ(5,*) IYEAR
C
C       TEST FOR YEAR BEING OUTSIDE RANGE OF TABLE
C
        IF(IYEAR.GE.YEAR(1).OR.IYEAR.LE.YEAR(N)) GO TO 25
        WRITE(6,*)'OUT OF RANGE OF THE TABLE'
        STOP
C
C       SEARCH TABLE FOR INTERPOLATION BRACKETS
C       WITH A BLOCK IF
C
     25 DO 50 I=1,N-1
        IF(IYEAR.LT.YEAR(I).AND.IYEAR.GE.YEAR(I+1)) THEN
     50    CONTINUE
        ELSE
          IPOP=POP(I)+(IYEAR-YEAR(I))*(REAL(POP(I+1))-REAL(POP(I)
       &))/(REAL(YEAR(I+1))-REAL(YEAR(I)))
        ENDIF
```

```
      C
      C     OUTPUT
      C
            WRITE(6,*)'THE POPULATION FOR',IYEAR,'WAS',IPOP
            STOP
            END



  19. C     LEAST SQUARES
      C
            DIMENSION PX(10),PY(10),A(2,2),B(2),R(2)
      C
      C     READ IN NO. OF DATA AND VALUES
      C
            WRITE(6,*) 'ENTER N '
            READ(5,*) N
            WRITE(6,*) 'ENTER POINTS'
            WRITE(6,*)
            READ(5,*) (PY(I),I=1,N)
            READ(5,*) (PY(I),I=1,N)
            SUMXY=0
            SUMXSQ=0
            SUMX=0
            SUMY=0
      C
      C     CALCULATING SUMS FOR NORMAL EQTNS
      C
            DO 100 I=1,N
            SUMXY=SUMXY+PX(I)*PY(I)
            SUMXSQ=SUMXSQ+PX(I)*PX(I)
            SUMX=SUMX+PX(I)
            SUMY=SUMY+PY(I)
        100 CONTINUE
      C
      C     FILLING ARRAYS FOR SOLUTION
      C     OF SIMULTANEOUS EQUATIONS
      C
            A(1,1)=SUMXSQ
            A(1,2)=SUMX
            A(2,1)=SUMX
            A(2,2)=N
            B(1)=SUMXY
            B(2)=SUMY
            CALL MATSOLVE(A,B,R,2)
            WRITE(6,*) 'SLOPE=',R(1),'INTERCEPT=',R(2)
            STOP
            END
```

Comment: Your particular site might not have a MATSOLVE Library subroutine. Check your Scientific Library for the subroutine that solves simultaneous equations.

21.
```
C234567
      SUBROUTINE MATADD(A,B,C,N,M)
      DIMENSION A(N,M),B(N,M),C(N,M)
      DO 10 I=1,N
      DO 10 J=1,M
   10 C(I,J)=A(I,J)+B(I,J)
      RETURN
      END
```

23. Careful examination of matrix multiplication as discussed in this chapter shows that [A] [B] cannot equal [B] [A]. Try it for several different [A] and [B] matrices.

25.
```
C234567
      SUBROUTINE MATTRN(A,N)
      DIMENSION A(N,N)
      DO 10 IR=2,N
      DO 10 IC=1,IR-1
      H=A(I,J)
      A(I,J)=A(J,I)
   10 A(J,I)=H
      RETURN
      END
C     MAIN PROGRAM
      DIMENSION A(3,3)
      DO 10 IR=1,3
   10 READ(5,*)(A(IR,IC),IC=1,3)
      WRITE(6,*)='BEFORE'
      DO 20 IR=1,3
   20 WRITE(6,*)(A(IR,IC),IC=1,3)
      CALL MATTRN(A,3)
      WRITE(6,*)'AFTER'
      DO 30 IR=1,3
   30 WRITE(6,*)(A(IR,IC),IC=1,3)
      END
```

27. $[A]^{-1} = \begin{bmatrix} 0.392157 & 0.352941 & -0.294117 \\ 0.656862 & 0.441176 & -0.617647 \\ 0.549019 & 0.294118 & -0.411765 \end{bmatrix}$

29.
```
C      SUBROUTINE TO TEST A MATRIX FOR SYMMETRY
C
       SUBROUTINE SYM(A,N)
       DIMENSION A(N,N)
       DO 50 I=1,N
       DO 50 J=1,N
       IF(A(I,J).NE.A(J,I))THEN
         WRITE(6,*)'NOT SYMMETRIC'
       ELSE
   50  CONTINUE
       ENDIF
       WRITE(6,*)'SYMMETRIC'
       RETURN
       END
```

31.
```
C      AN EXAMPLE OF MATRIX MULTIPLICATION
C
       DIMENSION D(4,4),P(4,4),S(4)
       WRITE(6,*)'INPUT DATA'
       WRITE(6,*)
       DO 10 I=1,4
C
C      INPUT THE TWO MATRICES
C
   10 READ(5,*)(D(I,J),J=1,4),(P(I,J),J=1,4)
       DO 20 I=1,4
       S(I)=0
       DO 20 K=1,4
C
C      THE COLUMN MATRIX IS THE DIAGONAL OF THE PRODUCT MATRIX
C
   20 S(I)=S(I)+D(I,K)*P(K,I)
C
C      OUTPUT
C
       WRITE(6,*) 'SHIPMENTS FROM PLANTS A,B,C,D ARE',(S(I),I=1,4)
       STOP
       END
```

CHAPTER 11

1.
```
C      CREATE FILE
C
       OPEN(13,FILE='JUNK.TXT',STATUS='NEW')
       DO 10 I=1,8
       READ(5,*)IVAL
```

```
      10 WRITE(13,*)IVAL
         CLOSE(13,STATUS='KEEP')
         END


   C     LIST FILE
   C
         OPEN(13,FILE='JUNK.TXT',STATUS='OLD')
         DO 10 I=1,8
         READ(13,*)IVAL
      10 WRITE(6,*)IVAL
         CLOSE(13,STATUS='DELETE')
         END

3. C     SEARCH THE FILE
         CHARACTER*20 LNAME
         CHARACTER*20 TARGET
         CHARACTER*10 FNAME
         INTEGER EXT
         LOGICAL HIT
         OPEN(8,FILE='STUDATA',STATUS='OLD')
         HIT=.FALSE.
      25 WRITE(*,*)'ENTER LAST NAME OF STUDENT WHOSE EXTENSION'
         WRITE(*,*)'IS DESIRED OR HIT ENTER KEY TO TERMINATE'
         READ(*,100)TARGET
         IF(TARGET.EQ.'                    ')THEN
           CLOSE(8,STATUS='KEEP')
           STOP
         ENDIF
      50 READ(8,200,END=75)LNAME,FNAME,EXT
         IF(TARGET.EQ.LNAME)THEN
           WRITE(*,*)'DESIRED EXTENSION IS',EXT
           HIT=.TRUE.
         ENDIF
         GO TO 50
      75 IF(HIT)WRITE(*,*)'NO SUCH LAST NAME'
         REWIND 8
         GO TO 25
     100 FORMAT(A20)
     200 FORMAT(A20,A10,I4)
         END

5. C     TABLE OF NATURAL LOGS
   C
         OPEN(20,FILE='DOUT',STATUS='NEW')
         DO 10 A=0.1,10.0,0.1
      10 WRITE(20,*)A,ALOG(A)
         CLOSE(20,STATUS='KEEP')
         END
```

```
7.  C       SEARCH TEXT
    C
            CHARACTER*80 LINE
            CHARACTER*8  KEYWD
            OPEN(10,FILE='TEXT',STATUS='OLD')
            KOUNT=1
            KEYWD='TERMINAL'
        20  READ(10,100,END=40)LINE
            DO 30 I=1,73
            IF(LINE(I:I+8).EQ.KEYWD)KOUNT=KOUNT+1
        30  CONTINUE
            GO TO 20
        40  WRITE(6,*)'NUMBER OF HITS =',KOUNT
            CLOSE(10,STATUS='KEEP')
       100  FORMAT(A)
            END
```

9. (a) eight file records are created
    (b) text file
    (c) 80 bytes
    (d) $80 \times 8 = 640$ bytes
    (e) by adding an OPEN statement and a CLOSE statement.

11. Random or direct access files allow the FORTRAN programmer to process any file record without having to sequentially access all the file records that precede the desired record. Random access is the better choice when selected file records are to be processed.

CHAPTER 12

1. The answer is site dependent. For most 8 and 16 bit micro computers integers range from -32768 to 32767. Real data has a precision of approximately seven digits and magnitude of $10^{\pm 38}$. Double precision data yields approximately 15 significant digits and a magnitude of $10^{\pm 308}$.

3. The answer is site dependent. Many micro computers support asynchronous communications in a terminal emulation mode.

5. The Newton-Raphson technique discussed in Chapter 10 is a good choice, where

$$f(x) = x**3 - 8 = 0$$
$$\frac{df(x)}{dx} = 3x**2$$

Replace FCN(X) $= X**2 - 4.0$
with   FCN(X) $= X**3 - 8.0$
and   DFCN(X) $= 2.0*X$
with   DFCN(X) $= 3.0*X**2$
in Figure 10.3

7. The answer is site dependent. Typically a library of subroutines and procedures is created and during linking these subroutines and procedures become part of the machine language program.

9. The plotting program requires little modification since y and z have the same range.

```
C      PLOTTING ROUTINE
       REAL X(33),Y(33),Z(33)
       CHARACTER LINE(61)
C      FILL THE ARRAYS
       DO 10 I=1,33
    10 X(I)=(I-1)/5.0
       DO 20 I=1,33
       Y(I)=SIN(X(I))
    20 Z(I)=COS(X(I))
C      OUTPUT RESULTS AS CHECK
       DO 25 I=1,33
    25 WRITE(*,26)X(I),Y(I),Z(I)
    26 FORMAT(3F10.5)
C      Y AND Z ARRAYS HAVE THE SAME RANGE
       YMAX=Y(1)
       DO 30 I=2,33
       IF(Y(I).GT.YMAX)YMAX=Y(I)
    30 CONTINUE
       YMIN=Y(1)
       DO 40 I=2,33
       IF(Y(I).LT.YMIN)YMIN=Y(I)
    40 CONTINUE
C      PLOT
       WRITE(*,100)YMIN,YMAX
       DO 50 I=1,61
       LINE(I)='+'
    50 CONTINUE
       IZERO=(0.0-YMIN)/(YMAX-YMIN)*60+1
       LINE(IZERO)='0'
       WRITE(*,150)LINE
       DO 60 I=1,33
       DO 50 J=1,61
```

```
 55 LINE(J)=' '
    LINE(IZERO)='0'
    IPOS=(Y(I)-YMIN)/(YMAX-YMIN)*60+1
    LINE(IPOS)='*'
    IPOS=(Z(I)-YMIN)/(YMAX-YMIN)*60+1
    LINE(IPOS)='*'
    WRITE(*,200)X(I),LINE
 60 CONTINUE
    STOP
100 FORMAT('1',7X,F5.3,51X,F5.3)
150 FORMAT(8X,61A1)
200 FORMAT(1X,F5.3,2X,61A1)
    END
```

index